COMPARATIVE
PSYCHOPATHOLOGY
Animal and Human

Officers of the

AMERICAN PSYCHOPATHOLOGICAL ASSOCIATION

for 1965

COMPARATIVE PSYCHOPATHOLOGY
Animal and Human

Edited by **JOSEPH ZUBIN, Ph.D.**

Department of Mental Hygiene, State of New York; Department of Psychology, Columbia University, New York City

and **HOWARD F. HUNT, Ph.D.**

New York State Psychiatric Institute; Department of Psychology, Columbia University, New York City

THE PROCEEDINGS OF THE FIFTY-FIFTH ANNUAL MEETING OF THE AMERICAN PSYCHOPATHOLOGI-CAL ASSOCIATION, HELD IN NEW YORK CITY, FEBRUARY, 1965.

GRUNE & STRATTON

NEW YORK • LONDON • 1967

SAMUEL W. HAMILTON AWARDS

NAME		SYMPOSIUM
Clarence P. Oberndorf, M.D.	1952	Depression
John C. Whitehorn, M.D.	1953	Psychiatry and the Law
David M. Levy, M.D.	1954	Psychopathology of Childhood
Stanley Cobb, M.D.	1955	Experimental Psychopathology
Sandor Rado, M.D.	1956	Psychopathology of Communication
Karl M. Bowman, M.D.	1957	Problems of Addiction and Habituation
Bernard Glueck, Sr., M.D.	1958	Trends in Psychoanalysis
Sir Aubrey Lewis, M.D.	1959	Comparative Epidemiology in the Mental Disorders
Franz J. Kallmann, M.D.	1960	Psychopathology of Aging
Nolan D. C. Lewis, M.D.	1961	Future of Psychiatry
Franz Alexander, M.D.	1962	Evaluation of Therapy
Heinrich Klüver, Ph.D.	1963	Psychopathology of Perception
Paul H. Hoch, M.D.	1964	Psychopathology of Schizophrenia
Curt P. Richter, Ph.D.	1965	Comparative Psychopathology

HENRY M. AND LILLIAN STRATTON AWARDS

Name		Symposium
James Birren, Ph.D.	1960	Psychopathology of Aging
Benjamin Pasamanick, M.D.	1961	Future of Psychiatry
Heinz E. Lehmann, M.D.	1962	Evaluation of Therapy
Charles W. Eriksen, Ph.D.	1963	Psychopathology of Perception
Ronald Melzack, Ph.D.	1963	Psychopathology of Perception
Robert W. Payne, Ph.D.	1964	Psychopathology of Schizophrenia
Kurt Salzinger, Ph.D.	1964	Psychopathology of Schizophrenia
David A. Rogers, Ph.D.	1965	Comparative Psychopathology

Library of Congress Catalog Card No. 67-13317

Copyright © 1967
Grune & Stratton, Inc.
381 Park Avenue South
New York, N.Y. 10016
Printed in U.S.A. (K-A)

CONTENTS

Part III: Behavioral Studies

Appendix

PREFACE

THE VARIETY OF SCIENTIFIC MODELS that have been proposed for investigating the etiology of mental disorders has given rise to hypotheses that have led to work with animals as well as with men. An attempt is made in this volume to juxtapose human and animal work in order to demonstrate similarities and differences between them. Whether or not animals may properly be said to exhibit mental illness remains an open question. Nevertheless, the development of "experimental neuroses" and conditioned emotional responses in animals has led to a number of behavioral and neurophysiological experiments with important implications for man, even though species differences make facile generalizations hazardous.

The phenomenological or naturalistic approach that has been the mainstay of psychiatry until recently is shown to have its counterpart in field investigations of the influence and expression of dominance, frustration, aggression, and sexual drives in animals, and in the interplay of these and other factors in producing normal or deviant behavior.

Developmental, genetic, internal-environment, and neurophysiological models are each represented in this volume; and examples of the learning-theory approach complete it. Studies of the last type demonstrate that reinforcement and conditioning laws in animals have their parallels in men, and that the mentally ill are subject to them too. Indeed, it would be surprising were it found that these laws—which are characteristic of the entire mammalian order, at least—did not apply to mental patients. Application of reinforcement principles to alter psychotic behavior or to eliminate neurotic behavior has created new approaches to management and therapy. Needed now are methods for determining (1) whether experimentally induced alterations generalize to other aspects of the patient's behavior, and (2) which approaches are most suitable to which disorders. To answer these questions adequately, we need objective indicators of "adjustment" as a whole, as well as of discrete behavioral changes.

Also, and perhaps more important, the comparative approach to psychopathology encourages a continuous cross-dialogue or cross-comparison between animal and human data. In some instances, we will be lucky enough to find animal analogues (or maybe even homologues) of the human situation that will permit the results of animal experimentation to bear directly and immediately on the solution of human

vii

problems. In others, and these probably will be more frequent, we will find that apparently obvious analogies are superficial and do not truly hold. To arrive at such discoveries, we will have been forced to analyze more closely the basic processes responsible for what is observed at each level, regardless of whether the processes are the same or different. The fallout in new knowledge here will be enormously beneficial.

In effect, continued confrontation between human and animal data, even when not truly analogous, challenges us and thus stimulates the development of knowledge about fundamental processes of importance to mental health. That such knowledge is good and worthwhile is an assumption, of course, but it has been so well supported already that we need not fear being forced to abandon it.

Joseph Zubin
Howard F. Hunt

CURT P. RICHTER

CURT P. RICHTER

Samuel W. Hamilton Memorial Lecturer, 1965

FOR OVER FOUR DECADES there has emerged from the Laboratory of Psychobiology of the Henry Phipps Psychiatric Clinic, Johns Hopkins University School of Medicine, a steady stream of researches which have progressively illuminated a number of significant facets of behavior, both healthy and deviant. The imaginative leadership of the laboratory, which has attracted as collaborators so many distinguished colleagues and talented young beginners in the field of psychopathology, has rested throughout this period in the hands of the man selected for the Samuel W. Hamilton Memorial Lectureship —Curt P. Richter, Professor of Psychobiology.

Perhaps in the early years of Dr. Richter's wide-ranging explorations casual reviewers of his publications may have been unclear as to the goals and contributions of the laboratory as they searched for a central theme or cohesive theoretical bent. Now one may discern a steady progression of researches that fall into a series of significant investigative lines. Perhaps self-regulatory behavior of animals and men, particularly periodic timing devices—biological clocks, as they have been called—have come to a more general recognition and acclaim than other lines of investigation. But the other lines are equally significant and interesting. Thus the laboratory centered one portion of its endeavors on the study of spontaneous behavior and activities, examining systematically their control through functional processes of the central nervous system, the endocrines, and variations in nutrition. Another long series of studies concerned with domestication of the Norway rat may now be appreciated as bearing on the biological consequences of civilization on organisms, and as contributing to our understanding of stress responses in different species. There was also a series of papers elucidating the role of the autonomic nervous system in relation to the functioning of the total organism in stress situations inducing emotional reactions, and also those highly penetrating investigations of the grasp reflex in animals and man under a variety of natural and experimental situations.

Only a man with a deep and abiding curiosity, a roving mind, a talent for bringing to association a variety of observations garnered from the behavior of animals and man, and an ability to devise experiments with technical niceties could effectively guide such a distinguished series of behavioral studies over the many years. Such a man is Curt Richter.

As a medical student and later as a young Fellow in neurology I remember him with warm admiration and respect. I came to know his work through visiting his laboratory to seek his advice on some interests of my own related to the grasp reflex. He had by then completed his examination of the changes in the grasp reflex in infants at various age periods, following various cerebral lesions and under the influence of bulbocapnine. He and his students had recently commenced examining the variables concerned in determining spontaneous running activity of rats, and were evolving a number of exceptionally delicate surgical procedures which allowed ablations of the various endocrine glands in these small mammals. This work, of course, led to the famous experimental observations on dietary self-selection of rats. Of course, as a young instructor in neurology, I was impressed by the stories told me of the expedition to Barro Colorado to examine the grasp reflex of those upside down mammals, the two- and three-toed sloths.

Curt Richter was born of German-Protestant parents, recent emigrants to Denver, Colorado. Their only child and son was born on February 20, 1894. As fathers often will, his father looked to his son to follow the parental profession, engineering, and eventually to share with him the direction of the iron and structural steel manufacturing company he had founded on settling in Denver. But this was not to be. At the age of eight Curt lost his father in a hunting accident. Parental wishes, nevertheless, seemed to influence his entry to the Technische Hochschule in Dresden, Germany, to study engineering following completion of high school in the United States. His interest in engineering wavered. After three years in Dresden he returned home to enter Harvard. At this time his goals seemed uncertain. There were thoughts of pursuing careers in international diplomacy or economics. At Harvard his passion for animal behavior was aroused when, by chance, he attended a course on the subject given by Robert M. Yerkes. Shortly thereafter, this interest was stimulated further on reading John B. Watson's book "An Introduction to Comparative Psychology." Immediately following his discharge from the U.S. Army in 1919, he enrolled at The Johns Hopkins University to study for his doctorate in psychology with Professor Watson.

These formative years gave Curt Richter a wide range of experiences;

they in turn provided the springboard for his future interest and the use of his unique talents. As a very young lad he was allowed to handle all kinds of tools and even assisted in the operation of a forge in his father's factory. Following his father's death, Richter worked for a time as a farmhand, herding cattle, milking cows, and operating heavy machinery. But his life was filled with more than work. Athletics drew him; he became an outstanding basketball player. In addition he found time to serve as editor of his class paper and, when a high school senior, was selected president of his high school class.

In Germany an entirely new cultural world opened to him in the operas, theatres, and art galleries of Dresden. Here for the first time he discovered as well the world of literature. And these many experiences were deepened in him by the comaraderie of, and discussions with, his fellow students in the cafés of the city.

His uncertain early days in Boston were depressing to him. But here again, as a Harvard student, his willingness to browse led him to discover another parameter of behavior: through a course in philosophy of nature he found psychoanalysis. His avid reading of Freud, as well as Jung, Adler, Jones, Ferenczi, Brill and others, opened vistas of subjective human experiences and their interpretation in dynamic biological terms. At about the same time there came to his awareness the beginning work on the endocrines, just coming to recognition as important structures in regulating the natural economy.

But it was the life of a graduate student under John B. Watson that did most to determine his future. Professor Watson allowed his student to roam at will, never requiring him to enroll in a formal course. At Hopkins he found the medical school courses in human anatomy and physiology, attended lectures in neurology, psychiatry, and pharmacology, and developed his flair for experimental techniques wherein the early experiences acquired in his father's factory and on the farm proved of value as a background for his developing aptitude in laboratory techniques. Within a year, backed by the richness of these experiences, his life-long research career blossomed in the publication of his first paper.

Curt Richter's contribution as a transmitter of our scientific culture and as a nurturer and model for those with an unfolding interest in the field of behavioral research is perhaps less well known to the scientific community, yet it certainly must command as much of our appreciation as his brilliant investigations. Through the Psychobiological Laboratory, from the early twenties to the present, there have passed a long line of student collaborators whose names have become independently known to us in their later contributions to psychiatry, neurology, and psychology. Richter's collaborating peers too were a distinguished group, known widely in their own right. Thus we find in the laboratory publications printed before World War II the names of G. H. Wang, C. Bagley, Jr., R. D. Gillespie, A. F. Guttmacher, H. C. Syz, E. F. Kinder, F. R. Ford, G. B. Wislocki, M. E. Brailey, O. Odegaard, O. R. Langworthy, Maurice Levine, M. B. Shaw, Sara S. Tower, H. G. Wolff, A. S. Paterson, F. F. Buchman, M. F. Hausmann, M. Hines, H. A. Benjamin, Jr., J. E. Eckert, L. E. Holt, Jr., Bruno Baralare, Jr., Alexander Kennedy, C. D. Hawkes, E. C. H. Schmidt, Jr., K. H. Campbell, William Honeyman, Lawson Wilkens, Harriet Hunter. As we view this list we recognize many of our present and past associates who have become renowned as researchers or as protagonists of investigation in holding important chairs in university centers in this country and abroad.

During the past two decades Curt Richter has been called upon to summarize his work in a series of distinguished lectureships: The Harvey Lecture in 1942, The Menas S. Gregory Lecture in 1952, The Thomas Salmon Lecture in 1959, The Percival Bailey Lecture in 1964, and now the Samuel W. Hamilton Lecture. Each of the lectures was used by him to synthesize his thinking, as he drew from the work of the laboratory the larger meanings from the long stream of ongoing observation.

His monograph "Biological Clocks in Medicine and Psychiatry" offers a splendid illustration of such a synthesis. From his review of the many data collected by him on periodic phenomena in the behavior of man and animals he postulated the existence of three groups of timing devices: homeostatic, central, and peripheral. The first was seen to operate as a feedback mechanism between a target endocrine organ and a central regulating function involving the intricate pituitary hypthalamic interrelationship. The oestrus cycle is an example of such a clock. The second, the central or 24 hour clock is located in the central nervous system—functioning, probably, in the hypothalamus— but operates independently of the homeostatic timing mechanism and without feedback. Thus Richter points out that body regulating systems operate under nonhomeostatic as well as homeostatic controls. These are, then, mechanisms which serve to determine fixed time schedules rather than fixed levels of physiological functioning. The former are regarded as the more primitive, since their existence may be discovered in unicellular organisms. Richter postulated as well the existence of peripheral timing devices which exist in tissues external to the central nervous system. Such peripheral periodic controls explain the highly regular periodicity of certain phenomena in illness such as occurs with the febrile course in Hodgkin's disease or certain joint manifestations in arthritis. To Richter, all cells function rhythmically. In some organs or systems the rhythms occur "in phase" and in others "out of phase," establishing thereby periodic and nonperiodic activity. In evolution the tendency is seen by him to be towards the reduction of in-phase activity. Shock, trauma, or other stresses are postulated as disrupting either in- or out-of-phase functioning of cells or organs, while he hypothesizes that the duration of the rhythms have been impressed upon the cell or organ structures by external cyclic changes which become reflected in metabolic activities. Curt Richter marshals well the evidence to support his positions. Fine scientist that he is, he concludes his essay on "Biological Clocks" with the statement that "at present we do not know anything about the anatomy of the clocks in a single cell . . . ," thus disclosing his own appreciation of the need and direction of future efforts if we are to understand the fundamental secrets of these biological factors in behavior.

One might analyze similarly his other lines of study. Those of us who know him and have followed him over these years would only be reinforced in our delight in his ways of probing issues critical for our understanding of healthy and abnormal behavior, of drawing upon and finding among natural phenomena that which is pertinent, and arranging the phenomena to offer us challenges for the future. This he has always done with a modesty and graciousness which have brought him both warm friendships and our deep and enduring respect.

To have been requested to prepare this biographical sketch has brought both an honor and a flush of pleasureable reminiscence of early laboratory work in Baltimore. It provides an opportunity to express a deep personal sense of gratitude to Dr. Richter and his collaborators, who filled the days of their juniors with excitement, stimulation, and understanding friendship, which hopefully we have carried forward in our relations with students in more recent years.

Lawrence C. Kolb, M.D.

COMPARATIVE
PSYCHOPATHOLOGY
Animal and Human

Part I: Sociocultural Environmental Factors

1

ECOLOGICAL FACTORS
IN THE DEVELOPMENT OF
BEHAVIORAL ANOMALIES

by JOHN B. CALHOUN, PH.D.*

1. INTRODUCTION

PATHOLOGICAL BEHAVIOR, by its very definition, denotes an inability to adjust to ongoing conditions. Behavior becomes incompatible with these conditions, at least to the extent that the individual fails to fulfill that role which contributes to the success of the biological or cultural system of which he is, or should be, a component part. In the normal course of events, both heredity and learning lead to adequate adjustments. Any failure to adjust indicates that the individual has become enmeshed or trapped by circumstances beyond his ability to cope successfully with them. Such unusual circumstances may be termed "ecological traps." As students of psychopathology we have two roles to play—that of the hunter and that of the hunted. As hunters we must devise better ecological traps, better ways of producing more psychopathological individuals with greater degrees of pathology. As the hunted we must devise better ways of recognizing and avoiding ecological traps. Beyond this comes the question of therapy; how do you readapt an individual from his altered state within the confines of the ecological trap, back to adequate functioning within a system in which this trap has been demolished.

My account here will be devoted entirely to the very personal effort to become a good hunter. In the process I have developed some fairly successful ecological traps to the point where certain principles of their structure and impact are beginning to emerge.

*Laboratory of Psychology, National Institute of Mental Health, Bethesda, Md.

Before embarking upon this account I would like to comment briefly upon methodology. A colleague once remarked to me: "There are so many variables in your studies you can't possibly draw any conclusions about anything." I do examine complex systems involving many variables. All mammals, not just man, live as part of the systems affected by many component variables. The question is, "What are the avenues through which we may gain understanding of these systems." I do not question the usefulness of the now-classical process of examining one variable at a time while maintaining all others constant at one of the many values each may have. However, it is difficult to conceive of any mammalian species not affected by more than one hundred variables. Even with this limited number of variables, the necessity for over a million kinds of experiments soon becomes apparent if one maintains the rigid position of working stepwise from the simple to the complex. We can justify neither the financial resources or the time for complete adherence to this logic. Somehow we must break out of this intellectual straitjacket and begin to deal with complex systems involving many simultaneously varying factors, while examining these systems over prolonged periods. This requires detailed probings of widely separated stages of complexity, while attempting to bridge the gaps by formulating mathematical concepts of the processes involved in bridging these gaps. The examples to be presented here represent such initial crude probings. Elsewhere[1] I have attempted the kind of mathematical formulations required to form a bridge between such probings.

2. Mass Panic

Naturally Among Lemmings

Several species of rodents, commonly called lemmings, inhabit the circumpolar tundra habitat of the northern hemisphere. Every three to four years in many localities the populations attain fantastic densities. At these times of obvious overabundance the majority of the members of the population suddenly die as the consequence of an associated stress syndrome.[2] Afterwards, over the next three to four years, the population builds up again to peak proportions. However, in some localities large-scale emigrations from the sites of overpopulation radiate outward into adjoining less-preferred habitats. Over most of the circumpolar range of these species no consistent pattern emerges in the direction or culmination of these emigrations, merely dispersal and eventual death.

However, in the Scandinavian peninsula these movements often take on additional characteristics. I am particularly indebted to Dr. Arnold Bakken for his thorough unpublished account.[3] In Scandinavia the tundra occupies an upland plateau. The primary opportunity for egress from the tundra lies downhill along the valleys extending from it toward the sea. Scattered individuals, gradually aggregating into compact groups and finally into massive waves of as many as a million individuals, represent the general pattern as the emigration flows from the tundra, through the coniferous zone, down into more hardwood forests, and finally out into lowland cultivated areas. The process may take weeks, and the trek may cover as much as a hundred miles. If the compact mass reaches the lowland area, its members by that time appear to have lost many former restraints on behavior. They enter and pass through villages, cross train trestles, swim across ponds, and may eventually reach the sea. There they continue their movement, swimming ever farther from shore until all drown.

No clearer example of pathological behavior exists. All who exhibit it die. This has long posed a dilemma. How can it have persisted over the centuries when all which exhibit it die, and the only ones which fail to exhibit it are the few survivors back on the tundra? If this is an hereditary trait, natural selection would long ago have eliminated it.

Obviously one cannot fall back on heredity for an explanation. Furthermore, over the extensive circumpolar area inhabited by such species it is only in the Scandinavian peninsula that these movements from areas of overpopulation culminate in this mass "suicidal" drowning. Something about this area must make it into an ecological trap. The outstanding characteristic here is the pattern of narrow valleys extending from the tundra toward the sea. As the lemmings move away from the tundra and down the valleys one aspect of their experience alone remains constant: Each day they move in a constant compass direction. The particular associates they encounter, as well as the particular configurations of the environment, vary over time. Only directional movement remains to be reinforced as the lemmings move from higher densities on the tundra toward lower densities in the lowlands. This directional movement becomes a highly learned, self-cycling one, requiring a long extinction period. When the lemmings finally reach the sea, the established necessity to keep moving in the established direction forces them to swim outward even unto death. Such is the general formulation I have arrived at as an approximate explanation of the phenomenon.

Experimentally Among Mice

Can this formulation be subjected to experimentation? Two conditions must be fulfilled: 1. There must be a gradient of a noxious stimulus capable of inducing movement from areas of higher to those of lower intensity. 2. The gradient must have a highly directional character over sufficient distance to maintain a movement for a fairly prolonged time.

Developing knowledge of small mammal communities suggested a strategy. Among many species inhabiting forests, field, and desert, each individual maintains its own circumscribed range, which, however, overlaps those of its neighbors. Each individual attempts to minimize its contacts with associates. This avoidance is apparently facilitated by vocal signals. Periodic emission of such signals by each individual enables each to know the whereabouts of its neighbors and thus to avoid them. Detection of such signals is not likely to be possible over distances as great as twice the diameter of the individual's range.

Now, suppose it were possible to remove suddenly all individuals within a circular area considerably greater than this maximum distance of perception of these noxious stimuli. Their absence would produce a signal void. Survivors at the periphery would then be at the boundary of a marked stimulus discontinuity. Inward they could detect no signals. Outward they could still detect the normal level of signals. The reaction of these survivors on the edge of the depleted area should be predictable from their former response pattern. This must have been one of equalizing the intensity of stimuli impinging upon them from surrounding areas. As an individual was approached by his neighbors from one direction, he would move in the direction of his more distant neighbors. Over time the movements of an animal within his range in response to his neighbors' movements would be much like a balloon surrounded by a circle of jets of air being emitted independently and at irregular intervals.

Thus we might expect the survivors at the edge of the circular depleted area to move into it and away from the relatively much greater stimuli originating from other neighbors who survived even farther outward. Now suppose that these individuals who enter the depleted area are also removed. Another tier of animals will be in the same situation. As each tier moves inward his neighbors will be left in the same circumstance. A chain reaction should thus be engendered in which, as far as the environment extends, successive waves are simultaneously moving inward in so long as the process is maintained by continually removing all animals invading the original central tract. Note that such a migratory "implosion" is overtly directly opposite to the migratory "explosion" characteristic of lemmings. Yet the theoretical processes involved are essentially similar; only the direction of movement is reversed.

Dr. W. L. Webb and his colleagues of the New York State College of Forestry offered to test this idea at their research forest near Newcomb, New York, which was inhabited by several species of small mammals.

Here they laid a circular trapline enclosing a 30 acre tract surrounded by extensive similar forest habitat. Along this line a trap was placed every five feet. The notion was that once the far fewer traps placed within the circle had removed the residents, the close spacing of traps along the peripheral line would suffice to capture all invaders as they encountered the line. Unfortunately this peripheral line of traps proved ineffective to that extent, with the consequence that animals accumulated in the center in greater numbers than the few traps there were able to remove them rapidly. An attempt was also made to trace movements inward by invaders by line-trapping along three one-mile long radii from the central area. Unfortunately 50 per cent of the animals captured each night died from exposure. This apparently set up "convexion" currents toward the radii, which "held" animals near the point of first contact with these trap-lines until at a later capture they also died from exposure. Even so, many animals maintained their induced movement (between the radii) toward and into the central area, where ultimately they also were captured. Con-

TABLE 1.—Results of Dr. Webb's Study of Induced Migrations of Red-backed Mice, *Clethrionomys*

Source	Number of Mice Trapped	
Invaders	Observed	Expected
Residents:	107	107
1st Wave:	88	96
2nd Wave:	111	107
3rd Wave	138	135
4th Wave:	165	163
Total	609	608

sidering only the socially dominant species, the mouse *Clethrionomys*, the results were as follows: Most of the residents were captured during the first 21 days of removal trapping. There followed four successive waves of invaders; each wave encompassed 15 days (Table 1).

Assume that each group of invaders originally inhabited one of four bands of width w and that the residents inhabited an area encompassed by the circular trapline plus an adjacent band of width w. Then we may calculate w and the distance of the successive bands from which invaders originated.

The radius from the center of the area being trapped to the circular trapline was 562 feet. Thus, the area sampled during the first 20 days equals $\pi(562 + w)^2$. Since each wave of invaders is presumed to represent a band of equal width, w, then the entire area sampled during the entire 80 days equals $\pi(562 + 5w)^2$. One-hundred-and-seven mice were taken from the central area and 608 from the total area. Thus, to the extent that number of mice is proportional to the area they inhabit, 5.626 as many mice inhabited the total area as the central area. It follows that:

$$5.626 \ [\pi(562 + w)^2] = \pi(562 + 5w)^2.$$
Thus w $= 302$ feet.

Radii to the limits of the central area and the four successive bands become 864, 1166, 1468, 1770, and 2072 feet. A w of 302 feet represents the approximate diameter of home range (i.e., radius $= 3\sigma$ of the bivariate normal distribution) found in other studies by Earl Patric for this species in this habitat.

Other details and related background have been discussed elsewhere.[1] This study of Dr. Webb's affirms the general logic of the initial phase of the hypothesis proposed to explain lemming migrations. It revealed that a directional movement can be generated. Much of their unpublished results indicated that the normal social structure of this community of small mammals had been disrupted. The mice were caught in an ecological trap beyond their control.

It has not yet been possible to pursue such a study to the point that individuals will persist in behaviors completely inimical to their survival. The lush deserts, such as lie 50 miles west of Idaho Falls, offer an ideal situation for such further studies. Preliminary calculations[4] suggest that 15 to 20 investigators working continuously 4 months represents the minimum effort. Opportunity for conducting an experiment of this magnitude has yet to materialize. Such is a far cry from controlled laboratory studies, but offers great possibility for developing insight into psychopathology associated with massive adherence to a single manner of behaving.

3. Group Size and Social Tasks

Animals other than man can also be faced with situations which make adjustment difficult or impossible. We will now consider a series of experiments in which domesticated rats were placed in situations somewhat remote from any that even their wild counterparts would have ever encountered.

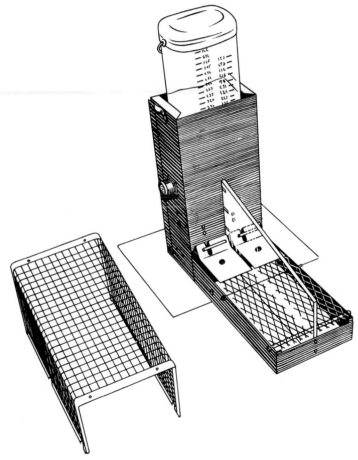

Fig. 1.—STAW, Socialization Training Apparatus Water.

Methodology

The basic instrument employed is designated "STAW," Socialization Training Apparatus Water (Fig. 1). It consists of a water reservoir on one of whose faces there are two levers. Depression of a lever may deliver a drop of water. A clear plastic partition, over which a screen hood is placed, produces two channels of access, each to a single lever. A rat on one side can see through to a companion on the opposite side. The diagonal meshed metal floor of each channel is affixed to an axle forming a fulcrum near the entrance end of the channel. The opposite end of this floor section rests on the arm of a microswitch by which it is supported. The weight of a rat on a floor section closes the microswitch. Appropriate circuits allow three conditions: (1) NO CONDITION. When this applies, a rat gets a cup of water every time it presses the lever, regardless of whether another rat is present on, or absent from, the other side. (2) COOP. Two rats must be on the STAW, one on either side, for the lever on each side to be unlocked. When only one rat is present, both levers remain locked; or when two rats are present, but one backs off, then both levers lock and the remaining rat can no longer obtain water. COOP stands for cooperation. (3) DISOP. One rat only can be present on the STAW for the lever on the side it is on to be unlocked. If a second rat enters the opposite side, both levers immediately lock. DISOP stands for disoperation. Disoperation is a negative social relationship in the sense that rats must cooperate by not interfering with each other. Rats exposed to either COOP or DISOP are said to be "on condition."

One STAW was placed in each of 24 pens, each measuring 2 feet 4 inches x 5 feet. A 2 feet high, solid metal partition, topped with a "cattle-fence" electrified wire, generally kept rats within their respective pens. Each of two 10 x 14 foot rooms contained 12 pens. Esterline-

TABLE 2.—Experimental Design

No., N, of Rats in a Group	Number of Groups	
	COOP	DISOP
2	5	5
4	3	3
8	2	2
16	1	1
32	1	1

Angus tape event recorders at 6 inch/hour indicated by an elevation of an inked recording pen if a rat was on each side of each STAW. Every press of a lever, whether or not a drop of water was delivered, made a mark. At a tape speed of 6 inch/hour, periods of lever-pressing effort left solid bands of ink due to the overlapping of adjoining marks. Examination of these records revealed whether the assigned condition was being met while the rat or rats were lever-pressing on any given STAW.

The 172 rats in this experiment were grouped as shown in Table 2. There was the same number of males and females in each group. Groups were formed at weaning at 27 days of age and allowed to remain on NO CONDITION for 35 days. Then each was allowed to remain on their respective "on condition" for the next 214 days. Inverted cardboard boxes, with holes cut in their sides, provided places of retreat. Females delivered young in them on the sawdust-covered floors and generally made nests from strips of paper toweling provided for this purpose. Young were counted and removed each 10 days. Both failure to conceive and failure to rear young to an average age of 5 days affected the obtained measure of reproductive success: Number of young surviving to removal per female per 100 days.

Detailed analysis of the records was confined to 6 24-hour periods. The first began at 2200 on a Friday after 10 days "on condition." The remaining five records analyzed began at the same time on the following five Fridays.

Basic Results

Numbers greater than 16 for COOP and 8 for DISOP reduced water consumption (Fig. 2). This reduced water consumption likely contributed to the lowered production of young and the reduced weight of males at these greater numbers. We may, therefore, suspect that in some way the efforts by one rat to obtain water were interfered with by its associates.

Opportunity for access to the lever must first be considered. The 6 24-hour periods analyzed in detail provided data encompassing 908 "rat days" (i.e., 908 24-hour periods). Equally weighting the means for the 10 basic subgroups gave a mean of 44 minutes per day spent by each rat in lever pressing. Except for a reduced effort by the survivors of the 32 DISOP group, this mean adequately describes the time (effort) spent in lever pressing by rats in all groups.

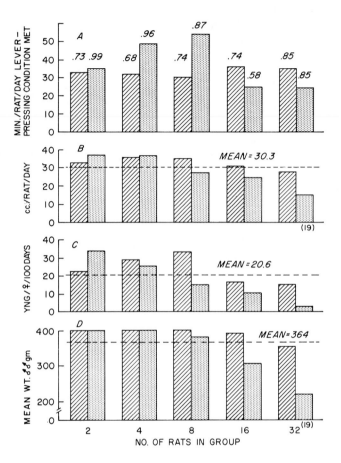

Fig. 2.—COOP-DISOP 2-4-8-16-32 N series study. COOP = crosshatched histograms; DISOP = stippled histograms. (A) Minutes of lever pressing per day per rat when the condition is met for securing water at each lever pressing. Histograms based on 6 24-hour periods, representing days 10, 17, 21, 28, 35, and 42 of "on condition." Rats also pressed the lever when the condition was not met. The proportion of total lever pressing during which the condition was met is given above each histogram. (B) Mean cc. of water consumed per rat per day for 53 days beginning with the 11th day of "on condition." (C) Number of young per female per 100 days for the 214 days following start of the "on condition," that is, for the period when the females increased from 61 to 275 days of age. The young were counted and removed each 10 days. (D) Mean weight of surviving males at 123 days of age after 62 days "on condition."

As may be seen from Table 3, with only 1440 minutes available in a 24 hour period, the 1408 minutes of effort required from 32 DISOP rats demanded that as soon as one rat stepped away from the STAW, another would be standing ready to replace him. But a great deal of time is excluded by sleep. My recently completed analyses of sleep indicate that 0.75 of all time is spent in this state. Furthermore, analyses of the lever-pressing records indicated that all groups persisted in a marked rhythm of activity and inactivity regardless of whether their water requirements were being fulfilled. Taking these several factors into consideration with respect to Table 3, it is obvious that at numbers of 8 and above for DISOP and 16 and above for COOP, rats will experience some difficulty finding a lever available when awake and

TABLE 3.—Use of Time per Lever in Pressing for Water by an Entire Group Based on 44 Minutes per Day per Rat

N	COOP		DISOP	
	Total minutes	Proportion of 24 hours	Total minutes	Proportion of 24 hours
2	44	.031	88	.061
4	88	.061	176	.122
8	176	.122	352	.244
16	352	.244	704	.489
32	704	.489	1408	.975

active. Thus both actual time available and restrictions on the use of available time imposed by physiological rhythms of sleep and activity increase the difficulty of obtaining water as the size of the group increases.

Under such circumstances too many associates simply become an ecological trap.

The two STAW conditions also generated behavioral changes, which, in aggravating the stresses arising from the use of available time, in themselves also represent ecological traps. Consider production of young by DISOP females, Figure 2(C). The mean number of young per female per 100 days declined from 34.2 to 25.4 to 14.9 to 10.6 to 3.0 through the N series 2-4-8-16-32, even though water consumption declined much less rapidly. I can only guess at the possible reason. Learning to avoid associates to the extent of not entering the opposite side of the STAW when one rat was already there on one side became a basic inculcated value. How this generalized to relationships outside the STAW is unknown. However, this avoidance may well have hampered proper execution of sexual and maternal behavior.

The marked inability of 32 DISOP females to produce young reflects the lasting impact of a temporary exceedingly restrictive condition. Within 15 days (Fig. 3) of being started on the DISOP condition nearly half of the 32 DISOP had died. This reduction occurred by 76 days of age, after which fell most of the reproductive span. And yet, although after this age the actual number of rats in the 16 DISOP and the 32 DISOP remained essentially the same, the latter produced less than one-third as many young during the next 178 days. Permanent impairment of performance appears to be a function of the magnitude of the initial stressful conditions.

A behavioral sink type phenomenon (see section 6), particularly among DISOP groups, greatly aggravated restriction on the opportunity for obtaining water imposed directly by increases in group size. For COOP groups, increase in number of rats fostered a more nearly equal use of the two sides of the STAW (Fig. 4). When one rat entered one side of the STAW the probability increased of another being awake and ready to enter the other side as the group size

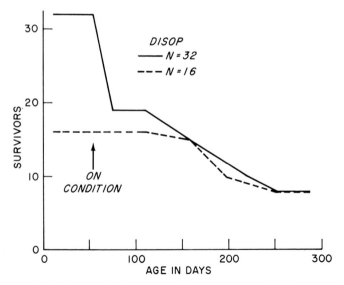

Fig. 3.—Survival curves for N = 16 and N = 32 for the DISOP groups. There was essentially no mortality among the other groups.

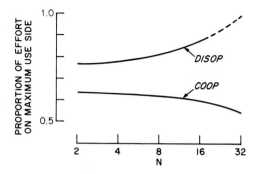

Fig. 4.—As the group size increased, COOP rats tended to utilize the two sides of the STAW more equally, whereas DISOP rats concentrated their efforts on one side. Theoretical curves based on least squares best fit values.

increased. However, the DISOP groups provided the more unexpected results. As the number of DISOP rats present increased, their tendency to concentrate activities on one side likewise increased (Fig. 4). Extrapolation of these data indicated that had all 32 DISOP rats survived they would have confined all activity to a single side of the STAW. Although all DISOP groups clearly developed a general preference for one side or the other, each shifted back and forth between the left and right side of the STAW over time. Thus, though a side preference became clearly established, each group clearly was a stochastic system within which the tendency of one rat to enter the STAW was influenced by which side a preceding rat was just completing his lever-pressing effort. In most instances, a DISOP rat entered the side immediately vacated by a predecessor.

At $N = 2$ for both COOP and DISOP most continuous lever-pressing efforts represented the activities of a single rat, and under each condition the mean duration of such effort was less than 3.0 minutes (Fig. 5). Where less than half a minute intervened between the termination of one burst of lever-pressing on a given side of the STAW and the start of another on the same side, the duration of the entire sequence was defined as a "continuous effort."

Prolongation of this mean duration of effort as the group size increased (Fig. 5) resulted from two or more rats lever-pressing in sequence. With only one side of the STAW effectively available to DISOP rats, the number of rats lever-pressing in sequence increased faster for DISOP than COOP groups as the number of rats present increased. Such increase in continuous effort as a function of increase in group size can be expected even if each rat behaves independently. Purely by chance, when one rat approaches the STAW, it will find

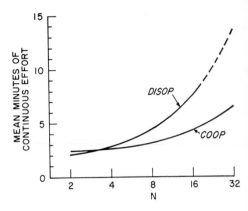

Fig. 5.—Queuing as a function of group size. With a mean of 2.3 minutes for lever-pressing efforts by individual rats, it may be seen that the number of rats pressing in sequence increases as the group size increases. Theoretical curves based on least squares best fit values.

another already there and will have to wait until this rat has finished before it can enter and begin lever-pressing.

Queuing

This queuing may result from chance or maybe intentional. Whenever a rat by chance immediately follows another, there exists the opportunity for associating opportunity for obtaining water with the presence of an associate at the STAW. A rat, having developed this association, will be attracted toward the STAW provided that some other rat is there, and pressing the lever. The larger the group, the more likely it is that development of such association may be anticipated and, therefore, the greater the queuing and the longer the spans of continuous effort.

Evaluation of the impact of queuing requires consideration of the lever-pressing by individual rats. When rats have not been exposed to the kinds of socialization training imposed by the COOP and DISOP conditions, the number of continuous lever-pressing efforts, as a function of their duration, conforms to a negative exponential of the form $y = e^{\,a+bx}$. In conjunction with my studies of the behavior of rats, many individuals have been temporarily isolated in a cage containing a single lever (a TAW, training apparatus water) similar to the two in the STAW. One group studied, designated as group 30.03, consisted of 75 rats which provided a sample of 12,563 separate efforts over a total of 4388 rat hours. The observed data, presented in Figure 6, are remarkably well described by a negative exponential equation. In terms of central nervous system function this implies that no matter how long an effort has already lasted, there is a constant probability of its terminating within an additional specified amount of time. For comparative purposes, one minute has been taken as the specified time, and p′ is assigned to denote the probability of terminating within one minute beyond any time the effort has already lasted; p′ here is 0.6546. Only 52 efforts lasted for longer than 5.0 minutes. Projection of the theoretical curve, shown as a dotted line in Figure 6, suggests that

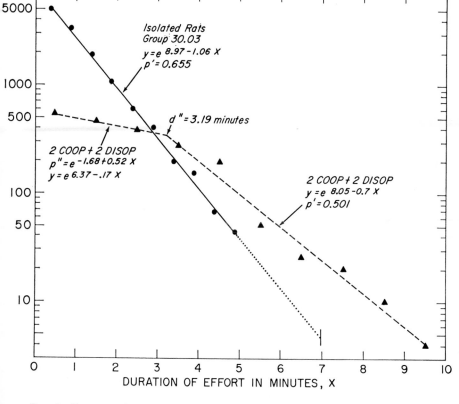

Fig. 6.—Frequency-duration curves of lever pressing by individual rats. All 75 of the 30.03 group, whose lever-pressing efforts were recorded in isolation, had previously lived as members of groups of either 3 or about 60 rats. Water was readily available to such rats in their normal habitat at all times by simply pressing a lever without having had to learn the COOP or DISOP task. Either COOP or DISOP learning tends to alter the curve, as in the illustrated example. This results in a longer mean duration of lever pressing by rats which have learned such a socially restrictive task.

in any rat's lifetime an effort of greater than seven minutes is highly improbable.

General observations indicated that queuing essentially never occurred among rats in two COOP and two DISOP groups. In other words, each measured duration of effort for rats among these smallest groups can be considered as the output of a single individual. Furthermore, the distributions of efforts for two COOP and two DISOP rats were sufficiently similar to justify pooling of data. Observed points are shown as triangle in Figure 6. Obviously, COOP and DISOP socialization training increases the average duration of effort. This increase is from a mean of 1.103 minutes for the group 30.03 rats to 2.253 minutes for the $N = 2$ COOP and DISOP rats.

This increase arises through alterations in CNS activity, which will be described in detail in a forthcoming paper. Beyond a duration, d'', here 3.19 minutes, the continuation of the effort is solely governed by the probability of a signal reflected by p', which here is slightly decreased to 0.501. At shorter durations than d'' there occurs a blocking of the circuit so that the CNS signal, which would terminate the effort, fails to exert its effect. The probability of this circuit *not* being blocked can be described by a probability, p'', which for this $N = 2$ COOP and DISOP data increases according to the equation: $p'' = e^{-1.68 + 0.52X}$. At 0.5, 1.5 and 2.5 minutes, p'' is respectively 0.243, 0.413, and 0.694; and at d'', $p'' = 1.0$. These remarks will be of assistance in relation to the more detailed discussion of these processes to be presented elsewhere.

For present purposes, the important conclusion is that such socialization training increases the mean duration of effort. In another comparable COOP-DISOP study, representative individuals from an N series of 3-6-12-24 were isolated from their social field, and the duration of their efforts were recorded. Regardless of the COOP or DISOP background, or the group size, blocking of the CNS circuit, which normally permitted termination of the effort, increased the duration of effort on an average very comparable to that shown in Figure 6 for the $N=2$ COOP and DISOP rats. Thus, without going into the details of this analysis, it seems justified to assume that the average duration of effort by individual rats is of the order of 2.3 minutes regardless of the particular COOP or DISOP condition or of the group size. Thus, queuing efforts lasting 30, 45, and 60 minutes respectively, must have included 13, 20, and 26 sequential efforts.

As the group size increased from 4 to 8, to 16, to 32, the influence of queuing on the frequency distribution of efforts was such that a quadratic equation, rather than a simple negative exponential, more precisely described the distribution. Present data are inadequate to determine the relative contribution of chance and learning to the increase in duration of continuous efforts.

However, for DISOP rats in both the $N=8$ and $N=16$ groups, there were 9 exceptionally long efforts which appeared too long to be attributed to chance queuing. Excluding these 9 long efforts, the observed points and calculated quadratic equations approximating them are shown in Figure 7. Extrapolation of the theoretical curve for the 8-DISOP to include an additional 9 efforts resulted in their having

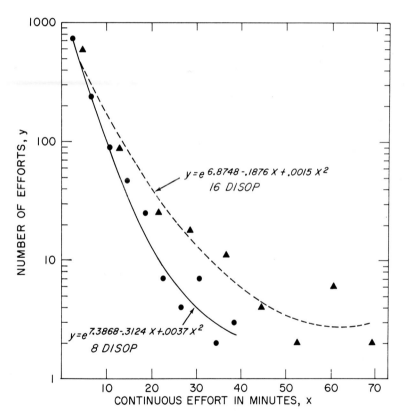

Fig. 7.—The impact of DISOP socialization training on the duration of lever-pressing effort. Dividing any point on the curves by 2.3 minutes, the average duration of lever pressing for water by an individual rat, indicates the approximate number of rats involved in a continuous queuing effort.

an expected mean duration of 47.1 minutes, whereas the mean for the observed exceptionally long means was 63.2 minutes. Similarly for the 16-DISOP rats, the theoretical mean for the 9 long efforts was 81.1 minutes, whereas the observed was 142.3 minutes.

These latter represent the best quantitative data indicating that social attraction increases the duration of queuing, at least for DISOP rats. Casual observations reinforced the conclusion that this learned social attraction could produce a behavioral sink (see section 6) with broad consequences. The following remarks equally describe the 16-DISOP groups through much of their history, as well as the 32-DISOP groups, until decimated by mortality.

Side preference was rapidly acquired by all DISOP rats. While the rats were still far from fully grown, the screen cover over the two sides of the STAW produced channels sufficiently large to accommodate several rats. One rat would enter and begin pressing. Another would then follow on the same side, and the two would simultaneously try to press and drink from the raised cup of water. Gradually, other rats would enter and jam themselves in toward the lever, even though they could not get to the lever or to the cup of water. Depending upon the age of the rats, the channel would become completely jammed by the time four to eight rats were present. This near-immobile mass would remain in the STAW channel for long periods. Gradually, the outermost rats would back off, frequently without having obtained any water. Then all would roam around for a short while before going to sleep. This resulted in a striking coordination of periods of activity and rest by all members of the group. Most would be sleeping, while the STAW remained vacant, or most would be jammed into one side of the STAW with few of the participants obtaining any water. As their accumulated water deficit worsened, their learning to avoid entering a side of the STAW if another rat was on the opposite side was overcome by the drive to approach the source of water. At this stage, at least in the 32-DISOP groups, both sides of the STAW would become jammed with rats, even though none could obtain any water. At this stage, long periods of sleep involving all members of the group were interspersed by shorter periods involving most members, during which they crowded into both sides of the STAW. This process led to the death of nearly half the rats of the 32-DISOP group within the first 15 days (Fig. 3).

This coordination of rest and activity also became fairly pronounced among COOP rats of N=16 and N=32. It is possible that such coordination of rest and activity is purely a consequence of chance factors in these very complex stochastic systems. And yet one must suspect that among these larger groups, on both COOP and DISOP conditions of social training, many rats do further associate the presence of other rats at the STAW with their own obtaining of water, to the point that the chance queuing phenomena becomes pathologically exaggerated.

Conflict of Values

What I shall say here is obviously anecdotal, a budding serendipity. If I am correct in the import of these observations, a whole field of comparative experimental research opens up.

We shall consider the 16-COOP and the 16-DISOP groups during the period starting about three months after they were placed on their respective conditions. All rats were physically mature at this time. The 16-COOP rats had learned their task sufficiently well that no rat experienced any appreciable deficit in water intake. Two slightly different ways of dealing with the situation had developed. Starting with no rat on or at the STAW, one rat would approach and enter one side and remain just in front of the lever without pressing it. One of his associates would immediately approach and enter the other side of the STAW. The rapidity of this second rat's response indicates an awareness by it of the first rat's intent and need. As soon as both were positioned in front of their respective levers, each simultaneously began pressing. As soon as one terminated pressing, the other did likewise, and both would back out of the STAW. An even more-refined procedure of initiating the paired pressing began with one rat positioning itself outside the STAW, but facing into one side. This stance served to attract another rate nearly immediately to position itself in front of the other side. Then they would simultaneously proceed into their respective channels and begin pressing. In either case, the behavior of the second rat may be termed altruistic. Both kinds of initiating cooperative behavior characterized all COOP groups.

In contrast, after five months on condition the very size of the 16-DISOP group continued to interfere with adequate securing of water. Despite a persisting slight water deficit for most 16-DISOP rats, it was clearly evident that every member had learned its task well. Rare indeed were the instances when one of these rats would enter an empty channel, if an associate was already on the other side.

Thus my term "disoperation" simply means to collaborate by staying out of each other's way.

In each group every rat had learned the role appropriate for maximizing benefits possible under the respective situations imposed by the STAWS. Such a role denotes a relationship of one rat to another. Assumption of these roles reduced constraints to action and indeterminancy of action. The role of one individual complemented that of his associates and led to an increase in the probability of realizing expectancies. Dr. Joel Elkes[5] refers to this as "increase in trust." This "increase in trust" can only follow from what Dr. Ernst Caspari[5] calls "ethical behavior"—that behavior by one individual which maximizes the realization of expectancies by others.

Every COOP and every DISOP rat had developed a role of behaving ethically appropriate to its own situation.

Still the constraint of time available for lever-pressing by the 16-DISOP rats interfered with acquisition of water, since they had to confine their activities to a single side of the STAW. In contrast, the STAW available to the 16-COOP rats was more frequently vacant due to the simultaneous use of both sides.

After a little over three months "on condition," one male rat among the 16-DISOP group learned to climb up on the water reservoir in its pen, jump over the electrified fence separating his home pen and that of the adjoining 16-COOP group, to the top of the water reservoir in their pen, and hence down into their pen. If not immediately, then after a short while he would find the 16-COOP STAW empty. He would enter and approach the lever. Before he had hardly started pressing, certainly before he could realize that pressing alone here provided him with no water, one of the COOP rats would come over and enter the other side.

To this invading DISOP male, his COOP companion's behavior was all wrong. He would immediately back out, grasp the "offending" COOP rat by the tail or hind feet and pull it out. This happened every time this invading male entered the COOP rats' STAW. I kept returning this male to his DISOP companions, but he persisted in jumping back over into the 16-COOP pen. During the following weeks he macerated the tails and hind feet of all the COOP rats. Most lost all their toes. Seven died from these wounds. And yet the invading male was never attacked. To the COOP rats this invading DISOP male was always behaving correctly when it entered the STAW and their ethical standards dictated that they come to his rescue.

Had it not been for this single male I would have confined my thinking about social behavior among rats to no more than to acquisition of roles. Through his activities it is clear that rats make value judgments as to the rightness or wrongness of the actions of the actions of associates. This insight now makes it possible to launch experimental research on integration and conflict of values with an animal so lowly as the rat.

Adjustment to COOP and DISOP conditions.

A second group size (N) series of 3-6-12-24 was run to gain additional insight. Prior to formation of these all-male groups, each rat was isolated from weaning to 112 days of age in a cage where each rat received all its water by pressing a mechanical lever. Groups were formed at this age, at which time the mean weight per group varied between 325 and 375 grams, and all groups were placed "on condition." This increase in size prevented the large aggregations on one side of the STAW, characterizing the early stages of the initial study. By the end of the 50 days on condition, the 18 surviving 24-DISOP had gained an average of only 9 grams whereas members of all other groups had, on the average, gained 58 to 94 grams. Thus, there had been fairly successful accommodation by all but the one group.

Detailed analyses of the Esterline-Angus records revealed many differences in the accommodation to the required conditions among the several groups. These proved so complex as to obviate any definite conclusions about the overall processes involved. Ignoring these details, water consumption alone provides the general picture (Fig. 8). Despite differences in rate of increase in water consumption among groups, all except the 24-DISOP presented a general picture of a twofold increase within the first 8 days. After this time the daily intake fluctuated about the mean of 37.3 cc./rat/day. All members of all these groups thus made a fairly rapid successful adjustment.

However, the 24-DISOP rats started off with less than one-third the necessary intake, and this continued through the first 7 days by which time each rat had, on the average, encountered a deficit of 207 cc. of water; each rat had consumed only 20 per cent of its normal requirements. All became extremely emaciated. Six died during the next 10 days. As the group became reduced from 24 to 18, learning ensued so that by the 20th day, and continuing to the 30th day, the survivors of the 24-DISOP group maintained an adequate water intake not diverging significantly from that of the other groups. On that day an accident occurred which engendered consequences justifying description.

"Memory trace erasure"

On the 30th day a severe summer storm caused a temporary failure of the electrical power. The overload accompanying resumption of power blew the fuse controlling the 24 hour cycle of bright lights in the experimental rooms. Four 10-watt lamps in each room on a separate circuit remained continuously on. The overloading did not affect that circuit, so they continued to burn. Normally, 4 150-watt lamps in each room came on at 2200 of one day and continued to 1000 on the following day. This "reverse" light cycle, with dim light from 1000 to 2200 each day, made it possible to observe rats more readily when they were in their period of heightened activity. The storm occurred on a Friday when only the dim lights were on, and I failed to realize until the following Tuesday that the bright lights were not being turned on at the appropriate time. Thus, for over 4 days the rats were subjected only to the continuous dim light supplied by the 4 10-watt lamps.

Despite this 4 day absence of the light cycle all rats but those in the 24-DISOP group maintained their normal intake of water. For the latter, water intake dropped precipitously to the level characterizing their first exposure to the DISOP condition (Fig. 8). Even after reinstitution of the normal 24 hour light cycle, low intake continued for four more days and all rats became quite thin.

During these four days the rats were observed to persist in entering both sides simultaneously. They presented a picture consistent with the interpretation that they had completely forgotten the task they had previously learned adequately. Between the fifth and ninth day after resumption of the light cycle, learning the task was again accomplished.

I do not know what happened within the central nervous systems of these 24-DISOP rats. Nor have I had the opportunity to explore further this potential bit of serendipity. However, one sees an indication of how tenuous the memory trace of learned behaviors may be when acquired under duress and maintained only through very precise coordination of periods of rest and activity among the members of the group.

However, one must question this possible interpretation—that there had been a loss of memory. On the basis of both COOP-DISOP studies, about 44 minutes of lever-pressing effort per rat per day is required to obtain adequate water. With 18 survivors this means 792 minutes per day or over half the available time, and most of this time must be utilized on "condition met." With every rat tending to sleep 75 per cent of the time this means that there must be extraordinary coordination of periods of rest and activity. Under continuous light conditions the endogenous circadian rhythm tends to be slightly different from 24 hours, and the exact duration differs among individuals. Therefore, among a group of 18 individuals over a 4 day period, the timing of each rat's activity might be anticipated to diverge from its prior relationship with its associates. This would increase the probability that, when one rat awoke, it would find another already on the STAW, and sleep might resume without this rat having obtained any water. As the water deficit became more intense, the drive to be near the lever would overcome the learned behavior not to go on the STAW if another rat was already there. I suspect that this interpretation is a more likely one, rather than there having been a loss of the memory trace of the learned behavior.

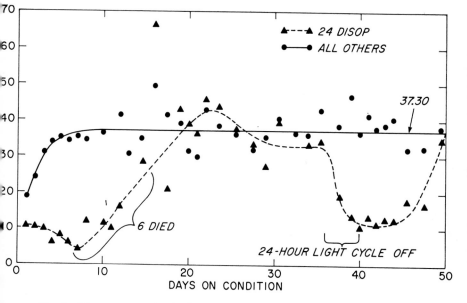

Fig. 8.—Water consumption in the 3-6-12-24 N series. Lines merely approximate trends. Each dot represents the mean of the mean water consumption for all groups other than the 24-DISOP.

It indicates the likely importance of an exogenous 24 hour cycle in preserving the timing of activities in which great precision is required in order to prevent interference.

4. AGGRESSION AND GROUP SIZE

Certain actions by one individual toward another may be designated as being aggressive. Any aggression may be reduced to a two-party action or interaction. And yet any two such individuals rarely live in isolation, but rather as members of some larger group. I shall attempt to show that an understanding of aggression requires consideration of the present size of the group, as well as of the evolutionary history of the species since it has influenced the typical group size. Examination of aggression from such an ecological point of view will introduce concepts not customarily introduced in the evaluation of the characteristics and consequences of aggression.

Development of a formulation applicable to many species, including man, is the basic objective. Though each species manifests species-specific reactions, I shall view all species as subject to a universal set of processes. I will present or describe the kinds of data which give rise to the general formulation and which suggest that it has utilitarian as well as heuristic value. Some of the concepts referred to here are elaborated elsewhere.[1,6]

BASIC GROUP SIZE

After circumstances force a species to persist for many generations within a narrow range of variability in group size, genetic adaptations arise which favor achievement of optimum physiological states by individuals who do live as members of groups approximating the typical size. As these genetic adaptations arise, they foster the origin of other adaptations, whose function is to assure that the size of the group will not diverge from the range imposed by external environmental conditions. These latter genetic adaptations further restrict the species to the habitat originally promoting their origin.

A *basic group*, N_b, refers to the mean number of adult individuals in a typical group of a species which has undergone those genetic changes making it advantageous for its members to live in groups of a particular size.

For the Norway rat, a species I have studied[7-9] intensively in both its wild and domesticated forms, the basic group appears to consist of about 12 individuals. Through most of his history, nearly up to historical times, the gatherer-hunter forerunner of modern cultural man likely conformed to a basic group of about 12 adults. Though many basic group sizes exist, it is no mere coincidence that many species, such as those which diverge so much morphologically as do rat and man, are characterized by a basic group of 12. I have shown that the physics of the utilization of space, by any form in which each individual maintains a fixed home and in which mutual antagonisms produce a wide spacing of home sites, must lead to the origin of a basic group of 12 as attractions between neighbors gain ascendancy over antagonisms.

ELYSIAN AGGRESSION

For the purposes of my thesis an ideal group will be considered as one of basic size N_b, in which every member is identical. Being identical here denotes that the actions of one's associates causes no divergence from, or inhibition of, an ideal way of behaving. At times each individual finds himself in a state of desiring some gratifying interaction with another individual. When two such individuals meet, each contributes through appropriate behavior to the fulfillment of the other's need for social intercourse. The behavior of each represents a *facilitation* culminating in the *gratification* of the other. *Gratification* becomes synonymous with a refractory state lasting for a period of time proportional to the intensity of interaction. The existence of such refractory periods following social interaction represents the basic premise necessary for understanding the origin of aggression. Any individual in such a refractory state may be called a "refractory individual."

When an animal is in a gratifying refractory state it can still interact with others who are still in the need state. However, this refractory individual will not respond appropriately for fulfilling the social need of the other. Such an inappropriate response is here defined as *aggression*. Its consequence is to place the individual, which had approached while in the social need state, into a state of *frustration*. This state of *frustration* continues through a refractory period which also lasts for a time that is proportional to the intensity of interaction.

Furthermore, such an individual while in a frustrating refractory state can still interact with associates. If they happen to be in the social need state, his action toward them will be inappropriate to the fulfillment of their needs, and they also will be thrown into a state of frustration as a consequence of this aggressive action from the individual already in a refractory state. Note that I have postulated that a state of frustration may arise from interacting with others regardless of whether they are in a state of gratification or frustration. The inappropriate behavior, the aggression, stemming from these two states may be qualitatively different, but for the purposes of the present formulation such differences may be ignored.

Contacts also occur between two individuals, both of whom are in a refractory state. No such contact contributes to either the gratification or frustration of either individual; any such social interaction is strictly of a neutral nature. Furthermore, every individual which exhibits an aggressive action toward an associate by so doing in no way alters the duration of the refractory state he happens to be in, whether it be of gratification or frustration.

These statements represent my basic formulation[1,6,10] within which aggression gains perspective. To reiterate, an aggressive act is merely one in which an individual in a refractory state of either gratification or frustration behaves inappropriately with respect to the requirement of fulfilling the need for social intercourse felt by another. An individual thus frustrated in his attempts at effective social intercourse is frustrated simply in the sense of failing to have his behavior rewarded. An aggressive act becomes synonymous with a negative sanction. An aggressive act may assume the form of violent action, but is just as effective in a more mild and sublimated form, so long as the individual in the social need state recognizes the behavior of the one with whom he sought interaction as being inappropriate to the fulfillment of his own needs.

We may now consider the consequences of membership in a closed group of the optimum basic group size. The time spent in either of the two refractory states, gratification or frustration, will be proportional to the intensity of interaction. That is to say the duration of a state will be proportional to the product of the intensities of action or behaving of the two individuals involved in an interaction. During evolution, animals will develop capacities for exhibiting intensities of action toward others compatible with maximizing the total amount of time spent in the gratification-type refractory state. It is this accommodation of intensity of interaction to the dynamics of life in a particular sized group which leads to the origin of the basic group size.

Even under the most ideal circumstances only one-fourth of the interactions involving any particular individual culminate in a refractory state of gratification. By similar mathematical reasoning it followed that when members of a group attempt to maximize the amount of gratification they can derive from social intercourse, they will equally frequently become involved in encounters culminating in the refractory state of frustration. Placed in terms of the behavior of the individual whose actions lead to the refractory state of another, it is plain that half will be facilitative and half aggressive with reference to satisfying social needs. Half of all interactions will also be of the neutral type, but they do not concern us for the moment.

Since aggressive acts are received as frequently as facilitative ones, there must have arisen through evolution a genetic constitution compatible with adjustment to the physiological consequences of this degree of frustration. Once this hereditary adaptation to aggression has arisen, any individual who happens to be receiving more facilitative than aggressive acts from associates will, in order to achieve the natural balance between gratification and frustration, actively seek situations increasing the probability that others will behave toward him in an aggressive way. Aggressive acts thus may be viewed as nonspecific stressors of physiology requisite to maintain the physiology of the individual in harmony with its genetic constitution. Thus, when I say that there is an Elysian amount of aggression, I mean just this. The dynamics of social interaction are such that aggression is as necessary a component of social life as is facilitation. For maximizing his well-being—happiness, if you wish—each individual must experience frustration as frequently as gratification (Fig. 10).

The consequences of aggression observed in a group of mice

All statements in the previous section are strictly theoretical and are documented in detail elsewhere.[1,6,10] We will now briefly examine empirical results[11] obtained from detailed observation of an experimental group of mice. This group consisted of 11 adult males reared together since weaning. Each had the opportunity of developing stable relationships with every other individual prior to my observations of their social interactions. These mice belonged to a genetic strain which had been brother-sister inbred for nearly a hundred generations. For this reason each of these individuals possessed as near identical heredity as it is possible to obtain from an artificial system of mating. Thus to the extent that genetic constitution determines behavior, each individual should respond in the same way as every other individual. All individuals had been reared in an identical physical environment, so that such nonsocial aspects of the environment should have in no way contributed to divergence in behavior from one individual to another. Furthermore, this physical environment was a comparatively rich one, one which should be compatible with a near-optimum-sized group as represented by these 11 individuals.

With lower animals, as with man, it is often difficult to judge every action in terms of its consequences being neutral, gratifying, or frustrating. Therefore, we will consider a variable which reflects the consequences of social interaction. This variable, which I call *velocity*, is a measure of the amount of time an individual spends in that portion of its home range or field of action where it is maximally exposed to contacting associates and thus becoming involved in social interaction. Figure 9 provides the results. The individuals are here ranked in terms of the velocity of their entering the social field. Despite genetic identity, there had developed a marked difference in behavior as reflected by velocity, in which the individual which exhibited the greatest avoidance of the social field had only 16 per cent the velocity of the socially most active individual.

In what way are these results compatible with the formulation of social interaction presented in the prior section? That formulation assumed that, despite some behaviors not being rewarded, no divergence of behavior from the ideal type would arise. Instead, let us consider that whenever an individual is frustrated in its attempts at seeking satisfaction of its need for social intercourse, its behavior will diverge somewhat from the ideal, appropriate manner of acting toward an associate.

In the beginning, as social relations develop among genetically identical members of the group, the manner in which any individual approaches any other will be identical. As a starting point, we may also assume each individual to be in the state of needing social intercourse. For the first two individuals which meet, each will be capable of contributing to the gratification of the other. Once this happens each will be for a while in the refractory state of gratification, during which time neither is capable of behaving appropriately for contributing to the gratification of any other individual they might meet. The third individual among the group, which meets another, might meet one of these first two. If this happened, he would be frustrated rather than gratified as a result of this encounter. Thus, the greater the lapse of time from the meeting of the first two individuals before a given individual meets some other one, the greater the probability will be that when he encounters some other individual this individual will already be in a refractory state. Once such a system persists over considerable periods of time, it is obvious that some individuals will, purely by chance, be much more frequently frustrated than others. Each time it is thus frustrated, it will by this very fact not be rewarded for behaving the way it did in seeking satisfaction of its social drive. This lack of reward will result, not because it failed to behave appropriately, but merely from the fact that the individual approached was in a refractory state and thus not receptive to such approaches. Each time such a behavior is not rewarded, its next expression may be anticipated to diverge from its appropriate expression. On this individual's next encounter with another, who also is in the social need

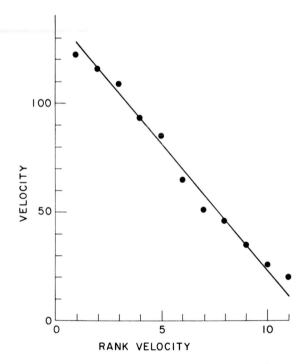

Fig. 9.—The relationship between the velocity of an individual and the rank of its velocity. These data are for a group of 11 inbred C57 Black 10 mice. See Table 7 (reference 11) and Table XIV (reference 1) for original data. The straight line was calculated using Equation (2) above and assuming $N_0 = 11$.

state, its behavior will not be completely appropriate. Therefore, there will result a certain amount of ambivalence in the total behavior of the other individual to this one with the slightly altered behavior. To the extent that this latter individual's behavior is appropriate, its partner will reward it for so behaving, by in return responding in such a way as to facilitate the other's behavior and thus contribute to its gratification. However, to the extent that the individual with the altered behavior fails to respond appropriately, his partner will respond so as to reject these advances. As a result, a mixed state of gratification and frustration will arise.

Continuing this process over long periods of time, these will arise an end state in which the behavior of each individual differs from every other, although all have identical heredity. At one end of the spectrum will be the individual who has preserved the ideal or prototype way of behaving which conforms to that whose original expression was most heavily weighted by heredity factors. On the opposite end we find individuals whose behavior has markedly diverged from the ideal prototype and who have experienced a high proportion of frustration in their effort to satisfy their need for gratification from social intercourse. The more an animal withdraws socially, as evidenced by its lowered velocity, the more deviant will be its behavior.

Furthermore, we may inquire as to the likely response to the heightened frequency of aggressive actions which culminate in frustration. Withdrawal from those places and times in which heightened aggression had been experienced represents a possible avenue of adjustment. Integration of this assumption leads to an equation from which the expected velocities in a closed group of basic size may be calculated[6] In relative terms we may assign a velocity of 1.0 to that individual whose behavior has diverged least, which has experienced the least excess of aggression, and which therefore has withdrawn least from the social milieu. This individual may be called the alpha member of the group. At the opposite extreme is the omega individual. Where there are N individuals in a basic group, the velocity of the omega individual will be only 1/Nth that of the alpha individual.

Let

$v_R^{(r)}$ = the relative velocity of any Rth ranked individual. Here (r) indicates that velocity is relative to the value of 1.0 for the alpha, highest velocity, individual. R = rank. There are N ranks in a group of N individuals; R_1 is the rank of the α individual, the one with the highest velocity.

N_o = the optimum group size. The basic group size N_b is always the optimum group size, but, under certain circumstances detailed elsewhere,[1] the actual group can vary from the basic size and still represent an optimum-sized group with respect to maximizing gratification.

Then

$$v_R^{(r)} = \frac{(N_o - R) + 1}{N_o} \ . \tag{1}$$

As N becomes greater than N_o, that is to say as the actual group size increases above the optimum, the relative velocities of all members will decline. Since the alpha, 1st ranked, individual will always have the highest velocity, the changes occurring in its velocity (Table 4) best reflect how the increase in group size dampens the dynamics of the entire group.

In actual practice in the study of an experimental group we obtain some estimate of velocity, v, for each individual which is merely the sum of the number of times the individual is observed to enter that

TABLE 4.—Effect of Increasing Group Size, N, on the Social Velocity and the Social Temperature of the Alpha-Ranked Individual

Conditions: N_o = 12, N varies, $v_\alpha^{(r)}$ at N_o = 1.0, $v_\Omega^{(r)}$ at N_o = .083.

N	Social Velocity $v_\alpha^{(r)}$ at N	Social Temperature $v_\alpha^{(t)}$* at N
12	1.000	1.000
24	.542	.501
48	.314	.251
72	.236	.167
96	.199	.127
120	.176	.101
144	.160	.084
168	.150	.073
192	.140	.062
216	.135	.057
240	.129	.050
264	.125	.045

*The log of $v_\alpha^{(t)}$ as a function of log N forms a straight line with a negative slope of minus one.

portion of the field where social interactions are most likely to occur. For experimental groups of mice and rats, such as I have studied, one structures the habitat so that food and water are available in one portion of the field and places for sleeping are in another part of the field. It regularly happens that most social interactions, including those not related to obtaining food and water, do take place in the vicinity where food and water happen to be available. For this reason each time an animal enters that portion of the habitat where food and water are available it is given a velocity score. v then represents the sum of these scores for some arbitrary period of time. Due to chance factors of sampling, these estimates of velocity will vary from that anticipated from the general theory, that aggression causes withdrawal and reduction in velocity in proportion to the amount of aggression received. Nevertheless, it is possible[1,6] to develop an equation permitting the calculation of the expected velocity of each member of the group in terms of such observational estimates of velocity.

Let

^{v}R = The expected velocity of any Rth ranked individual.

Then

$$^{v}R = \left[\frac{(N_o - R) + 1}{N_o} \right] \left[\frac{2 \sum_{R=1}^{N} {}^{v}R}{N_o + 1} \right]. \tag{2}$$

Such expected velocities are given by the straight line in Figure 9. $X^2 = 8.001$, which with 10 degrees of freedom has a p of 0.629. On this basis the observed certainly does not deviate significantly from the expected.

This conformity, of course, does not prove the validity of my formulation of social interaction, but it does suggest that I am possibly on the right track. And if the general formulation approximates the true processes involved, it follows that the particular aspects concerned with aggression and social withdrawal also approximate reality.

Groups of above optimum size

Even though evolution may have led to some basic group size being the usual optimum, various factors cause the actual group size to vary markedly from this optimum, at least on a temporary basis. This variability will affect the total amount of frustration and gratification experienced by the individual because frequency of contact between individuals will be altered. Elsewhere[1] I have presented details for calculating the total time in each of these two states under the special condition in which all individuals are identical and their behavior remains unaltered as a consequence of involvement in social interaction. Figure 10 presents such calculations diagrammatically, for the special case where $N_b = 12$.

At the basic group size each of these two states develops for equal amounts of time. This equality of time spent in frustration and in gratification represents the optimum condition. As the group diminishes in size, both frustration and gratification diminish from the optimum, until for the completely isolated individual none of either is experienced. As the group increases above its optimum size, frustration increases and gratification decreases. When the group becomes very large, each individual is in a state of frustration most of the time, with gratification only very rarely experienced.

Note that as the group increases in numbers above its basic size frustration increases much more rapidly above the optimum than

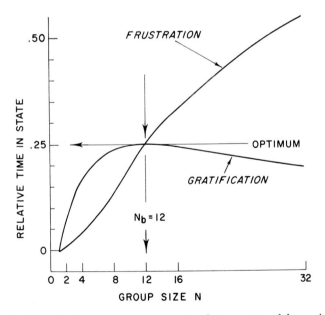

Fig. 10.—The relative amount of time spent in the two states of frustration and gratification will diverge from the optimum as the actual group size diverges from the optimum or basic group size, N_b. Curves are based on Table XI of my paper "The Social Use of Space."[1]

gratification declines below the optimum. This means that, as the group exceeds its basic size, aggression will play a more important role than facilitation.

Observed effects of increased group size and of a "tranquilizing" agent, vitamin A.

This section places particular emphasis on dietary vitamin A in relationship to the behavior of rats living in a fairly complex environment.[1,8,9] My concern with vitamin A had a chance origin. In a prior study[8] in this same habitat certain pathologies suggested a dysfunction of vitamin A metabolism; livers of adult rats contained much more stored vitamin A than would be anticipated on a diet of natural foodstuffs; and the Purina Ralston Co. verified that they did in fact fortify the diet we used with vitamin A. Since all rats involved in this earlier experiment obtained greater than normal levels of vitamin A, I could only speculate that it may have contributed to the observed behavioral pathology.[8] Systematic control of dietary vitamin A in the study reported here merely represents an exploration of this hunch.

We will here consider two closed groups of Osborne-Mendel albino rats in each of which 32 adult males survived through the period of study. Associated with them was an approximately similar number of adult females along with about 40 juveniles. Our concern will be only with the adult males as a group having a distinct social structure independent of their other associates. Each group was provided with an identical, synthetic, and amply nutritional diet, in which only one component, vitamin A, differed in amount between groups. The diet of the group living in experimental room 1A included 3 International Units (I.U.) of vitamin A per gram of diet, while the group inhabiting experimental room 2A included 12 I.U. vit.A/gm. diet. The 3 I.U. vitamin A diet approximates the level of this vitamin available from natural food stuffs, to which the animal is therefore best adapted. For reasons given below, vitamin A acts as a kind of tranquilizer. Its action appears to reduce the degree of aggression elicited by specific characteristics of behavior by associates.

It is not known whether the tranquilizing effect produced by the higher vitamin A diet is caused by the immediate effects of the greater intake level or by the higher storage level in the liver. These storage levels are given below for the 29 of 32 rats in each group which survived to the terminal autopsy. The two age cohorts, designated as Tier I and Tier II, are presented separately:

Tier I Rats			
Vitamin A Diet	No. of Rats	Mean Age in Days	Mean I.U. Vit. A. per Whole Liver
3 I.U.	16	500 ±20.6	27,823 ±6,401
12 I.U.	13	494 ±15.6	40,733 ±7,160

Tier II Rats			
Vitamin A Diet	No. of Rats	Mean Age in Days	Mean I.U. Vit. A. per Whole Liver
3 I.U.	13	409 ±28.5	18,278 ±3,236
12 I.U.	9	357 ±64.0	26,268 ±3,423

The measure of velocity was taken as the number of half hour periods, out of a sample of 32 such periods, that a rat entered the center of the field near the source of food and water. A mean velocity for each rat was derived from three such sets of 32 half-hours of observation. These mean velocities, $\hat{v}$ plotted against rank velocity are shown in Figure 11. Although the velocities of the 3 I.U. rats are depressed considerably below those of the 12 I.U. rats, lines drawn through the two sets of observed points converge at rank 32, the rank of the lowest velocity, omega rat. This convergence contributes a critical premise to the general formulation. It appears that there is some minimum velocity below which further social withdrawal cannot be made without the animal so disrupting its physiology as to augment the probability of dying. This minimum velocity becomes the velocity regularly reached by the omega individual within a basic group. Had there not been this limiting factor of a minimum tolerable velocity, and if 32 rats represented the basic group size, the velocity-velocity rank curves would be as shown by the dashed lines in Figure 11, as calculated by Equation (2).

However, given the limitation of a minimum velocity, it follows from Equation (2) that a curve, as shown by the upper double-barred line in Figure 11, would result. This curve represents the prediction that the velocity of the alpha ranked, highest-velocity rat would have been 106 rather than 38 in the 3 I.U. group and 58 in the 12 I.U. group.

However, there is every reason to believe that 32 rats far exceed the optimum-sized group. Therefore, the observed curves lead to the conclusion that when the group size does exceed the basic or optimum size there results a marked depression of the velocities of all individuals toward the minimum tolerable level. This general reduction in velocity conforms to that expected from the increased level of aggression, and thus frustration, which must accompany increases in group size above the optimum (Figure 10, "Groups of Above Optimum Size").

Furthermore, in terms of the prior symbols it may be shown that where the actual group size, N, may vary from N_o:

$$^v R^{(r)} = \left[\frac{(N - R)\ (N_o - 1)}{N\ (N - 1)} \right] + \frac{1}{N_o} \qquad . \quad (3)$$

Reference is here made to an optimum-sized group rather than to a basic-sized group. The latter refers strictly to an optimum-sized group in the habitat within which the evolution of the species took place. With reference to that species' heredity, an equivalent amount of frustration

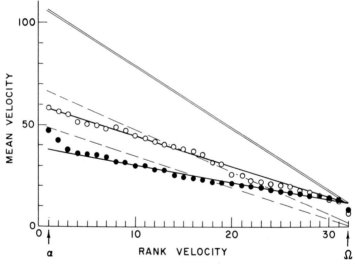

Fig. 11.—Some relationships between velocity and rank-velocity of Osborne-Mendel albino Norway rats. Open circles and the solid line through them represent the observed data for the 32 rats on the 12 I.U. of vitamin A per gram of diet. Solid dots and the solid line through them represent the observed data for the rats on the 3 I.U. of vitamin A per gram of diet. The upper and lower dashed lines are respectively those expected for the 12 I.U. and the 3 I.U. rats, provided 32 individuals represent the optimum-sized group and provided there is no hereditarily determined lower limit to velocity. However, provided there is a minimum tolerable velocity, as indicated by the convergence of the observed data, and provided that 32 is the basic group size, the expected curve becomes that shown by the double line.

and gratification may only be achieved at a slightly greater or lesser group size due to the fact that the particular configuration of the habitat alters the frequency of contacts among individuals. This different group size from N_b is therefore referred to as the optimum group size, N_o. Through procedures given elsewhere[1,6] it can be shown that the optimum group size for the albino strain of rat used in my experimental habitat is about 9, rather than the 12 which does closely approximate the size of groups formed by wild rats living under essentially natural conditions.[1,7]

Returning now to the observed data on velocities in Figure 11, the obvious fact stands out that, for some reason, those rats on the higher vitamin A diet exhibited less suppression of velocity than one would anticipate on the basis of the large-sized group in which the rats did live. From the theory, one would anticipate less aggression among the higher vitamin A rats. Although in an established group of rats much aggression is in the sublimated form of threats, there nevertheless does occur much overt fighting in which rats receive wounds, most frequently in the posterior dorsal region of the body. Usually wounds heal within two weeks, but the accumulated scar tissue prevents regeneration of hair. Periodically each rat was assessed on the basis of a five point rating scale as to the amount of scar tissue. A rating of one indicated practically no scar tissue, while a rating of five indicated that the posterior portion of the back was nearly a solid mass of scar tissue. The mean values of this scar tissue index for the 11 highest and 11 lowest velocity rats from each of the two vitamin A diet groups was calculated. At 12 months of age these means were:

Velocity	Vitamin A	Scar Tissue Index
High v	3 I.U.	4.2
High v	12 I.U.	3.4
Low v	3 I.U.	3.3
Low v	12 I.U.	1.7

Both high and low velocity rats on the high vitamin A diet received fewer wounds than the respective velocity categories on the low, that is the normal level, vitamin A diet. All the dominant and/or territorial rats on each diet fell within the high velocity category. At first glance one might anticipate that, contrary to the findings, the subordinate low velocity rats would be characterized by more scar tissue. However, what had taken place, as could be seen in the history of each group, was that by social withdrawal early in life, when aggression among young peer groups and from adults is generally of the mild sublimated threat kind, these low velocity rats by developing a low velocity avoided social encounters subjecting them to overt attack.

At the time the observations were made, which permitted calculation of a mean observed velocity, $\hat{v}$, for each rat, detailed records were also made of the majority of interactions between pairs of males, Many of these involved status relationships in which each member of the interacting pair could be designated as being dominant or subordinate. Without distinguishing between these two consequences of an interaction, one can utilize the total as indicating the degree of involvement in status interactions. In order to obtain a clearer picture of the possible relationship between velocity and involvement in social status interactions the 32 rats in each group were assembled into 8 velocity categories by rank. That is, a mean velocity was obtained for velocity ranks 1 to 4 (the four highest velocity rats), for ranks 5 to 8 . . . , for ranks 29 to 32 (the four lowest velocity rats). Mean social interaction scores for each group were similarly calculated. These data are graphically shown in Figure 12.

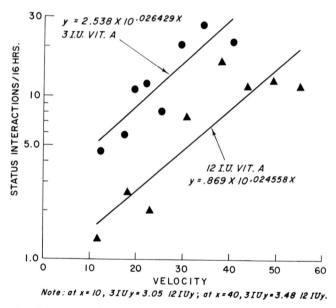

Note: at x = 10, 3IUy = 3.05 12IUy; at x = 40, 3IUy = 3.48 12IUy.

Fig. 12.—Relationship between velocity and social status interactions. Each point (dots for 3 I.U. and triangles for 12 I.U.) represents the mean of four individuals having adjacent velocity ranks, as indicated in the text.

The straight lines and their positive exponential equations shown in Fig. 12 serve as a first approximation of the observed relationship between velocity and involvement in social interactions. However, considering the developmental reduction of velocity over time the curves require interpretation from right to left. The more an animal reduces its velocity, as a consequence of aggressions received, the more it will reduce its involvement in social status interactions. Stated otherwise: The more a rat withdraws through reduction in velocity, the greater still its withdrawal both by reducing its initiation of interactions and by decreasing the exhibition of those behaviors which tend to elicit action toward it from associates.

Furthermore, for any level of velocity the reduction of involvement in social status interactions by the rats on the higher vitamin A diet is roughly proportional to the increase in vitamin A intake.

I suspect that the process of social withdrawal is a much more profound phenomenon than even intimated above. Prolonged observation of these lowest velocity rats shows them to be markedly different types from their higher velocity associates. When active, they frequently move among their associates as if these associates were not there, as if they were just so many sticks or stones. They give little evidence of being aware, through their responses, that their associates are nearby. They appear to have developed a perceptual blindness, an agnosia, to social stimuli.

Behavioral types

According to the formulation, an individual's behavior will deviate from the ideal norm in proportion to the frequency with which he is frustrated in his attempts at satisfying his need for social intercourse. Among my male rats, four types could be recognized on the basis of overt behavior. *Territorial* males maintained an area of the habitat to the near exclusion of other males. Other highly aggressive *dominants* occurred in those portions of the habitat which housed a high ratio of males to females. Some males, whom I call *probers*, rarely won in status encounters, but nevertheless continued to invade the vicinity where dominant or territorial males were active. *Homosexuals*, which make up the last category, were clearly recognizable by their persistent mounting of other males. In the order listed, other observed categories of behavior suggested that these types form a series of increasing deviation from normal behavior. As predicted by the formulation, the mean velocity (Fig. 13) declines with increasing deviation of behavior.

Adult body weight does not vary significantly among these groups. However, both adrenal weight and heart (ventricle) weight is positively correlated with velocity (Fig. 13). In other words, the more an animal withdraws from social interaction the less demands are placed on certain vital organs.

A fifth behavioral type, called *withdrawn* and recognizable only by very low velocity, is also included in Figure 13. The extreme infrequency with which such rats engage in any kind of social interaction, even with estrous females, necessitated utilization of the criterion of low velocity for their selection. As may be seen, they are very much like the homosexuals in terms of adrenal and heart size. However, they clearly stand out from the other groups in terms of the amount of abdominal fat, a factor which has a high negative correlation with velocity.

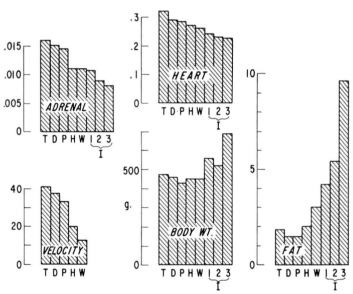

Fɪɢ. 13.—The influence of behavioral deviation and isolation on organ size, body weight, and velocity. All measures are means. The groups represented and the sample sizes in parentheses are: T, Territorial (7); D, Dominants (15); P, Probers (12); W, Withdrawn (18); I, Isolates: 1, LSC (12); 2, CCER (12); 3, Filthy (8). The symbols "LSC," "CCER," and "Filthy" designate special habitats in which one male was isolated with two females and are provided to facilitate reference to future publications in which they will be discussed in detail. The adrenal, heart (ventricle), and abdominal fat weights are expressed as (organ in grams/body weight in grams × 100).

These behavioral types are compared in Figure 13 with *isolation* males. Each such male was housed with two females, but had no opportunity to interact with other males. It may be seen that the adrenals and hearts of the lower velocity rats in the large social groups approached the small size of the isolated males. Similarly, the more the males in the large social groups withdrew from social interaction, the more nearly the increase of abdominal fat deposits resembled that of the isolated males. Such similarities of low velocity males to isolated males strengthens the inference that by social withdrawal rats effectively isolate themselves from their associates.

General Remarks Concerning the Effect
of Group Size and Vitamin A

So long as animals live in closed social groups, each increase in group size causes each individual to reduce its velocity further toward the minimum tolerable level. Although at $N =$ infinity all individuals are forced to this minimum level of velocity, to the maximum state of social withdrawal, for all practical purposes this degree of social withdrawal by all members is reached at a much lesser increase above the optimum size for the group (Table 4). This process of social withdrawal represents one end state, which circumstances may force the members of a species to experience.

For my rats the increased velocity of those within the group on the higher vitamin A diet indicates that those behaviors which normally elicit a more frequent or more intense aggressive action from associates no longer do so. There is a failure to integrate all those stimuli requisite to elicit a particular motor output. With regard to aggressive behavior, this hypothesis means that the actual intensity or number of stimuli emanating from one individual that would initiate aggression from a rat on a lower (normal) vitamin A diet fails to do so on the higher vitamin A diet. The price of reduced aggression appears to be a reduction in the capacity for involvement in, or execution of, complex behaviors.

Given any pharmacological agent which produces a perceptual blindness to behavioral stimuli, as vitamin A appears to do, we may justifiably ask: "What will be the consequences of continuing to increase the amount of this agent consumed by all members of a population?" Consider that such consumption originates from an endeavor to compensate for membership in groups of larger than optimum size. As the intake is increased above that of the present study, social withdrawal (as reflected by velocity) should further decrease. Velocities of all individuals should increase toward that characteristic of the alpha member. But consider again the implications of Figure 12. As the intake of vitamin A increases, involvement in social interactions should decline still more, at least with regard to those involving establishment of status relationships. Every individual sees every other individual as being no different from himself; no reasons are perceived for imposing restraints or negative sanctions on others. To the extent that development of social roles demands restraints, no social roles can develop. It is difficult to conceive of a complex society persisting in the absence of social roles being developed by its constituent members. As of 1965 the practice of adding vitamin A supplements to milk and milk products has reached such a magnitude that many children, now maturing, must be ingesting quantities of vitamin A, which per gram of body weight must be comparable to that of my rats on the 12 I.U. diet. If this increased intake of vitamin A has effects on the behavior of humans comparable to those on the behavior of rats, we may anticipate some very bizarre alterations in the fabric of social relations as an increasingly larger proportion of the adult population becomes characterized by high circulating levels of vitamin A. At this early stage of experimental research and with little known about the effect of vitamin A on human behavior, it is extremely hazardous to make projections. I merely wish to point out that when a chemical compound can produce changes such as vitamin A apparently does in rats we can slowly set an ecological trap of such magnitude that, once caught, society might experience extreme difficulty in extracting itself.

Social Temperature

The relative velocity of the omega individual, the minimum tolerable velocity, will always be $1/N_0$; it will be the reciprocal of the number of individuals in the optimum-sized group. Consider two optimum-sized groups, $N_0 = 6$ and $N_0 = 12$. In the former the minimum relative velocity will be 0.167, while in the latter it will be 0.083. Members of the species with the larger optimum-sized group will have evolved an hereditary constitution permitting toleration of a greater degree of social withdrawal than is possible for members of the species with the smaller optimum-sized group. Members of the species with the larger sized optimum group have a wider range of tolerance to social withdrawal. If, in these two species, we consider individuals with identical relative velocity, the ones in the species tolerating more social withdrawal will not have experienced as great a degree of change in its behavior and physiology. The important consideration is the level of withdrawal relative to the degree of withdrawal which can be tolerated. This I shall call "social temperature," $v^{(t)}$.

For any Rth ranked individual, where

N = the actual size of the group.

$v^{(r)}_{\alpha}$ and $v^{(r)}_{\Omega}$ are the relative velocities of the alpha, highest velocity member

and the omega, lowest ranked member at N_0.

$$v^{(t)}_{R} = \frac{v^{(r)}_{R \text{ at } N} - v^{(r)}_{\Omega}}{v^{(r)}_{\alpha} - v^{(r)}_{\Omega}} = \frac{(N - R)\,(N_0 - 1)}{N(N - 1)\left[v^{(r)}_{\alpha \text{ at } N_0} - v^{(r)}_{\Omega}\right]} \tag{4}$$

Social temperature reflects the social and physical kinetics of the individual. As may be seen from Tables 4 and 5, each increase in rank or group size produces a greater decrement in social temperature than it does in social velocity. As the minimum velocity, social temperature is zero. We may, therefore, refer to a "social freezing point," $v_{R=N}^{(t)}$ Both social velocity, $v^{(r)}$, and social temperature, $v^{(t)}$, decrease as velocity rank, R, increases. The omega individual will always have a social temperature at the social freezing point. It can be shown that at an infinite N all individuals have been forced to a minimum velocity and thus all are at the social freezing point. At this point social life is patently impossible. The real question is: "Is there some smaller density greater than N_0 where for all practical purposes social life can no longer continue?"

Decision on this point again requires consideration of the omega-ranked individual in an N_0 group. Any social group is not a "sure" or "static" one but is subject to stochastic processes. This means that during some period of time the omega individual will receive less restraints from his associates than would be anticipated from the actual group size. During these times its velocity and social temperature would increase. At other times its velocity will be reduced in relative terms below the tolerable, $1/N_0$, limit, and its social temperature would drop below the social freezing point. Every omega individual in an optimum-sized group will, for these reasons, fall below the social freezing point for considerable periods of time. Each of these times will force the passage of the individual into a state of detachment and

TABLE 5.—Relationship Between Rank, Velocity, and Social Temperature
Conditions: $N_o = 12$, $N = 12$.

Velocity rank, R	Social Velocity $v^{(r)}$ R	Social Temperature $v^{(t)}$ R
$1 = \alpha$	1.000	1.000
2	.917	.909
3	.833	.818
4	.750	.727
5	.667	.636
6	.583	.545
7	.500	.455
8	.417	.363
9	.333	.273
10	.250	.182
11	.167	.091
$12 = \Omega$	.083	.000

behavioral deviation, making it impossible for it to function as a member of the group.

As N increases above N_o, the social temperature of every member approaches the minimum. Thus a larger proportion of the group will be exposed to developing such nonfunctional social states. I have[6] arbitrarily assigned this critical social temperature as the mean of the two lowest velocity individuals ($R = N - 1$ and $R = N$) in an optimum-sized group. This $v^{(t)}$ is called the "Social Frost Temperature."

Since there is reason to believe that 12 individuals form an optimum group size for many mammals, including man, I further explored the effects on social temperature expected from increases in the actual size of the group. Utilizing Equation (4) for a series of arbitrary sized groups, the highest velocity individual in each group whose social temperature fell within the social frost zone was determined. In each case all lower velocity individuals (i.e., those with a larger R) would also fall within the social frost zone. These results are shown in Figure 14. When an animal's velocity becomes so reduced as to force its social temperature into the social frost zone, its behavior will then become so deviant from the norms of the group that it can no longer operate effectively as a member of it.

The percentage of the group which falls within the social frost zone, as a function of the size of the group, increases monotonically. There is no a priori basis for judging from Figure 14 what percentage of a group can become deviants and still permit the group to continue functioning. When the group has increased to the square of its optimum size, over 50 per cent of its members will fall within the social frost zone and will presumably become markedly deviant in their behavior. It is difficult to conceive of any group long persisting intact with such a large deviant membership.

Relevance to Phenomena On the Human Level

The present theoretical formulations have considered all social relations as taking place within the framework of a closed social group. Membership in such groups provides the opportunity for a certain number of contacts, and thus social interactions, per unit of time. During evolution the physiology and behavior of the species becomes adapted to permit attainment of an optimum amount of gratification (along with an equivalent amount of frustration) as a consequence of the existing rate of contact characteristic of the typical group size. *The key to the problem lies in the rate of contact.*

Evolutionary history modifies physiology to demand a given rate of contact in harmony with having lived in a particular group size in a particular habitat. Man is no exception. Through most of his evolution he has lived in relatively closed groups of relatively small size. There are reasons to believe that man lies along an evolutionary path on which the optimum group size (of adult members) has a range of 7 to 19 with a mean of 12.

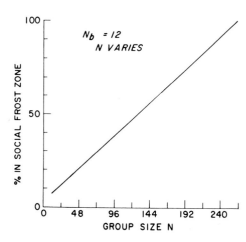

Fig. 14.—The influence of increase in the size of the group above its optimum size on the proportion of its members which exhibit sufficient social withdrawal to fall within the social frost zone. Those falling within this zone have a heightened probability of developing highly deviant behavior.

Obviously, modern man lives in close proximity to many more associates than this. So then what is the group? It can only be conceived of from the viewpoint of a single individual. It becomes that entire assembly of others with which that particular individual can regularly have satisfactory relations half of the time. Yet, although there may be many more than 11 others involved in these relationships, at any moment in time this individual, and therefore all others, must be participating in some structured assembly which on the average involves 12 others. Maintaining an integration in several such partially overlapping groups in time and space places a strain on cultural mechanisms, particularly in a mobile population which periodically forces the new resident to find channels for being accepted into such a system. All such periods of adjustment are initially unsatisfactory and the increased frustrations accompanying acceptance make the individual live through a period when the consequences to him are comparable to having low velocity in a greater than optimal sized closed group.

5. The "Musical-Chair" Trap

Any population, any group of contiguously distributed members whose numbers through successive generations are maintained by reproduction, may be considered as inhabiting a spatially closed universe. In the simplest case only the peripheral impermeable barrier interferes with movement from one place to another. However, in most universes, internal barriers exist which prevent straight line movements from one place to another. Thus, in most cases, an animal at any one point may be considered as being in a cell of the universe from which passages of variable width provide access to adjoining cells. In natural habitats the size of cells, the number of passages from them, as well as their width, all vary. This extreme variability of natural habitats makes difficult any rigorous analysis of the impact of such configurations upon the contained population.

The entomologist Huffaker has presented[12] the basis for logical experimentation. Assume that the universe consists of a series of cells all of which are identical in size and internal conditions appropriate to the members of the species living in the cells. The center of every cell is equidistant to the centers of all immediately adjoining cells. Each cell is connected by a single passage to each of, or a portion of, such immediately adjoining cells. All passages are identical in form. Huffaker uses the term "universe" specifically to apply to such a system of interconnected cells. "Universe" will hereafter be used in this restricted sense. Through continued travel, any individual could, in time, theoretically get from any one cell to any other cell.

In the light of the concept of a basic group size characteristic of each species, we may now pose the question, "Does the configuration of the universe affect the aggregation of its contained members?" My first contact with this problem arose purely accidentally. The previous sections on aggression, velocity, and withdrawal among members of

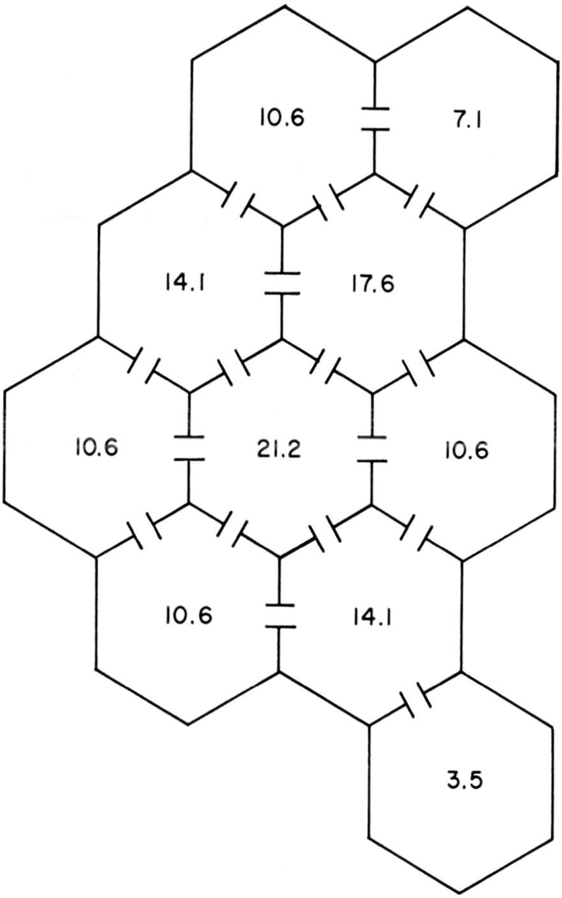

Fig. 15.—A 10 cell universe. For animals which behave like rats, an initial introduction of 12 individuals in each cell will rapidly lead to a steady-state number of individuals per cell, as indicated by the numbers within each hexagonal cell.

closed social groups of rats were based upon analyses of groups contained within universes consisting of 4 identical 5 x 7 foot cells. In terms of the connecting passages, these universes consisted of four cells in a row with each cell connected to each adjoining one by a single passage. Thus, a rat in one of the two end cells had only one passage of egress available to it providing access to the adjoining more central cell of the series. In contrast, a rat in either of the two more centrally located cells had two passages of egress available to it; one to the adjoining central cell and one to the adjoining terminal cell in the series. This factor operating alone produced a situation in which twice as many rats aggregated in either of the two central cells as in either of the terminal cells.[8] In other words, the size of the resultant aggregation in a cell became proportional to the number of passages connecting it to other cells. This differential density arose from a behavior of rats which differs from random or Brownian. Every so often each rat appeared to develop the urge to leave the cell it was then in and go to an adjoining one. In such relatively simple cells each rat could always find its way out of the cell it was then in, regardless of the number of passages present. In the following discussion of "behavioral sinks" an effect of such differential densities is discussed.

However, for the present, I shall wish to delineate the general expectations of differential aggregation in any such universe by animals which behave like rats. Although I can offer no proof at present, I suspect that the movements of most species of mammals, including man, will conform to the formulations below for those members in the universe not yet having spatially fixed home sites.

Consider any universe in which the exchanges between cells have resulted in a steady-state density in each cell.

Let:

M_i be the steady-state mean number of individuals in any i^{th} cell, C_i in a universe of n cells.

t_i = the number of passages from C_i.

$T = t_1 + t_2 \ldots t_n$.

T = twice the number of total passages in the universe.

Consider that all animals move simultaneously from the cell they are then in to an adjoining one. Then M_i/t_i individuals will move from C_i to each adjoining cell. For any particular cell the relative contributions from all adjoining cells may be calculated for these steady-state moments of exchange. Take the simplest possible case of three cells in a row which the center one is connected by one passage to each of the end ones. Let M_1 and M_3 be the steady-state means for the two end cells C_1 and C_3, and M_2 similarly for the central cell C_2: Obviously M_1 or $M_3 = \frac{1}{2} M_2$. Therefore, $M_2 = 2M_1$ or $2M_3$.

In this case M_i is proportional to t_i. This relationship holds true for several universes analysed in this way. I am indebted to Frederick Mosteller of Harvard for the development of this insight. As universes become more complex through addition of cells or by an increase in the number of cells connected to any given cell, the actual proof of this relationship becomes somewhat more cumbersome. However, Mosteller believes that the cases analysed are sufficient to indicate the generality of M_i being proportional to t_i.

It follows that where N is the total number of individuals inhabiting the universe

$$M_i = N \ (t_i/T)$$

Empirical data on this subject are few. It therefore behooves us to examine a theoretical case to see the magnitude of the effects engendered by this musical-chair phenomenon. A 10 cell universe of hexagonal cells is shown in Figure 15, in which t_i varies from 1 to 6. Suppose that there were introduced N_b animals in each cell for a species in which $N_b = 12$. The M_i number of animals per cell is indicated by the number within each cell of Figure 15. After a very few exchanges, the one cell connected with only one passage to a single neighboring cell will have less than one-third the optimum number of individuals, whereas the cell connected to six others will contain nearly twice the optimum number. Vertical lines drawn from N = 3.5 and N = 21.2 on Figure 10 reveal the magnitude of changes in amount of frustration and gratification from optimum levels. As pointed out in the discussion of that figure, theoretical considerations indicate that in any group living under optimum conditions, each animal may be expected to experience equal amounts of frustration and gratification. For N = 3.5, gratification and frustration are respectively reduced to 0.61 and 0.14 of normal, whereas these values become 0.91 and 1.68 or normal for N = 21.2. Thus, even though we must rely mostly on theory for the present, some simple changes in the physical environment affecting movement can become ecological traps having profound effects upon frustration and gratification.

6. BEHAVIORAL SINKS

The term "behavioral sink" refers to the entire process whereby an initially fairly uniform distribution of a population over the space available to it becomes transformed into one in which there are one or more localized aggregations, each of which far exceeds the optimum group size. This localization may be in either time or space. Two primary kinds of processes are involved.

First, some aspect of the environment or of the behavior of the animals must make the density greater in some places or at some times than at others. Restricted sources for obtaining food or water, or for conducting breeding activities, have likely been important in long-term evolutionary changes. However, for present conceptual purposes, it is more pertinent to consider only those situations in which every animal at any time or place can readily obtain any needed resources. Even then, 24 hour cycles of activity and rest will produce greater aggregations at some places than at others. Such processes as are involved in the musical-chair phenomenon can produce spatial aggregations.

Second, animals must come to associate the presence of associates with some originally unrelated activity. Consider a resource such as food, which though readily available, is sufficiently restricted spatially that when one animal is eating there is a fair chance of an associate doing likewise nearby. At some critical frequency of engaging in similar actions side by side, each participant will associate the presence of another with the execution of the act. Each animal will serve as a secondary reinforcing stimulus for engaging in the act by others. Once this happens, each animal will tend to be held in areas where there are more associates already there or will actively seek places where there are more associates. Fairly rapidly, animals will vacate areas where for other reasons fewer lived and will congregate in those where there was initially a slightly greater-than-chance expectation of encountering associates.

I have previously described in detail this whole behavioral sink process among rats inhabiting a four cell universe.[1,8,9,14] At its culmination, over 0.60 of the total food consumption within the universe was in the single "sink" cell, whereas, in contrast, considerably less than 0.05 of the total food consumed was in one of the other cells.

The overall importance of the behavioral sink process derives from the consequence of animals living or being active in groups whose numbers far exceed the optimum. In the sink, social withdrawal becomes accentuated, as does the prevalence and severity of behavioral pathologies. Among males, homosexuality and pansexuality become rampant, while females largely lose their capacity to build nests and care for their young.

REFERENCES

1. Calhoun, J. B.: The social use of space. *In:* Physiological Mammalogy, Vol. 1. Mayer, Wm. and Van Gelder, R., Eds. New York, Academic Press, 1964; pp. 1-187.
2. Christian, J. J. Phenomena associated with population density. Proc. Nat. Acad. Sci. USA 47:428-449 (1961).
3. Bakken, A.: Aspects of the emigrations of the lemming. Unpublished review of the literature from 1885 to 1952. 1953, 32 pp.
4. Calhoun, J. B.: Induced mass movements of small mammals, a suggested program of study. U.S. Dept. of Health, Education and Welfare. 1962, 33 pp. (Available from the author.)
5. Remarks by Joel Elhes, and Ernst Caspari made at a conference called by the National Institute of Mental Health, May 19, 1960.
6. Calhoun, J. B.: The study of velocity. (A manual prepared for informal distribution to those contemplating initiating studies of velocity with animals.) Mimeographed Sept. 1962, 55 pp.
7. Calhoun, J. B.: The ecology and sociology of the Norway rat. U.S. Dept. of Health, Education, and Welfare. Public Health Service Pub. No. 1008, Washington, D.C. Government Printing Office, 1963, 288 pp.
8. Calhoun, J. B.: A "behavioral sink." Chap. 22, in E. L. Bliss (Ed.) *In:* Roots of Behavior—Animal Behavior. New York, Harper & Row (Hoeber), 1962.
9. Calhoun, J. B.: Population density and social pathology. Sci. Amer. 206: 32, 139-146, 1962.
10. Calhoun, J. B.: Social welfare as a variable in population dynamics. Sympos. Quant. Biol. 22:339-356, 1957.
11. Calhoun, J. B.: A comparative study of the social behavior of two inbred strains of house mice. Ecol. Monog. 26:81-103, 1956.
12. Huffaker, C. B.: Experimental studies in predation: dispersion factors and predator-prey oscillations. Hilgardia 27:343-383, 1958.
13. Calhoun, J. B.: Determinants of social organization exemplified in a single population of domesticated rats. Trans. N. Y. Acad. Sci. (Series II) 23: 437-442, 1961.

2

SOCIAL STRUCTURE AND PSYCHIATRIC DISORDER: A THEORETICAL NOTE

by JOHN CUMMING, M.D.[*]

and

R. JAY TURNER, Ph.D.[*]

THE JOINT COMMISSION ON MENTAL HEALTH, after exhaustive effort to define mental health, finally stated that "there is no general agreement on what constitutes mental health or mental illness; mental health means many things to many people . . ."[1] This state of affairs, of course, has long been indirectly evidenced in the proliferation of both conceptual and operational definitions of mental illness (See, for example, reference 21.) and directly evidenced by published difficulties in achieving consensus on just what constitutes a psychiatric case.[†] One of the obvious consequences of this confusion about the character of the object of our study is a lack of comparability of research findings, a fact which markedly reduces the cumulative character of investigation.

Fundamentally, there are three major definitions of mental illness in use in research: (1) mental illness as exposure to psychiatric treatment; (2) mental illness as the presence of symptoms; and (3) mental illness as social deviance or maladjustment.

Most studies employ the first definition, the fact that an individual is involved in psychiatric treatment.[21] The shortcomings of this definition are, of course, many. First, since there is a shortage of treatment personnel, such a definition sets an absolute limit upon the number of psychiatric patients who can exist at any one time. Many factors, for example the differential availability of personnel to patients of

---

[*]New York State Mental Health Research Unit, Syracuse, New York.

[†]See the discussion entitled "Definition of a Case for Purposes of Research in Social Psychiatry" in "Interrelations Between the Social Environment and Psychiatric Disorders," Milbank Memorial Fund, New York, 1953.

different income and education levels, can produce spurious correlations between sociocultural factors and rate of illness, if illness is to be defined this way.

While this definition seems to be operational rather than conceptual, it does imply a particular interpretation of mental illness. Essentially, it implies that there is a real dichotomy between mental health and mental illness in which anyone regarded as sufficiently disturbed to require hospitalization or other treatment is mentally ill and anyone not so regarded is mentally healthy.

Recognition of the inadequacies of this definition leads to a rejection of the notion that there are fundamentally two subgroups of psychiatric patients: those who are sick and in the hospital and those who are well and in the community. It is now rather widely agreed that there may be more mentally ill people in the community than in mental hospitals. A new definition of mental illness is therefore needed.

The second definition or criterion of mental illness that we cited was a measure of the level of pathology. Pathology ratings based on the clinical detection of symptoms have always been the standard against which psychometrists and others attempting to devise objective indices of disorder have validated their efforts. In spite of the desirability of defining illness by pathology level, psychiatrists frequently have difficulty in agreeing upon just how much pathology is present in any given individual. Dohrenwend and Dohrenwend[7] have pointed out that reported estimates of psychologically impaired individuals vary from less than 1 per cent to more than 60 per cent of the evaluated populations. These data suggest a lack of consensus concerning what behavior is to be regarded as pathological and suggest that there is confusion over how much pathology need be present before the individual is regarded as mentally ill. Nor is this the end of the difficulty: Even within the same study, variations in procedure have produced different rates of psychopathology.[19]

Where level of psychopathology is used to predict level of performance or chance of hospitalization, the amount of variance in performance (or outcome in the case of prediction of hospitalization) that can be accounted for by degree of pathology is very small. For example, during World War II psychiatrists were unable to predict military performance.[14] Similarly, Pasamanick[20] and others have demonstrated the many cases of unrecognized and untreated psychosis in the community.

We have found, in a study of diagnosed schizophrenics drawn

randomly from the Monroe County Psychiatric Register, that *pathology ratings cannot effectively distinguish hospitalized from nonhospitalized patients nor the employed from the chronically unemployed.*

The inability of judgments of pathology to account for differences in adequacy of work performance, which, from some points of view, is not only related to mental health but is an integral part of it, poses some interesting and vital questions. In a sense, mental health *is* simply personality somehow evaluated by some criterion, but any reasonable evaluation of "personality" considers more than just those mechanisms regarded as pathological. Why then does pathology remain a focus which crowds from attention the more positive elements? It seems reasonable to imagine that the explanation lies in a tendency to regard strengths as the reciprocal of pathology. Regarding pathology as the absence of strength effectively dilutes any impulse to develop measures of strength because of the scarcely conscious belief that in dealing with any factor its reciprocal is automatically dealt with.

It may now be time to challenge this long-standing habit of regarding strengths and weaknesses as negatively correlated and to open the questions of their distributions and their actual relationship.

In our study of diagnosed schizophrenics, referred to previously, we are not in a direct or deliberate fashion attempting to investigate or measure strengths. It seems possible, nevertheless, that our extensive social data will allow some general comparisons on this important variable. For example, if "working" can be taken as a rough index of strength and if the implied strength does have important effects, then there should be a relationship between working and hospitalization. Using the first 100 cases of our sample, we categorized hospitalized patients as employed if they had worked any time during the six months prior to admission. Nonhospitalized subjects were counted as employed only if they were working at the time of interview. By these procedures it was determined that 83 per cent of the nonhospitalized group were working, while only 43 per cent of the hospitalized group could be counted as employed.* Since, as indicated earlier, pathology ratings could not effectively distinguish the hospitalized from the nonhospitalized or the employed from the unemployed, it is clear that this finding cannot be attributed simply to a difference in symptoms.

The definition of mental illness as social deviance (the third category that we mentioned) has been prominent in investigations of the rela-

---

*These proportions are significantly different at the .01 level.

tionships between social variables and mental illness. In a review of studies of the "Social Psychological Correlates of Mental Illness and Mental Health," Scott[22] has pointed out that "A variety of . . . defini-tions of mental illness have been used in these studies, but the one which appears conceptually appropriate to most formulations is that of maladjustment, or deviance from social norms." The use of this definition leads to two major difficulties. First, variation in the demands of different social structures and the personal frames of reference associated with them make the formulation of operational definitions very difficult. Second, variability in personal frames of reference is likely to result, on the one hand, in some behavior being labeled deviant when it is not, by any other criterion, associated with illness. On the other hand, behavior which by all other criteria would be regarded as symptomatic is not labeled as deviant. The primary advan-tage of defining mental illness as deviance is that it incorporates, if incompletely and unevenly, traditional symptomatology at the same time that it takes account of the norms and expectations of the society in which the individual participates. Moreover, implicit in this definition is the premise that ego failure, however expressed, cannot be under-stood independently of the setting of the failure any more than a figure can be perceived independently of its ground.

What follows is an attempt to synthesize the thinking of several social-psychological theorists in ways that will provide heuristic approaches to the three problems that we have already raised: (1) the need to estimate strength or competence in evaluating personality; (2) the relationship—not necessarily dependent—between personality estimates and social performance; and (3) the relationships among the definitions of illness that we have so far proposed.

Our theoretical assumptions are those usually termed "ego psy-chology." In this view, the adult ego is considered rational and responsible for intellectual and social achievements; it is not solely dependent upon the id since it has its own source of energy, its own motives, and its own objectives.

Ego psychology perhaps began with Hartmann's postulation (1939) of a conflict-free or executive portion of the ego independent of the conflict-generated or synthetic portion.[16] He proposed that not only does the ego have its own source of intrinsic energy, but that growth yields an intrinsic pleasure. Having observed that children's speech and motility develop with remarkable uniformity, Hartmann con-cluded that the *instrumental* ego functions must emerge, not through id-superego conflict, which is variable from person to person, but by the interaction of the effects of the environment with a process of biological maturation in a manner similar to overt learning.

This insight of Hartmann's led to a revision of Freud's "libido-quantum" theory and hence to a questioning of the doctrine of an inherent priority of synthetic ego function. This in turn reduced the weight given to psychopathology in the assessment of function. If the bases of the executive and synthetic functions of the ego are indeed independent of each other, then the customary notion that effective executive function is a *consequence* of the well-being of the synthetic function cannot be wholly accurate. There seems, in fact, no theoretical reason why the reverse may not be equally true. Synthetic functioning, in short, expressed in terms of the adequacy of defense systems, is no more vital to a description of personality than is executive function, expressed in terms of skills or strengths. Even though the two functions are entwined in any complex behavior, the synthetic and executive functions of the ego can be productively regarded as separate and relatively independent factors wherein *skills are to the executive portion of the ego what defenses are to the synthetic portion.*[5,6]

Erikson has conceived of the development of executive function in terms of "mutuality." He asserts, in relation to the onset and duration of developmental phases,* that ". . . individual makeup and the nature of society determine the rate of development of each of them, and thus the ratio of all of them."[10]Precipitation of each psychosocial crisis is the product of the individual's readiness and society's pressure. Thus Erikson's theory postulates a "fit" between the developing individual and his particular social environment. This "fit" is not accidental since individual psychosocial development is, within limits, malleable, and society provides training conditions and institutions specific to each phase.†

According to Erikson's view, the disciplines of society do not

---

*Erikson distinguishes a total of eight stages or phases of development. Although he invests much in the designation and description of these stages, it should be noted that their contents are not crucial to the basic conception of personality growth through crises resolution which is to be discussed. In short, it is quite possible to accept the principle that the solutions of crisis encounters have profound effects upon personality development without accepting the substantive content of the stages described.

†This formulation of Erikson's is very similar to Hartmann's concept of an "average expectable environment."

impinge upon and mold an otherwise asocial organism, but rather upon inborn predispositions for both growth and differentiation. This inborn predisposition of the individual is both played upon by, and plays into, his particular social milieu. Every new development carries with it its own specific vulnerability, and it is to each of the successive vulnerabilities that the training agents of society most effectively address themselves.

Each of Erikson's sequential phases of development is seen as a crisis, the outcome of which is described in terms of successful or unsuccessful resolution. The successful steps are systematically interrelated, each depending upon the proper resolution of the one before it. In other words, the subjective achievements derived from previous phase solutions are the building blocks for present and future solutions.

While Erikson specifically uses the term "vulnerability" to characterize the individual's state during crisis, he seems to be referring to a kind of openness—openness to both harm and enhancement. This is evident from his contention that ego growth occurs through the resolution of phase-specific crises and hence that the disequilibria which characterize these crises offer potential for forward developmental leaps as well as for ego damage.

It is Erikson's contention that developmental—and therefore normative—crises differ from imposed, traumatic crises in that the growth process provides new energy for their solutions. However, since unexpected crises are frequently experienced, it seems reasonable to propose that such crises when *successfully resolved** also promote ego growth and hence influence identity.

It is Erikson's argument that the encounters of each successive developmental step constitute potential crises because they demand a "radical change in perspective." These "potential crises" seem quite similar to what Tyhurst calls "transition states." Tyhurst applies this label to conditions in which ". . . there is actually some sign of disequilibrium or turmoil" (p. 156),[24] turmoil resulting from a ". . . passage or change from one place or state or act or set of circumstances to another" (p. 149).[24] He recognizes that change is ubiquitous but that it usually takes place within the context of a

---

*It is quite clear that to speak in terms of success is to admit into the formulation certain value assumptions. The term "resolved" is employed in the conventional sense to refer to attainment of closure or a return to a stable state. The term "successful" implies that the state achieved and the means utilized in achieving it are of a culturally valued quality.

coherent system of ". . . certain personal values, assumed roles, [and] definable expectations and responses" (p. 156),[24] which are taken for granted. Change, then, is intensely experienced subjectively only when the individual's premises are called into question or, in our terms, only when "identity" is challenged.

We thus use the term "crisis" to refer to any event, *whether developmental or normative, imposed or traumatic*, that challenges the assumptive state and forces the individual to change his view of, or readapt to, the world or himself or both. We, therefore, understand crises to be personal experiences rather than objective social or physical occurrences.

In summary, Erikson's concept of ego identity seems to include three elements: the definition of the self, the state of congruence between the self and the requirements of the environment, and the expectation that this congruence will continue. This is, of course, the definition of a system whose equilibrium, or steady state, depends on positive feedback. Experimental and clinical evidence that the sense of self is importantly dependent on continued confirmation from the environment supports this concept of identity. The ego in a state of identity is in a dynamic equilibrium with its environment and requires continued reinforcement of the nature and appropriateness of its roles, skills, and abilities. All parts of the environment—the physical, the interpersonal, and the social-organizational—are involved in the process of ego reinforcement.

The importance of the interpersonal relationships to ego integrity is the subject of much psychological literature. That physical and social structural factors might be equally important has been pointed out by Wallace.[25] He observed that a "disaster syndrome" sometimes occurs "partially or wholly as a result of the perception that a part of . . . [a person's] . . . culture is ineffective or has been rendered inoperative" (p. 24). In such cases, the individual reacts to this perception as if a beloved object had been lost. He contends that the individual's physical milieu ". . . can be cathected in such a way that the mere perception of these objects is satisfying, and their mere absence, or presence in damaged form can set in motion responses of anxiety."

In our terms, the real or imagined loss of the cathected milieu, or a portion of it, disrupts its important function of providing and reinforcing self-definition and, therefore, maintaining the sense of ego identity. If self-definition—including status, abilities, and roles, by or through which problems are solved—is not maintained, the individual may *feel* he no longer possesses such capacities and thus may be unable to make the adaptive responses of which he is capable.

The importance of the milieu, we are arguing, cannot be over-emphasized. In daily interaction with the environment, the individual not only learns new concepts and new skills, but also receives new proofs of already achieved and cherished abilities and, of course, of continuing areas of ineptness. The environment, then, must be regarded as an inextricable partner in the identity system. It provides the framework for carrying out actions, defines the paths open for solution of problems, and determines whether or not group support will be forthcoming.

It is clear that if this formulation is sound personality and social structure cannot ever be regarded as wholly independent. Nevertheless, we do not deny that for many purposes personality adequacy and social factors can be treated as though they were independent variables. Our view is simply that when dealing with such dependent variables as responses to stress, solution of problems, adjustment to hardship or disability, or even ego disorganization, it is necessary to consider the intimate relationship between personality functioning and the social milieu.

Our formulation thus far has suggested only that the social milieu continually influences individual personality functioning. Since, however, individuals generally have available an array of social settings, there remains the question of what particular social structures exert important influence upon what individuals.

That the structure of the social situation can produce important effects on its members has been shown by a number of authors. For example, Turner[23] studied the extent to which the crisis experienced by medical patients as a result of hospitalization was influenced by nursing technique and organization. He contended that the structure and organization of nursing services would determine the quality of ongoing interactions and thus create the effective milieu.

Turner tested this hypothesis with samples of patients from two medical wards located in separate hospitals. These wards organized their nursing services in markedly different ways—known as "team" versus "functional" nursing—and it was hypothesized that patients nursed by the team method would make a significantly better hospital adjustment. This hypothesis was clearly confirmed by the results of the experiment.

Hospitalization is, of course, only one kind of crisis. Following Erikson, we assume that all crises are characterized by vulnerability or "openness," and this assumption is of great theoretical importance and practical consequence. Its credibility is suggested by numerous researches, including those concerned with reactions to natural disasters. For example, the generalization that "in the absence of reliable guidance from past experience for perceiving or acting, suggestibility is high," first stated by Cantril,[1] has been applied by Kilpatrick[17] in relation to crisis situations.

Glass[15] thinks "suggestibility"—a form of openness—is a primary characteristic of soldiers who break down in the face of acute combat stress. During World War II, the occurrence of suggestibility among "combat exhaustion" casualties led, in some places, to the formulation of an entirely new therapy—a system centered on the concept of "expectancy." According to Glass, "Military experience has demonstrated that situationally induced . . . disorders worsen or improve, depending upon what is expected of the patients by persons responsible for their treatment and disposition" (p. 12).[15] Nonverbal attitudes and actions were found to be far more effective than words in communicating such expectations. The success of this expectancy-centered therapy as compared to conventional psychotherapy, in terms of length of time to recovery, led to the institutionalization of these procedures in treating victims of both combat exhaustion and large-scale disaster and, we believe, can best be explained theoretically by the previously stated propositions.

The relationship between involvement in difficult or unsettling situations and openness to environmental influence has been noted by Caplan.[2] He and his colleagues have proposed a process of "therapeutic intervention" based, at least implicitly, upon this proposition. Klein and Lindemann,[18] for example, conclude, in reference to therapeutic intervention, that beyond the goal of restoring the equilibrium existing prior to the crisis ". . . is the opportunity in some cases to foster a more desirable equilibrium between an individual and his immediate human environment . . ." (p. 286). "Thus, it is clear that hazards provide opportunities for promotion of emotional growth as well as the occasions for preventive measures" (p. 305).[18]

Let us now consider the response of social systems to deviant members. It has been suggested by several authors that the different rates of hospital admissions in different areas of cities, different social classes, different occupations, and so on, probably reveal more about relative tolerance of deviant behavior than about its relative prevalence.[3,8,9] Felix and Bowers (1948)[12] long ago observed that case-finding is done by the community rather than the clinician. In a more recent study, Freeman and Simmons (1963)[13] report that family members, rather than community agents or the patients themselves, were the principal arbiters of the patients' community tenure (p. 45).* These authors point out that "The hospitalization process, though involving professional and community persons in subsequent steps, most typically is initiated by persons in the patients' familial network" (p. 45).[13]

These findings suggest that the relationship between social deviance and involvement in psychiatric treatment—two distinct and popular definitions of mental illness—is both important and direct. The members of any social system are active agents in encouraging or causing any member who has violated certain expectations or norms to become involved in psychiatric treatment. Thus deviant behavior, however variously interpreted and variably tolerated, appears to be directly and causally related to involvement in *psychiatric* treatment. Involvement in psychiatric treatment, however, usually requires that a psychiatrist confirm the need for it—presumably because upon examining the patient he discovers psychiatric symptoms. Psychiatric symptoms, after all, are the names given to deviance from expected patterns of thought and feeling. We would expect that these would be related, if imperfectly, to deviance in action.

Thus it seems that our three definitions, all imperfect in different ways, are related to one another. If empirical research can elucidate the nature of this relationship we may arrive at a more satisfactory definition. If we can add to such a new definition some satisfactory way of estimating competence, we should have a most useful clinical and experimental instrument.

REFERENCES

1. Cantril, H.: The Psychology of Social Movements. New York, Wiley and Sons, 1941.
2. Caplan, G., Ed.: Prevention of Mental Disorders in Children. New York, Basic Books, 1961.
3. Clausen, A. A., and Kohn, M. L.: The ecological approach in social psychiatry. Amer. J. Sociol. 60:140-151, 1954.
4. Clausen, J. A., and Yarrow, M. R.: Paths to the mental hospital. J. Soc. Issues 11:25-32, 1955.

*A similar observation has been reported by Clausen and Yarrow.[4]

5. Cumming, J.: The inadequacy syndrome. Psychiat. Quart. 37:723-733, 1963.
6. Cumming, J., and Cumming, E.: Ego and Milieu. New York, Atherton Press, 1962.
7. Dohrenwend, B. P., and Dohrenwend, B. S.: Field studies of psychological disorder: the problem of construct validity. J. Abnorm. Psychol. In press.
8. Dunham, H. W.: Current status of ecological research in mental disorder. Soc. Forces 25:321-326, 1947.
9. Dunham, H. W.: Some persistent problems in the epidemiology of mental disorders. Amer. J. Psychiat. 109:567-575, 1953.
10. Erikson, E. H.: Identity and the life cycle. Psychol. Issues 1 (No. 1): 1959.
11. Ewalt, J. R.: In: Americans View Their Mental Health. G. Gurin, J. Veroff, and S. Feld, Eds. New York, Basic Books, 1960, x.
12. Felix, R. H., and Bowers, R. V.: Mental hygiene and socio-environmental factors. Milbank Mem. Fund Quart. 26:125-147, 1948.
13. Freeman, H. E., and Simmons, O. G.: The Mental Patient Comes Home. New York, John Wiley and Sons, 1963.
14. Ginzberg, E., Anderson, J. K., Ginsberg, S. W., and Herma, J. L.: The Lost Divisions. New York, Columbia University Press, 1959.
15. Glass, A. J., Psychological considerations in atomic warfare. Army Medical Service Graduate School, Walter Reed Army Medical Center, Washington, D.C., No. 560, March 1955.
16. Hartmann, H.: Ego Psychology and the Problem of Adaptation. New York, International Universities Press (Translated by David Rapaport, originally published in German in 1939), 1958.
17. Kilpatrick, F. P.: Problems of perception in extreme situations. Hum. Organ. 16:20-22, 1957.
18. Klein, D. C., and Lindemann, E.: Preventive intervention in individual and family crisis situations. In: Prevention of Mental Disorders in Children. G. Caplan, Ed. New York, Basic Books, 1961, pp. 265-283.
19. Leighton, D. C., Harding, J. S., Macklin, D. B., Macmillan, A. M., and Leighton, A. H.: The Character of Danger. New York, Basic Books, 1963.
20. Pasamanick, B.: A survey of mental disease in an urban population. IV. An approach to total prevalence rates. Arch. Gen. Psychiat. 5:151-155, 1961.
21. Scott, W. A.: Research definitions of mental health and mental illness. Psychol. Bull. 55:29-45, 1958.
22. Scott, W. A.: Social psychological correlates of mental illness and mental health. Psychol. Bull. 55:65-87, 1958.
23. Turner, R. J.: Social structure and crisis. N. Y. State Mental Health Research Unit Report, Oct. 1963.
24. Tyhurst, J. S.: The role of transition states—including disaster—in mental illness. In: Symposium on Preventive and Social Psychiatry. Washington, D. C., Walter Reed Army Institute of Research, April, 15-17, 1957.
25. Wallace, A. F. C.: Mazeway disintegration: The individual's perception of socio-cultural disorganization. Hum. Organ. 16:23-27, 1957.

3

BEHAVIORAL FACTORS STABILIZING SOCIAL ORGANIZATION IN ANIMALS

by WILLIAM ETKIN, Ph.D.*

M ODERN BIOLOGY is, of course, committed to the concept that man is a product of primate evolution. The post-Darwinians interpreted this as indicating merely quantitative differentiation of human characteristics from those of other primates. This interpretation is indeed fruitful in respect to most physical and biochemical characteristics. The hand, jaw, endocrines, blood proteins, etc. in man are readily interpreted as modifications of those characteristic of the primate group generally. The brain has presented a little more difficulty; not a few claims of unique new features in man have been made and denied. When we turn to behavioral or psychological characteristics, the strenuous insistence of evolutionary biology on the gradualistic view has been giving way to the point where many modern evolutionists do not hesitate to speak of the uniqueness of man.[2,7] This uniqueness of course lies in the cultural determination of his social organization and in his use of language. Indeed Julian Huxley one time even proposed placing man in a phylum separate from all other vertebrates on the basis of his psychological isolation. I do not propose to discuss so large and philosophical a question here, but mention it in order to bring out a change in the orientation of modern zoology that I think is pertinent to an understanding of the appropriate relation of the study of animal behavior to medical psychology. The rigidity with which older zoologists could see only similarities in the mental functioning of animals and man has led to an unfortunate schism between animal-oriented study of behavior and the major trends of human psychology, particularly of social and medical psychology. The animal work, in confining itself to objectively observable events, lost contact with the mental life of man. The willingness to recognize the uniqueness of man thus should free us for new avenues of approach between animal and human studies.

*Albert Einstein College of Medicine, Bronx, N.Y.

I propose first to discuss certain aspects of animal social behavior and organization from the point of view of the factors stabilizing animal societies. I will then try to indicate in evolutionary terms how the human behavioral system might have been derived from that of lower primates. Finally I will consider to what extent the factors of stabilization are similar in human cultures and animal societies. Thus, although I am not specifically concerned with psychopathology, I hope to contribute to the breaking of the stalemate between those who contend that man is an animal like any other and those who insist that man, being psychologically unique, cannot be approached through animal study.

GENERAL NATURE OF ANIMAL SOCIETY

Systems of Organization

The first point I wish to make about animal social organization is that the kinds of behaviors an animal shows form an interrelated system of checks and balances. Altogether they add up to a system that achieves the ecological success necessary for the survival of the species. Let me illustrate. The song sparrow is monomorphic—i.e., male and female are alike. The male sets up a defended territory before mating. The female invades this. He drives her off. She persists. He learns to accept her. Simultaneously they develop nest-building behavior. Then they both become sexually active in coition. After egg laying both develop the incubation drive, then the feeding drive, etc. The final fruit of all this is the successful raising of a brood. In late summer the family members lose all tendency to stay in the territory or to associate especially with each other. Sociality takes the entirely different form of flocking.

It can be seen that the kind and timing of the aggression shown is related to the kind of territoriality the animal shows. Also it correlates with their monomorphism, since in dimorphic species the sex-specific characteristics could serve to suppress aggression between sexes. But monomorphism and defended territoriality also correlate with the fact that both sexes show parental care and seasonal monogamy. The mates learn their territorial limits and recognize each other individually, but they do not recognize their own eggs or young. In other words the kind of learning capacity shown is part of the adaptation that fits in with the kind of territoriality, morphism, etc. characteristic of the species. If one of these characteristics were to be changed, a change in all would be required for the species to survive.

Adaptiveness of Behaviors

The second point about animal social behavior that I wish to make is that the psychological characteristics are adaptive to the particular needs of the animal's ecology and social organization. For example where a behavior is governed by an innately determined S-R relation the effectiveness of the S-R linkage is enhanced by the evolution of special devices that make the stimulus more specific and more conspicuous. Thus the inside of the mouth of many birds is conspicuously colored or otherwise decorated with the result that when the young begs for food by gaping, the stimulus value of the exposed surface is greatly increased. This type of evolutionary development is called ritualization. It is possible in social interactions because both "sender" and "receiver" partners (kumpans), being organisms, are capable of change by evolution. The stimulus provided by the "sender" and the response of the "receiver" evolve pari passu to make the bond between them more effective. Many examples may be cited whereby movements, as well as structures, are ritualized. The technique of making such movements more conspicuous often depends on making them contrast by slowness, awkwardness, etc. with normal functional movements. The slow awkward strutting display of the deer in rut or the courting turkey cock are familiar examples.[4] These movements stand out because they are so different from functional movements.

The particular movement which has become ritualized is often a result of the conflict of two motivations. Thus certain gulls have a ritualized facing-away posture as part of their courtship display. Tinbergen regards this as derived from a compromise movement between flight from an antagonist (these birds are monomorphic) and sexually motivated approach behavior. The important point for us to recognize is that this highly stylized and apparently useless movement serves to inhibit the aggression normally evoked by close approach of another bird. To older naturalists such ritualized movement often seemed incomprehensible because so useless. We now recognize that it is their very uselessness that helps make them effective signals by sharpening the contrast with normal functional movements.[4]

A second important way in which psychological characteristics are adaptively specialized is seen in the kind of learning capacities an animal shows. Thus chickens are extremely facile in learning to recognize individuals and position in the hierarchy. Rats learn the topography of their home range or the experimenter's maze with great facility. Some of this specialized learning behavior, as in the phenomenon of imprinting of ducklings to their parents or the learning of song in certain birds, is so extraordinarily facile and durable as to excite our wonder. Indeed the specialized character of learning in animals is one of the important discoveries of the ethological school of animal behaviorists and puts the entire question of learning capacities in a very different light from that conventional in American psychology. The learning capacities of animals for specific items is seen to be much more dependent upon the animal's ecological requirements than upon its phylogenetic position or brain structure.[13]

A third element in the ecological specializations of behavior is that the motivations or drives shown by an animal likewise differ from animal to animal in adaptive ways. The enormous exploratory drive of rats is today seen to be part of their adaptation as defenseless nocturnal ground feeders which must know their environment thoroughly to facilitate escape. Chicks are characterized not only by the capacity for imprinting but by the drive to follow a moving object and thus achieve the imprinting experience. Wolves are socialized within their ingroup hierarchy by the drive for rough play they show throughout their lives. The peculiar grooming drive of monkeys helps maintain their ingroup socialization.

I believe there is a fourth element in the adaptive character of psychological characteristics. This is an emotional involvement or commitment to a particular behavior. For example a territorial animal in defending its territory shows aggression much more intensely and "indignantly" than when it is out of its territory. Similarly the "self-confidence" of the alpha animal in a hierarchy is usually readily recognizable. One can hardly characterize this aspect of behavior except in anthropomorphic terms, which is perhaps why little is usually said about it. Zoologists generally hesitate to use such terms as "indignant" or "despotic" in reference to an animal, although it must be noted that Schjelderup-Ebbe[12] in his original descriptions of hierarchy did not. It is exactly because this phenomenon seems so anthropomorphic that I wish to emphasize it now, since I think it is a characteristic with which we must come to terms if we are to relate animal and human behavior.

The Limitations of Behaviors by Ecological Adaptation

The adaptive character of the behavior capacities of an animal is only one side of the coin seen by ethological studies. The other, much less emphasized but no less important, I think, is that the animal's capacities are generally limited to those which are of ecological significance. The learning capacities for example of animals are often strikingly limited. The songbird that can learn the fine points of its own melody by hearing it sung just a few times months before it itself sings that melody is not influenced by other melodies it hears. The same songbird is remarkably obtuse about recognizing other individuals, even its own young. Chickens, on the other hand, which form strict hierarchies, learn through only one experience to identify other members of the flock. Similarly the laboratory rat, whose capacity for maze running approximates that of man with a finger maze, rates so much lower in almost any other capacity.

The animal's drives, as well as its capacities for learning, are likewise limited to the appetitive behaviors appropriate to its mode of living. The following-response is found in precocial birds, which must learn to follow their mothers if they are to survive. The playful hunting drive of kittens is obviously adaptive. So is the playful fighting found in puppies and young monkeys, for these animals establish hierarchies by such activities. The existence of play and the form it takes is specifically suited to the particular mode of life of the species. In fact the young of sheep and goats cannot play-fight together successfully because their forms of expression of this drive differ. Tinbergen tells us from his experience with arctic huskies that not only does the dog not show territorial behavior until it reaches sexual maturity, but it cannot be trained to recognize territorial limits in spite of severe drubbings.[14]

I think it important to recognize that as a result of the adaptiveness in both the positive and negative aspect of animal learning it makes little practical difference whether a behavioral response is innately determined or learned. In the normal development of the species the outcome is equally automatic. For this reason it is not only extremely difficult to distinguish the role of genetic determination versus learning in producing particular behavior patterns, but from a practical viewpoint the distinction is unimportant since the learning capacities themselves appear to be genetically determined. Furthermore, if we apply Waddington's concepts of genetic assimilation the distinction, even at the theoretic level, dissolves away.

From our present point of view, the important conclusion that emerges is that irrespective of the role of heredity or learning the social behavioral system possible for each species is confined within strict limits. Its innate S-R relations and its learning capacities and drives are so arranged that they automatically yield only one effective pattern of social life. That pattern is well stabilized within a narrow range. We are only beginning to realize the implication of this concept. For example, domestication and the use of animals in the zoo or laboratory is possible only when their natural behavioral system coincides with the demands we put upon them. Dogs are still essentially wolves. Cats are still lone hunters. Only some species reproduce under zoo conditions, etc.

If this is so, pathologists will ask what happens when the species-specific social behavioral system is prevented from developing by some interference by man or nature. When I accepted the invitation to speak here, I emphasized to Dr. Zubin that I had no competence to discuss behavioral pathology and would stay clear of it. Yet the temptation to express the zoological viewpoint more effectively leads me now to offer a few speculations. The primary point I wish to make is, of course, that the use made of an animal in behavioral investigation and the interpretation of the results must always be viewed against the specifics of its normal behavioral system. This is a generalization which, like other pious thoughts, is not likely to arouse any opposition and therefore will have no effect. Let us instead offer some thoughts on the application of this concept to the problem of the effects of the stresses of social crowding on rodents. We have already heard Dr. Calhoun's description of his elegant experiments on the "behavioral sink" in rats, as an example.

What I think the zoological viewpoint suggests here is that perhaps the very form of the behavioral and physiological breakdown that occurs in each rodent is species specific. The thought derives from the well-known fact that in nature many rodent species exhibit the phenomenon of rodent plagues accompanied by strange changes in behavior whose end result is self-destructive. The great rabbit plagues and years of dying off of the Canadian arctic hare are well known to all students of behavior. But perhaps the best known case is that of the lemmings of Norway. These normally nocturnal, timid, and furtive creatures become extremely bold and careless of danger as they enter the phase of mass migration which ends in their inevitable destruction. However maladaptive this behavior appears to be, some zoologists, Wynne-Edwards[15] in particular, see in this phenomenon a mode of population regulation suited to the ecology of the species. I have interpreted the rodent behavioral system as one which allows the species to take rapid advantage of enormously variable food supplies by extremely rapid population increase. Population crashes, then, are a mechanism for reducing this population level and thereby preventing exhaustion of the environment. In other words these rodents have a peculiar mechanism that stabilizes their population on a violently cyclical basis rather than as we ordinarily think on a constant basis. If this is so, the physiological and behavioral consequences of crowding, whether physiological breakdown or migration, may be a specific adaptation. Other animals have other very different adaptations to their particular population stresses. Thus many males in birds and fish are well known to be unable to breed unless they achieve territory establishment. Their reproductive tracts fail to proceed further in their normal seasonal development. The omega chicken when the flock is under stress does not fight for its share of the food or roost or whatever. It simply withdraws to die. Are these failures to express sexual development or competitiveness to be considered pathological? If so, they are species-specific "normal pathology," if you will allow the phrase.

APPLICATION TO MAN

The Origin of the Unique Human Behavioral System

To the biologist an understanding of a zoological fact must include a concept of how it arose in evolution. The unique human behavioral system has been the subject of much speculation in this regard in the the post-Darwinian period. However, the few facts relevant to the problem were soon exhausted; thus it has been in disfavor until recent years when a flood and new and revolutionary insights from the South African fossil finds has inspired renewed interest in this problem among anthropologists and zoologists. Although this is an area in which I have had a particular interest,[3] we cannot here take the space for a discussion of the problem. However, some of the conclusions reached will be useful as the basis of our further discussion.

Human origin from a large-bodied forest-living primate is conceived of as resulting from the selection pressures for the development of cooperative hunting to replace the usual individual food-gathering economy of primates. Presumably this shift was dictated by a desiccating climatic change, leading to the reduction of forests and the formation of open plains.

To achieve cooperative hunting of large fast-moving animals, the usual primate social organization must necessarily have shifted in a number of ways toward the type of organization we find in wolves. The primary changes envisioned include:

(1) Integration of all males into a cooperative family unit in which the males constitute the hunting pack; (2) assumption of parental and cooperative role by the males toward females and young; (3) suppression of behavioral estrus, pair formation being stabilized by socializing factors; (4) differentiation of male and female economic roles, the females not entering into hunting but retaining food gathering and domestic roles, in contrast to the hunting role of males.

In good part these changes seem to be built into the human organism by genetic change, in the sense developed previously—namely, that whether responses are learned or not, they automatically develop in the appropriate environment. In other words, man is believed to have achieved these particular changes by ordinary evolutionary processes and they are not culture dependent. The major part of this evolutionary change is conceived of as having taken place by the australopithecine level of evolution and did not involve major cerebral expansion. This leaves untouched the unique characteristic of man—namely, cultural transmission and its major instrument, speech. How did these arise? In this theory the biological meaning of culture is sought in its efficiency as a means of adapting the pack-hunting primate to many different ecological niches. Because cultural modification permitted rapid adaptation to different situations, man became the most widely distributed and variously adapted of higher vertebrates. Why did not this efficient mode of change develop in other species? Simply because they did not start from the basis of the highly intelligent primate. Why did not the cultural mode of adaptation appear in other primates? Because they did not face the ecological revolution to cooperative hunting. The first primate (the hominoid) to move into this niche pre-empted it and effectively closed it to late starters.

I have only given a threadbare sketch of the evolutionary problem since our main concern here is with the nature of the finished product —modern man. What are the characteristics that make possible the cultural mode of adaptation? I would put first what I would call a time- and space-binding imagination (modifying Korzybski's term for our use; see Montagu[11]). Although animals show memory in being able to give a learned response to a stimulus often after long periods, there is little evidence that animals can respond to remembered stimuli that are not physically present. A good example of the limitation of the ape mind in this respect is the extreme difficulty Köhler's apes had in using boxes in their problem-solving when these were out of sight, even though the animals had played with the boxes only moments earlier.[9] The time- and space-binding quality of the human mind is here thought to have arisen under the selection pressure for complex communication about events not immediately present. Such communication is unnecessary in other primate groups in which all members of the group stay together. But with the separation of the sexes into two spheres, the domestic and the hunting, while maintaining the highly integrated family group, such communication became necessary for the first time in evolution. The preparation of tools for hunting would be an additional factor to which a time-binding mentality would contribute, for such time-binding permits foresight in the planning of tool production. Most significant of all, I believe, is the relation of time- and space-binding to language. I believe the significant thing that differentiates human language from the communication systems of animals is the fact that the signals of true language refer to and evoke concepts of items not present to the senses of the communicators, whereas animal signals simply direct attention to things present. (Bee communication provides at least an apparent exception.[10]). Furthermore animal signals serve primarily to convey emotional responses to present events, whereas language, insofar as it deals with things absent, can have a purely intellectual content as well. This is especially evident in the denominational function of words. As Geschwind[5] points out— the physical basis in the cerebral cortex for such naming processes is peculiar to the human brain. It lies in the possession of direct cross-modal connections between somatic sensory areas independent of limbic connections.

This line of thinking leads us to consider that once the hunting primate had been well started on its way to evolution the emergence of a time- and space-binding mentality with associated primitive language made further adaptation by cultural transmission rather than by genetic change possible. The much greater efficiency of such cultural evolution over that by genetic change then permitted the emerging man to spread quickly over the earth and take advantage of the changing environmental conditions produced by the ice ages. It was in this period that the explosive increase in the human cortex occurred, presumably under the selection pressure to make cultural determination of human social systems more effective.

Dobzhansky[1] has stressed the autocatalytic relation between genetic and cultural change. Once an organism is effectively started on a cultural mode of adaptation each genetic change promoting culture-forming abilities makes possible greater culture dependence. With greater culture dependence comes greater pressure for genetic change in this direction. Such a positive feedback system makes possible the extraordinary rapid evolution of the human behavioral system and brain that occurred in Pleistocene times[2] and helps account for the psychological uniqueness of man.

Stabilizing Factors in Cultural Systems

Whether or not the above concept of the origin of the cultural mode of social organization in man is valid, we must regard this system as having received its impetus in some way from animal organizations. Indeed modern studies are showing us more and more instances in which a primitive kind of cultural transmission plays some role in animal organization. But even among Japanese monkeys,[8] of which, I believe, our knowledge of cultural transmission is richest, we see that such transmission is very minor compared to biological factors. I expect no one disputes the concept that in man social organization is predominantly determined by learned forms transmitted from generation to generation.

Man is unique, then, in being a single species with a multiplicity of different social behavioral organizations, each acquired and trans-mitted by learning. Each such culture consists of an assemblage of behavioral patterns. These vary from systems of land tenure, sexual and parental relations, etc., through religion and esthetic displays. It is now a commonplace of anthropology that the elements of such an assemblage form an interlocked system in which each part fits with the others to make a stable culture. We emphasized previously analogous characteristic of animal social systems above. What we would wish to inquire into, then, is to what extent the same techniques of behavioral determination which help to stabilize animal societies in their variety are operational in human cultures.

Since culture is learned, we may begin by asking about learning capacity and motivation for learning. In animals we saw that these were both specialized and limited in ecologically suitable ways. But, of course, the human organism must be capable of learning any cultural system. Thus, unlike the chaffinch, which is amazingly adept in learning its own song but no other, the human child is able to learn any language. There is thus a measure of generality in human learning ability notably absent in animals.

Yet when we think about language learning we see that in a sense it too is specialized. Thus language learning is well recognized to be much more facile in the young than in the older person. The appetitive behavior of babbling in infants and imitative repetition of words in the young child are motivations as specialized as any we find in animals. Indeed Hayes[6] was convinced that it was the absence of these factors that was the basis of the failure of her chimp, Vicki, to respond to language teaching.

I think it must be apparent that the socialization of the child depends thus upon specialized motivations and capacities for learning that are quite comparable to what we find in animal life. Of course this is familiar ground to modern psychology. Yet I cannot help but think that an explicit formulation of this principle, and a realization of how far ranging its application is in animal life, would enlarge our appreciation of human learning drives. For example, though it is easy to find discussions of this phenomenon in children, much less is said of the teaching drives in parents. Yet, of course, in the cat and dog not only do the young like to play-hunt but the parent also likes to play-teach. Human children, like monkeys, develop ingroup socialization through their enormous drive for play; children who play together stay together. Adult monkeys groom; adult humans make do with small talk, committee meetings, and other nonfunctional exchanges of social stimulation.

Although man shows some specialization in learning, he also seems to have a generalized learning capacity quite independent of any possible ecological meaning. To me this represents an intriguing puzzle. Is it really unique or can animals too learn or show other capacities that have no ecological significance for them? Several biologists have protested to me that animals could do so. But I find that the examples they give, such as monkeys riding bicycles or crows "counting," are unconvincing. In any case whether the distinction is absolute or relative it seems basic in the difference between animal social organization and human cultures.

In animals we have seen that the innate S-R relations are commonly stabilized by ritualization. In man we find an analogous ritualization of social signals, even though these are culturally learned. Thus in class-organized societies the distinction between classes is maintained by differences in dress, speech, manners, etc. Many of the forms of politeness maintain the distinction between male and female. I would stress again that it is precisely the nonfunctional or, from the human viewpoint, the irrational character of these rituals that make them effective as signals. Tipping one's hat on a cold winter day just does not make sense. That is why it is polite. Veblen described many of these rituals under the rubric of "conspicuous consumption."

We saw above that many of the ritualized behaviors of animals are invested with an emotional commitment that greatly increases their effectiveness. We illustrated this with the "indignation" of the territory defender at a violation of his territory. It is similarly an important element in the effectiveness of ritualized cultural customs of man that they draw on a similar emotional commitment. We call it "propriety," "decency," or, if we think it important enough, "morality." In our rapidly changing world this investment of emotional commitment has become somewhat elusive. But I think that, in analogy to animal behavior, we may recognize that this emotional garment, the sense of righteousness, is one of the stabilizing factors for each cultural pattern.

Of course, a zoologist, as such, is not concerned with value judgements as to whether stability is good or bad. My only point in these very brief and superficial comments on the human predicament is that by comparative study of animal life we can enlarge our understanding of what kinds of behavioral characteristics promote or interfere with social stability in man. This is not to deny that factors exist in man that are not found in animals and that these may indeed be the predominant ones in human society. I stressed before that the human mind does seem to have evolved unique characteristics.

In summary then I would make the following points from the point of view of psychopathology.

Each animal species has evolved behavioral characteristics that enable it to achieve a stable social organization adaptive to its mode of living. Even what appear as modes of behavioral breakdown may be species specific and adaptive.

Prominent stabilizing factors in animal societies are (1) Ritualization of signals of innate S-R relations; (2) specialized learning capacities and motivations; (3) emotional commitments to particular behavioral patterns. Even superficial observation indicates that analogous phenomena are operative in stabilizing human cultural patterns.

In his evolution, man has achieved unique mental characteristics here characterized by the phrases time- and space- binding imagination, generalized intelligence, and language. To the extent to which man's social behavior is governed by these characteristics, his behavioral patterns have no analogues in animal life.

REFERENCES

1. Dobzhansky, T.: Evolution, organic and superorganic. Bull. Atom. Sci. 20: 1964.
2. Eiseley, L.: Fossil man and human evolution. *In:* Current Anthropology. Thomas, Ed. Chicago, University of Chicago Press, 1956.
3. Etkin, W.: Social behavioral factors in the emergence of man. Human Biol. 35:299-310, 1963.
4. Etkin, W., Ed.: Social Behavior and Organization Among Vertebrates. Chicago, University of Chicago Press, 1964.
5. Geschwind, N.: The development of the brain and the evolution of language. *In:* Monograph Series on Languages and Linguistics. C. I. J. M. Stuart, Ed. No. 17, pp. 155-169. Institute of Languages and Linguistics, Georgetown University, Washington, D.C.
6. Hayes, C.: The Ape in Our House. New York, Harper & Row, 1951.
7. Huxley, J.: Eugenics in evolutionary perspectives. Perspect. Biol. Med. 6: 155-187, 1963.
8. Imanishi, K.: Social behavior in Japanese monkeys. *Macaca fuscata.* Psychologia 1:47-54, 1957. Reprinted in "Primate Social Behavior." C. Southwick, Ed. New York, Van Nostrand Co., 1963.
9. Kohler, W.: The Mentality of Apes. London, Routledge and Kegan Paul, 1927.
10. Kroeber, A.: Sign and symbol in bee communications. Proc. Nat. Acad. Sci. 38:753-757, 1952.
11. Montagu, M. F. A.: Time binding and the concept of culture. Sci. Monthly 77:148-155, 1953.
12. Schjelderup-Ebbe, T.: Social behavior in birds. *In:* Handbook of Social Psychology. C. Murchison, Ed. Worcester, Mass., Clark University Press, 1935.
13. Thorpe, W. H.: Learning and instinct in animals. Cambridge, Harvard University Press, 1956.
14. Tinbergen, N.: Social behavior in animals. New York, John Wiley and Sons, 1953.
15. Wynne-Edwards, V. C.: Animal dispersion. New York, Hafner Publishing Co., 1962.

4

ABNORMAL STEREOTYPED MOTOR ACTS

by GERSHON BERKSON, PH.D.*

AMONG THE MORE INTRIGUING ASPECTS of abnormal psychology is the study of the stereotyped motor acts which are often associated with mental deficiency, mental illness, and blindness in childhood. These stereotyped acts are for the most part reptitive movements, but also include nonrepetitive movements or postures. Among them are whole body movements (body rocking and twirling), other repetitive movements (head rolling, head banging), nonrepetitive behaviors (limb and body posturing, digit sucking, eye poking and gouging, self-biting), stereotyped complex hand movements, repetitive manipulation of objects, and the repetitious utterance of meaningless sounds. These motor acts may be differentiated, on the one hand, from disorders of motor organization such as tremors in voluntary movements which have a fairly specific and well-determined neuropathology and, on the other, from certain tics and ritualistic compulsive acts whose origin and form are specific to an individual and which often seem to have a complex symbolic basis. Although these defining characteristics should not be too rigidly adhered to, it does appear that the stereotypd acts with which we are concerned are voluntary and that they represent a level of behavioral complexity somewhere between postural mechanisms and patterns of ideation.

It has been pointed out frequently[23] that some of these abnormal behaviors are similar in form to certain patterns seen in active normal infants. Thus, body rocking and thumb sucking are relatively common, and head banging occurs in some infants who have previously rocked.[30,34] In early childhood, these patterns are apparently not ordinarily associated with any pathology, and typically they disappear with age.

This paper was supported by grants from the National Institute of Mental Health, the National Association for Retarded Children, and Illinois State Psychiatric Training and Research Fund. Dr. William A. Mason collaborated in much of the research, and I am indebted to him for his contribution.

*Illinois State Pediatric Institute, Chicago, Ill.

Of special relevance to this paper is the fact that when certain animals are separated from their mothers at birth, they develop behavior patterns which are strikingly similar in form to the stereotyped behaviors of abnormal humans and normal infants. Forty years ago, Richter[44] reported that a coatimundi, a kinkajou, and a spider monkey who had been separated from their mothers by three months of age engaged in stereotyped sucking of a part of their bodies. Jacobsen, Jacobsen and Yoshioka[28] were the first to describe repetitive body swaying in a hand-reared infant primate, and it has since become clear that, among animals, it is the higher monkeys and apes which develop these and other abnormal behavior patterns to the fullest extent. *More recently, the similarity in form between the stereotyped movements of subhuman primates and of abnormal children frequently has been pointed out,[14,25] and this has encouraged their comparative study.

The similarity of the movements in the animal and human groups is striking, and it is one of the purposes of this paper to describe some of the common features of the acts in monkeys, apes, and human mental defectives. However, there are also a number of differences among the groups which are at least as interesting and significant as the similarities. These differences will also be pointed out.

---

*It is important to differentiate these stereotyped behaviors of hand-reared animals from other repetitive acts which are manifested by caged wild animals and by monkeys reared in the laboratory with their mothers. The "cage stereotypies" develop in some active species of animals who are kept in small cages.[26] Large carnivores often pace their cages;[12] horses show a variety of repetitive acts such as "weaving" and "crib-biting"[22] and young macaque monkeys pace, back-flip and jump repetitively on all fours.[17] It is likely that the cage stereotypies share some common mechanisms with the stereotyped acts of animals raised in isolation. For instance, both are increased by placing the animals in small cages.[8,17,33] However, there are also clear differences. For one thing, the form of the two groups of behaviors is different. Although they share the characteristics of being repetitive, the cage stereotypies usually involve repetitive locomotion while the "deprivation" acts almost never do. Second, eliciting the cage stereotypies seems to be specific to restricting the animal to a small cage, while the movements resulting from isolation-rearing are often seen when the animal has freedom of movement. Finally, there seems to be a fairly sharp division in the origin of the two groups of activities. The "deprivation" stereotypes develop in animals who have been separated from their mother soon after birth, while mother-reared animals have never been reported to show them.[14,37] On the other hand, isolation-reared animals can show some cage stereotypy, and it remains to be seen what the two types of stereotyped acts have in common.

DESCRIPTION OF THE BEHAVIORS

Monkeys who have been reared in isolation rock their bodies, clasp themselves, and crouch with their heads between their legs. Sucking a digit or the genitalia is common, and self-biting and eye poking also occur occasionally. At least 25 different stereotyped behaviors and postures have been reported for chimpanzees,[14] with body rocking or swaying, head rolling, eye poking, limb posturing, and thumb sucking the most common. Among severely defective humans, body rocking and complex movements of the hands are most frequent, and self-biting, sucking, eye poking and gouging, head banging, and other more individual activities are also seen. Some mental defectives play in a stereotyped manner with a single object for long periods of time, and some utter certain verbal phrases repetitively.

The basic similarity of the movements among the animal and human groups lies in the form of certain movement patterns. Behaviors such as rocking and sucking occur in all groups. Also, the frequency of these movements is controlled by some of the same variables in the different groups. However, there are also clear species differences in the form and expression of the stereotyped activities. One difference is in the variety of responses manifested. The number of different behaviors that have been observed increases from monkeys to apes to humans. It is possible that the greater variety seen as one goes up the phylogenetic scale reflects a generally greater differentiation of the innate response repertoire.[36,46] In addition to species differences in the variety of behaviors, there are also differences in the frequency of expression of various behaviors. Body rocking or swaying develops in most, if not all, isolation-reared chimpanzees, but preliminary observations of crab-eating macaques in our laboratory indicate that while some kind of sucking is very common, rocking does not occur in all animals. Furthermore, there are apparently species differences in the specific mode of expression of the various types of acts. Rocking is typically performed by macaque monkeys as a forward and back motion of the torso while the animal is sitting. In chimpanzees, seated rocking also occurs, but in addition rocking may be seen when the animal is standing on two feet, and chimpanzees often sway from side to side in prone, seated, and erect positions.

Variations in variety, frequency, and mode of expression also reflect differences between the stereotyped movements of humans and of the subhuman primates. In addition, while body rocking of monkeys and apes almost always is accompanied by clasping a part of the body or the environment, clasping seems to be "optional" in much human rocking.

There are species differences also in the individuality and complexity of unusual stereotyped responses to objects. Isolation-reared monkeys and apes may respond in a stereotyped manner to a soft cloth with which they have been raised. A similar attachment to a blanket is commonly seen in normal human children. In human mental defectives, idiosyncratic complex ritualistic responses to a wider range of specific objects may occur over long periods of time,[3] and it may be that these complex manipulations are related in some way to the stereotyped hand movements seen in other mentally deficient patients.

The form of stereotyped behaviors is therefore determined partly by individual and species characteristics, and any analysis of these behaviors should take both the similarities and differences into account. Besides the form of the behaviors, there are also other aspects which differentiate the groups. One of these is the relationship of stereotypy to the environment. Stereotyped behaviors are often performed with reference to the environment. Animals tend to choose a single area of any situation in which to rock or sway, usually next to a wall or on a smooth floor, and it is not uncommon to see an animal go to his "favorite" place and then begin to rock. The situation with the severely deficient humans is more complicated. Those who frequently perform stereotyped movements also tend to be stereotyped with regard to the area of the room in which they stay. With some patients, this tendency is so marked that it is possible to predict almost perfectly the location in any room of their cottage in which they will be found simply because that is the place they ordinarily go to on entering the room.[3]

This stereotypy in choice of location is worth considering when one does experiments on stereotyped movements because the location in which a subject is tested may affect the level of expression of stereotypy.[5,8] On the other hand, this factor should not be emphasized too heavily because it is the case that changing the location never limits the performance of stereotyped acts completely. An animal or person who does these acts at all will do them in many environments. However, the fact that there is a tendency to prefer locations indicates that these activities are done to some extent with reference to the environment and that they are therefore not "autistic" in any extreme sense. Perhaps more significant is the idea that at least for some behaviors, it is not only the motor acts which are stereotyped but that perceptual aspects are also involved.

Finally, there may also be species differences in the function of particular acts. Beginning with Louri[34] and Greenacre,[24] there have been a number of classifications of rocking which have emphasized the fact that rocking may occur when a child is quiet or when he is in an excited state (e.g., Brody;[10] Provence and Lipton[42]). Nissen[40] has also pointed out that chimpanzees tend to rock when they are "bored" or when they are excited. Whether this two-way division is useful remains to be demonstrated. Nevertheless, it does seem that, although human children and chimpanzees rock when they are quiet and when they are excited, macaque monkeys rock mainly when they are apparently afraid of some external stimulus. This fact has led some workers to characterize rocking as emotional behavior in monkeys (Bernstein and Mason;[9] Saxon[45]).

Determinants of Stereotypy Level

This brings me to an overview of the experiments we have done with chimpanzees and mental defectives. In these studies our major interest was to determine the kinds of variables which affect moment-to-moment changes in the level of stereotyped behaviors once they have been developed. Our major findings were that in chimpanzees, rocking or swaying is determined by the general arousal level of the animal and also by the extent to which the environment elicits activities other than the stereotyped behaviors. With the defectives, the main variable seemed to be the extent to which the person responds to the environment.

The chimpanzees had been reared in varying degrees of isolation for the first two years of life[14] and thereafter had been housed in groups for at least two years. At the time they entered the experiments, they were at least four years old. The mental defectives were severely deficient institutionalized male adolescent and adult patients. All were ambulatory, but most had no speech. This particular group of patients was studied because it is the case that the prevalence of stereotyped motor acts is greater with lower intelligence and also that older defective patients tend to show more stereotypy than do younger ones.[4]

We studied both chimpanzees and mental defectives partly because of an interest in the generality of our findings. That is, we asked whether the stereotyped movements were similar for the two groups in other respects besides their form. We also hoped that by doing the research concurrently with the two groups, using the same kind of variables, it might be possible to get a broader look at the problem of stereotyped behaviors than would have been possible with a single population.

Our main interest was in body rocking, or swaying, since this behavior was evidenced by almost all chimpanzees and many of the mental defectives. Digit-sucking* was not frequent among the chimpanzees, and we rarely saw it among the defectives. However, we did employ a behavior category in our observations which included sucking, posturing, eye poking, and other nonrepetitive acts. In addition, the observations involved notations of other classes of behavior such as locomotion, manipulating the environment, and self-manipulation (e.g., scratching or rubbing any body part). It was particularly important to study other behavior classes besides stereotyped movements because, as will be shown, the level of stereotyped behaviors depends partly on the extent to which the environment elicits alternative activities.

Some preliminary experiments[5,8] showed that, in both the chimpanzees and the defectives, stereotyped behaviors were most frequent in a bare, spatially restricted environment which was new to the subject. These results were consistent with previous findings that repetitive acts occur in environments which restrict movement[17,33] and which are novel,[37] and we therefore proceeded to a series of studies examining more specifically the factors in these environments which affect stereotypy level.

Novelty of environment was one factor considered, and we tested its influence by observing chimpanzees and defectives repeatedly in a situation which was initially new to them. It was expected that if novelty was important the stereotypy level would decrease with repeated testing. The results with both chimpanzees and defectives indicated that repeated experiences had no influence on the level of rocking and complex hand movements, and we therefore concluded that novelty by itself does not influence stereotypy level.

A second variable considered was spatial and visual restriction. We compared rocking of chimpanzees in two cages of the same size, one an indoor cage out of which the animal could not see and the other an outdoor cage which faced the animal colony. If restriction had been the only variable involved, no difference in level would have been expected between the two cages. However, it was found that in

---

*See Benjamin[2] for a more adequate review of sucking.

the outdoor situation in which there was more to do, the level of rocking was lower.

After showing that novelty of the environment and environmental restriction were not by themselves sufficient to account for variations in stereotypy level, we were still left with the problem of indicating what the important variables were. We knew that when an animal is placed in a new situation, his level of excitement is high, and we remembered that other workers had suggested that rocking is related to the level of excitement or emotionality. We generalized this notion and suggested that rocking and swaying in chimpanzees is directly related to the general level of arousal rather than to any particular situational variable. We then did a series of studies with chimpanzees attempting to relate arousal to rocking by employing conditions which are ordinarily used in psychological experiments to vary arousal or drive.[7]

In the first study, ambient sound level and food deprivation were varied; and it was found that, with each of these variables, rocking or swaying was positively related to arousal. In a second experiment, we tried habituation to the environment again. In the earlier experiments, the animal had been exposed to the environment repeatedly, and rocking did not decrease; in this experiment the animal was left in the same environment continually for 12 days. Using this kind of habituation procedure, the level of rocking and swaying did decline over time as the animal became relaxed in the situation.

As part of this same experiment, the animal was given amphetamine after he had settled down. The idea was that this drug, which is said to increase general arousal level, would increase repetitive activities, and it did. Another drug study by Fitz-Gerald[20] is consistent with this finding and also indicates that chlorpromazine and a barbiturate (which tend to reduce arousal level) will decrease rocking and swaying.

The arousal notion therefore seems to have merit when applied to chimpanzees. Its status with mental defectives is less clear. One study examined the effects of amphetamine and barbiturates on the stereotypy behaviors of four blind severely defective individuals, and no drug effect was observed (Berkson, unpublished). However, Levitt and Kaufman[32] have shown that increasing noise level raises the rate of rocking, at least in mentally deficient boys. Hutt, Hutt, Lee, and Ounsted[27] have provided evidence of EEG arousal during the performance of stereotyped behaviors in autistic children. Thus the arousal notion may have some generality in humans.

However, arousal level does not by itself account for moment-to-moment changes in the level of stereotypy. Another important variable is the extent to which the environment elicits activities which interfere with the stereotyped acts. Soon after we began our studies, Menzel[38] reported that as isolation-reared chimpanzees begin to manipulate objects of which they are initially afraid, their stereotypy level declines. He also showed that as they become satiated with an object they again begin to perform stereotyped movements. This finding suggested that there is a reciprocal relationship between object manipulation and stereotypy. In one of our habituation studies we had seen a similar reciprocal relationship between stereotypy and manipulations of the animal's own body, and we therefore began to think that *any* behavior can interfere with stereotypy if the environment brings this alternative activity into play. By the same token, increasing the probability of rocking by increasing arousal level can have a reverse effect so that when rocking is made very high it can interfere with any other behavior class.[7]

Thus stereotypy level is related not only to arousal level but also to factors which affect the likelihood of performance of other behaviors in the animal's response repertoire. The environment is of course an important factor in determining the balance among stereotyped behaviors and various other behavior classes, and it is the case that in different experiments stereotypy has varied both with the inversely to self-manipulation, environmental manipulation, and locomotion. It is well to remember this variability of the relationship between stereotypy and any other behavior class in considering correlations between stereotyped movements and other behaviors. It may, for instance, be at the basis of inconsistencies that have been reported in the relationship between stereotypy and self-manipulation.[6,8]

The determinants of the relationship between stereotyped movements and other behaviors go beyond environmental effects and can also be sought in individual differences in characteristic patterns of responsiveness to the environment. This principle is most clearly seen in the studies with mental defectives in which individual differences in responsiveness to objects were shown to be related to the type of stereotyped movement the patient performed. Our first experiments with defectives showed that patients who perform stereotyped movements tend to manipulate objects less than do those who show no stereotypy of behavior.[13] However, it soon became clear that among those patients with stereotyped movements there are at least two groups: those who do mainly body rocking and those who do mainly complex movements of the hands.[6] Comparisons of these groups with a group which showed no stereotypy indicated that the three groups had different tendencies to respond to the objects with which we presented them. The "rockers" tended to respond somewhat *more* to the objects when they were not performing the stereotyped acts than did the control group, although when rocking occurred it did interfere with object manipulation. The situation was different for the group that did complex hand movements. These patients did less object manipulation both when they were performing the hand movements and when they were not. *It therefore appears that stereotypy can interfere with object manipulation in defectives as well as chimpanzees. †However, it is also the case that a stereotyped act in an individual may or may not represent a *generally* lower responsiveness to the environment. Whether or not it does, can be predicted at least partly from the character of the acts performed.

To summarize, experiments with chimpanzees have indicated that body rocking and swaying are positively related to the animal's general level of arousal and that they can be suppressed when the environment evokes alternative activities. Among mental defectives, changing environments and presenting objects do affect the level of stereotyped

---

The individuals who do some kind of repetitive complex hand movement appear to represent a group, within the profoundly defective population, different from the rockers. We have suggested[6] that they might be "autistic" since they do perform stereotyped movements and do not respond to people. However, they also tend not to respond to objects and therefore do not fit strictly the usual definitions of early infantile autism.[19] They seem to be more like Earl's description of the "catatonic psychosis of idiocy."[18] An intensive investigation of these profoundly defective individuals with psychotic features would be significant.

†It has been suggested[3] that one approach to the therapeutic control of stereotyped behaviors might be to develop the functioning of alternative forms of behavior with the expectation that performance of alternative activities would interfere with the expression of the stereotyped movements. This approach has been successfully used on an experimental basis by Lovaas et al. with self-destructive behaviors of a schizophrenic child.[35] Other means of reducing a stereotyped act that have been effective have been withdrawal of an incentive and also presentation of an aversive stimulus when the stereotyped act is performed.[1,49]

It is therefore clear that stereotyped behaviors can be controlled at least to some extent with a careful use of programmed rewards and punishments. The studies cited have been limited, however, to a consideration of the changes in stereotyped behaviors during an experiment. It would be of interest to know what behaviors increase as stereotyped behaviors decrease and to what extent the effects are generalized beyond the experimental situation.

acts. Defectives who do complex hand movements tend to be generally less responsive to the environment than those who do mainly rocking.

ORIGIN AND FUNCTION OF STEREOTYPED BEHAVIORS

Our program began with an analysis of variables which affect moment-to-moment changes in the level of stereotyped behaviors once they had been developed. Although it was possible to show that arousal level and competing responses could affect the level, the changes exerted in these ways tended to be ephemeral. These manipulations could increase or decrease the stereotyped acts for a short period but did not affect their form or suppress them permanently. The reason for this is that arousal and competing responses affect the likelihood that the stereotyped behaviors are expressed but do not interfere with the basic organization of the patterns.

For the most part, the stimuli which initiate, guide, and reward stereotyped behaviors have their origin within the organism performing the act. That is, while normal behaviors ordinarily involve some aspect of the environment, the basic organization of most stereotyped acts is only partially dependent on external stimulation. This means that the stimulus-response organization of most stereotyped behaviors is to a great degree enclosed within the individual, and the investigator of stereotyped acts has the special problem of trying to break this circle to find ways of controlling their organization as well as their level of expression.

One way of getting a hint of the kinds of mechanisms involved in stereotyped behaviors might be to concentrate study on those few behaviors which do incorporate the environment. The stereotypy of location, repetitive manipulations of objects, and cage stereotypes are organized with respect to external stimuli and an understanding of them might give some clue to the organization of other stereotyped behaviors.

However, the most fruitful approach thus far has been the study of the movements as they first develop. Many of the behaviors are seen during infancy or early childhood, and some of them are clearly similar in form to aspects of the normal infant's behavior repertoire. The study of infants provides the opportunity for investigating the conditions necessary for the development of stereotyped behaviors and also permits one to observe the movements as they develop in relationship to the rest of the organization of the infant's behaviors.

The fact that infant monkeys and apes show stereotyped behaviors similar in form to those of infant and abnormal humans has provided the opportunity for an intensive experimental analysis of their origin. Undertaking such an analysis assumes that there is a fundamental similarity in the abnormal acts of animals and humans, an assumption which has some empirical support in the case of body rocking and digit or genital sucking.

In the case of sucking and self-clasping, the stereotyped behaviors of monkeys and apes can be traced to activities present in the behavior repertoire of the neonate.[36] The newborn monkey clasps tightly to its mother's fur and is capable of sucking at her nipples. The occurrence of these behaviors is not dependent on the presence of the mother; the neonate monkey will eagerly clutch at furry cloths and suck small, soft cylindrical objects placed in its mouth. The tendency to perform these acts is very strong, and it is also the case that objects which have only a very general similarity to the mother's body can also elicit them. Thus, in the absence of a cloth, the infant may clasp and become "attached" to the wire mesh of his cage. However, a primary stimulus generalization principle is probably operative at this time, and it is likely that the infant will clasp or suck objects to the extent that they are physically similar to the mother.

Thus, at least two factors determine what will be sucked and clasped: The first is the availability of the object during the neonatal and early infantile period, and the second is the extent to which the object is physically similar to the mother. The infant himself is one object that is similar to his mother and, of course, is always available to himself so that it is not surprising that self-sucking and clasping are seen in isolated animals.

The conception that sucking and self-clasping are basically normal neonatal responses suggests that, with age, they should decline in strength as do the same behaviors in the infant raised with the mother. Although this suggestion has not been formally evaluated, a decrement with age does occur. However, the abnormal acts generally persist longer than do their normal homologues. One possible explanation for this is that isolated animals who are reared in restricted environments do not have the opportunity to develop behaviors alternative to the stereotyped responses. In this view, infantile acts remain when more mature forms of activity are not developed to compete with their functioning. It would predict that monkeys reared in restricted environments would retain stereotyped behaviors longer than monkeys reared in situations in which the environment stimulates the development of alternative behavior patterns.

Another possible explanation of the long retention of stereotyped behaviors is that animals raised in a restricted environment have not had the opportunity to experience novel stimulation during development and have not gone through the long process of habituation to stimuli which a jungle-reared animal has experienced. Since novel stimuli tend to arouse an animal, it is possible that isolation-reared monkeys are at a generally higher level of arousal than are mother-reared monkeys. As previously shown, a higher level of arousal tends to increase the expression of at least some stereotyped movements. Thus it may be that, through an arousal mechanism, continued isolation in a restricted environment provides the conditions for the maintenance of stereotyped acts beyond the time when they would ordinarily have been given up.

The similarity in form between abnormal sucking and self-clasping, on the one hand, and normal sucking and clinging, on the other, are fairly obvious. There are other behavior patterns, however, which are not as clearly related to normal neonatal acts in form but which nevertheless have some important similarities to them. Among these are crouching and the tendency to perform stereotyped acts in a particular area of the cage.

Within a few days after separation from its mother, the infant crab-eating macaque begins routinely to sleep in a particular body posture in a restricted area of the cage. Which posture and which area are chosen is not always predictable, but aspects of the environment such as a heat source, a raised portion of the cage, a corner, a smooth or soft surface, or a place where there is something to grasp may all increase the likelihood that a particular area and posture will be chosen. Frequently, especially when no heating pad or soft cloth is provided, the animal begins to sleep in a seated position with his head between his legs. This crouching posture maximizes contact with the animal's own smooth and soft body surface (similar to the mother's) and also probably minimizes the loss of body heat. The sleeping posture is rather similar to the stereotyped crouching seen under conditions of stress, and the two patterns may actually be identical.

The specificity of the area in which the animal sleeps may have some similarity to the mechanism of a stereotypy of location, for it is also the case that when the monkey is fearful he retires to the area in which he sleeps and performs a stereotyped act there.

Thus the place and posture in which the animal sleeps, escapes, and performs stereotyped acts tend to be the same. It is noteworthy that mother-reared infant monkeys rush to her when threatened and sleep with her until at least well into the second half of the first year. It appears that a particular part of the cage can also serve as a "refuge" in the same way in the absence of the mother, and it is tempting to speculate on the mechanism of this attachment. It may be that the animal originally chooses a particular posture and area in which to sleep on the basis of the environmental factors noted and that a more permanent "attachment" is maintained partly by these factors. It is also possible that the stimuli of that area become conditioned to the low level of arousal maintained in sleep. It may be that after a short time the animal learns to go to the sleep area and get into the sleep posture when excited, with the resultant reward of a conditioned lower arousal level.

It therefore appears that at least some stereotyped behaviors may be closely identified with neonatal motor patterns which normally function to maintain close contact with the mother. There are, however, other behaviors such as self-biting, repetitive vocalizations, eye poking and gouging, body rocking and swaying, head banging, and complex hand movements which probably have their origin later in development and have a different organization from the neonatal responses. For some of these it is possible to speculate on homologous patterns during later development. Thus, self-biting may be fundamentally the same as the biting which occurs in the play-fighting of juvenile primates. Complex hand movements may originate in the hand play of normal three-month-old infants. However, such homologies are yet to be demonstrated, and this kind of demonstration depends upon intensive longitudinal studies of the development of these movements during infancy.

Among the more intriguing of this group of later-developing behaviors are the repetitive movements such as rocking, swaying, and head banging. These patterns are of special interest partly because some of them are seen in a diverse group of populations. Isolation-reared primates, normal human infants, psychotic children, blind children, mentally deficient children and adults, and normal human adults, all can show rocking. In addition to their widespread occurrence, the repetitive behaviors are of interest because they seem to have some relationship with one another. There is evidence that head banging develops in children who previously have been rockers and head rollers.[16,30] Moreover, since these are repetitive movements done more in physically restricted situations, they have some similarity to the "cage stereotypes" of caged feral-reared animals.

The origin and function of rocking and head banging have been widely discussed, and there seems to be some disagreement regarding them in the literature. Rocking has been variously regarded as a normal expression of a movement urge in active infants,[39] as a frustration response developed during transitional stages in locomotor development,[34,42] and as resulting from an abnormal relationship with the mother.[47] Other hypotheses implicate bareness of environment or a high level of unorganized stimulation in institutions.[29] Some workers have regarded rocking specifically as genital masturbation,[41] while others see it as a more general kinesthetic or tactual self-stimulation[5,11,31] or as a way of relieving anxiety.[34] Head banging has been thought to be a way of bringing sources of tension under the infant's own control,[30] simulating the sound of the mother's heartbeat,[21] and establishing the reality of the body.[24] De Lissavoy[15] has presented evidence that it is related to the early incidence of middle ear infection and has suggested[16] that the stimulation derived from head banging originally has the function of interfering with the pain of the otitis media.

Most of these ideas have only been illustrated with case histories, although some have received more formal support.[16,42,47] However, the results of the two most extensive studies which attempted an experimental approach are conflicting.* Thus, the empirical basis of these ideas is tenuous.

As might be expected, the situation is more complicated with humans than with the subhuman primates. In the animals it can at least be said that deprivation of the mother is probably necessary for the development of rocking. In humans, none of the factors which have been suggested is relevant to all cases. For instance, some aspects of institutionalization may be a contributory cause. However, many children develop rocking prior to institutionalization, and not all children who

---

*Provence and Lipton[42] reported that all of the institutionalized babies they studied rocked, while Spitz and Wolf[47] found that almost none of the babies that were without their mother in an institution did repetitive movements. These conflicting results point to both the difficulty in doing this kind of research and the need for more of it.

are institutionalized develop a stereotyped act. As another instance, complete deprivation of the mother apparently does not always increase the likelihood of rocking. When the relationship with the mother is unusual and an increase in the prevalence of rocking results, not all cases show this increase.[47] Furthermore, rocking occurs in normal human infants when there is no reason to believe that there is an unusual relationship with the mother,[43] and rocking develops along with the general deterioration of Heller's disease when the relationship with the mother is probably not an important etiological factor.

Although it is thus not likely that a single factor forms the etiology of repetitive movements, it is possible that analysis of their development might contribute to an understanding of their later organization. No doubt the *form* of the repetitive act is limited by the rate of the infant's postural and locomotor development. Head rolling, rocking on all fours, and seated rocking can be seen only after the child is able to assume the posture in which the particular behavior occurs. In addition, since in a single individual, one repetitive movement (such as head rolling) can be superseded by another (such as all fours rocking) as postural abilities advance, it appears that developmental level of posture can dictate which particular movement will develop.

This notion has some importance when one considers species differences in the form of abnormal stereotyped movements. It will be remembered that although humans and chimpanzees show head rolling, body rocking or swaying, and head banging in a variety of postures, the main abnormal repetitive stereotype of macaque monkeys is seated rocking. Although this could be a function of the greater richness of the innate response repertoire of the more phylogenetically advanced animals, it may also be related to the rate of postural development prior to the acquisition of advanced motor abilities. It may be that the macaque infant does not stay at a particular postural level long enough to develop a stereotyped act before he proceeds to a higher level of maturity. It is only when he has achieved a relatively stable developmental stage that any repetitive stereotypy becomes possible, and since the level of maturity may determine the form of the movement, only the more "mature" activity (rocking) develops.

Developmental levels and rates affect not only the form that the repetitive act takes but also seem to influence the time when it will first be seen. Although locomotion of isolation-reared monkeys develops rather quickly, it remains quite awkward until between the fourth and eighth week of life. It may be coincidental that rocking is first seen at about this time (personal observation; personal communication: G. P. Sackett; G. W. Meier), but it is possible that a repetitive act develops only when the motor system involved in it is well integrated. This view is rather different from the idea that rocking is a frustration response to the infant's inability to control his motility.[34] It would tend to de-emphasize rocking as having a role in the *development* of the organization of a sensorimotor system (as, for instance, by some kind of practice), but would give more importance to it as an unusual pattern expressed by a mature response system when the system is active but relatively unguided by the environment.

This idea is consistent with a concept of stereotyped acts as normal movements which are organized independently of the stimulus situation. This view assumes that these movements are ordinarily directed to some object (e.g., an aspect of the mother's body) but that when this object is unavailable, generally the same act must occur, even if it appears in a distorted form.

A different idea is that stereotyped behaviors serve some self-stimulatory function. This general view involves the assumption that the organism has a need for certain levels of more or less specific types of stimulation. In the ordinary course of events, these needs are met by the social or physical environment. But when isolation or some other unusual condition is imposed, these sources of stimulation may be reduced and the organism, in order to fill the deficit, begins to provide his own stimulation.

It is doubtful whether it is possible to determine whether one or the other of these two approaches is correct. Since every movement involves at least some proprioceptive stimulation and every kind of self-stimulation must be accompanied by a movement, it probably is impossible to determine whether an infant rocks in order to stimulate himself or rocks to express a motor urge and as an epiphenomenon also receives some stimulation. Therefore, opposing these two views does not now appear to be possible operationally, and it may be that the distinction is not useful.

Perhaps the best approach for the future will be one that continues to deal with aspects of stereotyped behavior that can come under observation and experimental control. The conditions under which specific behaviors develop and what determines their form need study. It would also be fruitful to look further into the relationship between stereotyped behaviors and normal patterns. Finally, the consequences of performing stereotyped movements could also be examined. As an example, a study by Stone[48] suggests that a sleeplike electroencephalogram follows body rocking or eye pressing in some blind children, and he has hypothesized that the repetitive stimulation acccompanying rocking has the effect of inducing a drowsy state. Further support for such an hypothesis depends on an extension of Stone's general method of doing psychophysiological recordings at the time that the stereotyped act is performed. This method has many technical difficulties associated with it, but Stone's work demonstrates that it is promising.

Conclusions

The fact that isolation-reared monkeys and apes perform stereotyped acts which are similar to those seen in abnormal humans has provided the opportunity for their intensive experimental investigation. A comparison of the movements in the various animal and human groups has revealed significant similarities and differences in their manifestation. It has been possible to vary the level of at least some of these behaviors once they have been developed. The effects of general arousal and of competing behaviors are significant but tend to be ephemeral since they do not involve the fundamental organization of the behaviors.

Most stereotyped acts are organized without important reference to the environment. Thus, the study of stereotyped behaviors presents the special problem of attempting to gain control over internal stimuli. This approach probably is not feasible at this time. Instead, it would be useful to study those few stereotyped behaviors which do incorporate the environment. Even more fruitful will be an investigation of their development, emphasizing the relationship between stereotyped acts and normal behaviors.

REFERENCES

1. Baer, D. M.: Laboratory withdrawal of thumbsucking by withdrawal and representation of reinforcement. J. Exp. Anal. Behav. 5:525-528, 1962.
2. Benjamin, L. S.: The non-nutritive sucking behavior of the infant rhesus monkey. Ph.D. Dissertation, University of Wisconsin, 1960.
3. Berkson, G.: Stereotyped movements of mental defectives. V. Ward behavior and its relation to an experimental task. Amer. J. Ment. Defic. 69:253-264, 1964.
4. ———, and Davenport, R. K., Jr.: Stereotyped movements of mental defectives. I. Initial survey. Amer. J. Ment. Defic. 66:849-852, 1962.
5. ———, and Mason, W. A.: Stereotyped movements of mental defectives. III. Situation effects. Amer. J. Ment. Defic. 68:409-412, 1963.
6. ———, and ———: Stereotyped movements of mental defectives. IV. The effects of toys and the character of the acts. Amer. J. Ment. Defic. 68:511-524, 1964.

7. ——, and ——: Stereotyped behaviors of chimpanzees: Relation to general arousal and alternative activities. Percept. Mot. Skills 19:635-652, 1964.

8. ——, ——, and Saxon, S. V.: Situation and stimulus effects on stereotyped behaviors of chimpanzees. J. Comp. Physiol. Psychol. 56:786-792, 1963.

9. Bernstein, S., and Mason, W. A.: The effects of age and stimulus conditions on the emotional responses of rhesus monkeys: Responses to complex stimuli. J. Genet. Psychol. 101:279-298, 1962.

10. Brody, S.: Self rocking in infancy. J. Amer. Psychoanal. Ass. 8:464-491, 1960.

11. Casler, L.: Maternal deprivation: a critical review of the literature. Monogr. Soc. Res. Child Develp. 26:1-49, 1961.

12. Cooper, J. B.: An exploratory study of African lions. Comp. Psychol. Monogr. 17:1-48, 1942.

13. Davenport, R. K., Jr., and Berkson, G : Stereotyped movements of mental defectives. II. Effects of novel objects. Amer. J. Ment. Defic. 67:879-882, 1963.

14. ——, and Menzel, E. W., Jr.: Stereotyped behavior of the infant chimpanzee. Arch. Gen. Psychiat. 8:99-104, 1963.

15. De Lissavoy, V.: Head banging in childhood: a suggested cause. J. Genet. Psychol., 102:109-114, 1963.

16. ——: Head banging in childhood: review of empirical studies. Pediat. Dig. 6:49-55, 1964.

17. Draper, W. A., and Bernstein, I. S.: Stereotyped behavior and cage size. Percept. Motor Skills, 16:231-234, 1963.

18. Earl, C. J. C.: The primitive psychosis of idiocy. Brit. J. Med. Psychol. 14:230-253, 1934.

19. Eisenberg, L., and Kanner, L.: Early infantile autism. Amer. J. Orthopsychiat. 26:556-566, 1956.

20. Fitz-Gerald, F. L.: The effects of drugs upon stereotyped behavior in young chimpanzees. Ph.D. Dissertation, McGill University, 1964.

21. Fitz-Herbert, J.: The origin of head banging: a suggested explanation with an illustrative case history. J. Ment. Sci. 96:793-795, 1950.

22. Fraser, A. F.: Behavior disorders in domestic animals. Cornell Vet. 53:213-223, 1963.

23. Gesell, A., and Amatruda, C. S.: Developmental Diagnosis. New York, Paul B. Hoeber, 1947.

24. Greenacre, P., in Kris, E.: Problems of infantile neurosis. Psychoanal. Stud. Child 9:16-71, 1954.

25. Harlow, H. F., and Harlow, M.: Social deprivation in monkeys. Sci. Amer. 207:137-146, 1962.

26. Hediger, H.: Studies of the Psychology and Behaviour of Captive Animals in Zoos and Circuses. New York, Criterion, 1955.

27. Hutt, C., Hutt, J. J., Lee, D., and Ounsted, C.: Arousal and childhood autism. Nature (London) 204:908-909, 1964.

28. Jacobsen, C. F., Jacobsen, M. M., and Yoshioka, J. G.: Development of an infant chimpanzee during her first year. Comp. Psychol. Monogr. 9(1): 1932.

29. Kaufman, M. E.: Stereotyped self-oriented behaviors among the profoundly retarded residing in institutions. Paper read at meetings of Amer. Assoc. Ment. Defic., Portland, Oregon, 1963.

30. Kravitz, H., Rosenthal, V., Teplitz, Z., Murphy, J. B., and Lesser, R. E.: A study of head banging in infants and children. Dis. Nerv. Syst. 21:3-8, 1960.

31. Kulka, A., Fry, C., and Goldstein, F. J.: Kinesthetic needs in infancy. Amer. J. Orthopsychiat. 30:562-571, 1960.

32. Levitt, H., and Kaufman, M. E.: Sound induced drive and stereotyped behavior in mental defectives. Amer. J. Ment. Defic. 69:729-734, 1965.

33. Levy, D. M.: On the problem of movement restraint. Amer. J. Orthopsychiat. 14:644-671, 1944.

34. Lourie, R. S.: The role of rhythmic patterns in childhood. Amer. J. Psychiat. 105:653-660, 1949.

35. Lovaas, O. I., Freitag, G., Gold, V. J., and Kassorla, I. C.: Experimental studies in childhood schizophrenia: Analysis of self-destructive behavior. J. Exp. Child Psychol. 2:67-84, 1965.

36. Mason, W. A.: The social development of monkeys and apes. *In:* Primate Behavior. De Vore, I., Ed. New York, Holt, Rinehart and Winston, 1965.

37. Mason, W. A., and Green, P. C.: The effects of social restriction on the behavior of rhesus monkeys: IV. Responses to a novel environment and to an alien species. J. Comp. Physiol. Psychol. 55:363-368, 1962.

38. Menzel, E. W., Jr.: The effects of cumulative experience on responses to novel objects in young isolation-reared chimpanzees. Behaviour 21: 1-12, 1963.

39. Mittleman, B.: Motility in infants, children and adults. Psychoanal. Stud. Child 9:142-177, 1954.

40. Nissen, H. W.: Individuality in the behavior of chimpanzees. Amer. Anthropol. 58:407-413, 1956.

41. Potter, H. W.: An introductory study of the erotic behaviour of idiots. J. Nerv. Ment. Dis. 65, 497-507, 1927.

42. Provence, S., and Lipton, R. C.: Infants in Institutions. New York, International University Press, 1962.

43. Richmond, J. B., and Lipton, E. L.: Observations on the psychological development of infants: The development of feeding, sleep and motility. *In:* Emotional problems of childhood. Liebman, S., Ed. Philadelphia, Lippincott, 1958.

44. Richter, C. P. Some observations on the self-stimulation habits of young wild animals. Arch. Neurol. Psychiat. 13:724-728, 1925.

45. Saxon, S. V.: Effects of asphyxia neonatorum on behavior in the rhesus monkey. J. Genet. Psychol. 99:277-282, 1961.

46. Schiller, P. H.: Manipulative patterns in the chimpanzee. *In:* Instinctive behavior. Schiller, O. H., Ed. New York, International University Press, 1957.

47. Spitz, R. A., and Wolf, K. M.: Autoeroticism. Psychoanal. Stud. Child. 3:85-120, 1949.

48. Stone, A. A.: Consciousness: Altered levels in blind retarded children. Psychosom. Med. 24:14-19, 1964.

49. Tolman, C. W., and Mueller, M. R. Laboratory control of toe-sucking in a young rhesus monkey by two kinds of punishment. J. Exp. Anal. Behav. 7:323-325, 1964.

5

SOCIAL BEHAVIOR AND SOCIAL HIERARCHY IN THE FORMATION OF PERSONALITY PROFILES IN ANIMALS

by BENSON E. GINSBURG, Ph.D.*

by BENSON E. GINSBURG, Ph.D.*

THERE IS A SENSE in which all matter is form, in which simple forms determine more complex ones, and in which all animate relations depend upon form. Our world is composed of configurational patterns associated with all levels of reality, from the molecular and material to the molar and the ideational. The individual physical components of a pattern—those material ingredients that constitute the scaffolding, the outline, the boundaries, and all other definable hallmarks—these can change without doing violence to the persisting configuration, which is the organizing principle according to which the components are related. In a temporal sense, forms may have either static or dynamic persistence. They may also undergo sequential changes. Some of these are cyclical, others vectorial. Of these, a portion shows accretions of magnitudes of complexity and others dissociate into progressively simpler components. Similar patterns can arise convergently from diverse origins. Dissimilar ones can emerge as a result of differential arrangements derived from common origins.

We describe a hydrogen atom in terms of such spatially organized matter in motion, and these concepts also apply to our solar system. The recent breakthroughs in molecular genetics involve the application of just such concepts. The gene is literally the spiral staircase leading to a new understanding of the organizing role of form in living matter. Embryology and taxonomy have long made use of such configurational affinities in sequential, temporal progression. They will be used here to analyze the social structure of groups of organisms that maintain their

Preparation of this paper and the researches described therein were aided by grant MY-3361 from the National Institutes of Mental Health. The paper was written while the author was in residence at the Center for Advanced Study in the Behavioral Sciences.

*The College, Department of Biology, University of Chicago, Chicago, Ill.

patterns of existence through social group behavior, as well as the behavioral imperatives, both normal and abnormal, imposed by such evolved patterns in animal societies.

Just as a cell may be said to maintain its individual identity from one period of time to another, even though not one atom of which it was previously composed remains the same, so an individual may be said to be the same (but not identical) person today that he was at some time in the past, even though the majority of his body cells are not the same ones now that he had then. May we say the same of a clone of unicellular organisms whose members have all undergone fission? They are not only the descendants of the previous generations of Protista, they *are* also the previous generations. Not one of their ancestors has ever died. There has been protoplasmic continuity, just as in the case of the multicellular individual whose cells have largely been replaced over a period of time. We regard the latter as having kept his identity, yet we think of the products of unicellular fission as new individuals. In each case it appears to be a matter of what is the whole and what are the parts. The atoms and molecules within a cell are replaced, but they are replaced in kind, and this replacement does not alter the configurational pattern of the cell which constitutes the whole; therefore, its integrity has been maintained. In the multicellular individual, it is now the cell that can be a transient part and that is subordinated to the organizational form of the whole, which, through having maintained this form, has maintained itself.

Looking to a future in which organ transplants may become commonplace, the same relationships hold at yet another level of organization. Heart, liver, kidneys, spleen might all be replaced without changing the essential identity of the recipient. Hormones may increase his stature, plastic surgery may modify his external features, but he still transcends the sum of his parts and remains a singular and identifiable individual. Suppose, however, that our organ transplantation procedures were extended to include the brain. What, then, is the identity of the recipient of the new part? If one were to regard the donor brain as mere substrate to which one could transfer the engrams, memory traces, and accumulated molecular configurations representing the life experiences of the host, such a transplant would have no more effect than that produced by providing a new kidney. If, however, the donor brain retained all that was previously encoded within it, then it would maintain its former identity even though it is materially a part of a larger whole. It is not, therefore, the proportion of the total configuration that is at issue in the problem of the determination of subjective identity, but rather qualitative considerations involving continuity of experience which the brain alone mediates. While anatomically and physiologically a substructure with distinct and reciprocal relations to all other bodily parts, it contains the psychic representations of everything that has happened to the individual, and as such it is unique. Were we able to wipe it clean, as occurs in a limited sense in victims of amnesia, the integrity of the rest of the body (including most of the physical aspects of the brain itself) would only serve as a configurational signal to other minds that had previously encountered this same gestalt. It is the same brain in terms of physical continuity in time, but it is no longer the same mind. The amnesic individual is only a representational effigy, a key with which to unlock percepts and expectations in others who had known "him" before and a potential returnee to his previous selfness whenever the connections between then and now can be re-established. Even though the same brain sits in a body whose feedback mechanisms have not changed, the identity of the amnesic phase is as dissociated from the preamnesic as if one were dealing with a monozygous twin. The similarities in the two situations rest on the possibility of others reacting to one as though he were the other, as well as on the material and formal identities involved due to the fact that in both instances we are dealing with a single genotype. In the case of the interrupted continuity of conscious experience, the actualization of a given genetic potential must be the same in "both" individuals. In the case of the replicated manifestations of a single genotype, there are undoubtedly differences in the way in which the genetic potential has been realized in the formation of the effective phenotype. In addition, there can be no continuity of consciousness between them, and the encoded experiences comprising the materials of their psychic lives are different.

If the brains of our two identical twins were to be transposed, our first supposition would undoubtedly be that they have now exchanged identities. However, as we shall shortly see, this cannot be entirely so. Were this reciprocal exchange to be effected neonatally or at some earlier stage that predates conscious experience, th supposition would be easier to defend, but would still pose difficulties. From the moment that development begins in two equipotential systems (here, genetically identical) some divergence between the two systems becomes possible. There is lability in the relationship between the physical genome and the effective genotype, and between the latter and its final phenotype expression. The highest potential lability exists in the behavioral realm, where differences in intra-uterine environment, let alone postnatal experiences, have determining influences on the realization of the genetic potential.[12]

The mind-brain, while physically an interacting part in the complex of the organism, is director, coordinator, and physical seat of those events that are translatable as psychic phenomena. It is not, however, the arbitrary determiner of psychic life. As experiments with various cybernetic mechanisms have shown, its capacities can be modified (within limits) by input, and by the results achieved through this on other organs. Imprinting is one example of such a modification at the behavioral level. Adrenal responses as a result of early stress or stimulation provide an example of the second kind. Here, such stimulation activates neurosecretory cells in the hypothalamus, which in turn cause the pituitary to secrete ACTH, thereby producing adrenal cortical responses which speed up maturation and render future reactions to stress more adaptive.[14,16,21] The organism with such a history is at a different dynamically maintained equilibrium with respect to the interactions among brain, endocrines, and behavior than is a comparable con-specific that has encountered a different temporal phasing of applied stresses. Its brain is operating in a different internal environment and is affected by it.

The degrees of freedom of the interacting system are determined by its genes. If one had several sets of individuals, in which each set represented a collection of identical genotypes distinct from that in any other set, and repeated the early stimulation experiments with these, one would expect that the optimal timing for producing a behavioral effect would vary from set to set, and that the magnitude and direction of the effect would show similar intra-set consistency and inter-set variation. One would also expect the lability of the sets to vary. Such work has in fact been done, using sets consisting of six different highly inbred strains of mice, and all of these parameters have been shown to be genotype dependent.[10] It is interesting that some of the measures encompassed by the tests were reactions associated with emotionality and aggressiveness, including actual combativeness on the part of previously isolated sexually mature males in a standardized situation. These are certainly aspects of personality as we generally use the term. The measures were, as might be expected, affected by experience. They were, however, affected in the same way by similar experience within a set or genotype and in quite different ways when the same experience was imposed upon different genotypes. Since we know that the level of adrenal steroid production under controlled stimulation is also genotype dependent in these same strains of mice,[21] it is possible to infer that the differences in personality profile are due primarily to the endocrines and that the brain of any genotype would respond in the same way to the same internal environment. Using this model, one may conceive of the hypothalami and pituitaries as responding identically to the result of similar stimulation, but of the adrenals responding differentially to comparable levels of ACTH. Had these strain correlations with adrenal steroid responses not existed, one could as easily imagine that the brains were differentially affected by comparable steroid levels. There is no reason that we should not expect to encounter both kinds of situations. In either case, the genotypic prism refracts the environmental input according to their joint characteristics. At present, the best interpretation of the situation seems to be that genetic mechanisms are primarily involved in enzymatic differences in synthesis and degradation of adrenocortical hormones, since such conditions are known clinically.[16] However, since closely related polypeptides are involved as releasing factors for particular trophic hormones by the pituitary, there is no reason to suppose that genetic mechanisms controlling the synthesis of these will not also be found or that the quantities of corticotropin-releasing factor necessary to stimulate the pituitary may not vary according to the genotype of the latter or that the adrenal threshold for response to ACTH and/or the thresholds of target cells in the brain for responses to steroid hormones may not also vary genetically. In addition to the neurosecretory cells of the median eminence of the hypothalamus, several limbic structures have a role in the regulation of the release of ACTH.[16] Moreover, it is the subjectively experienced stress rather than the more directly mediated physical stimulus that is responsible for the changes in ACTH level; for example, cold, fasting, or exercise are not effective in the absence of a concomitant emotional arousal, whereas emotional arousal independent of external physical stress is sufficient to produce changes in steroid levels.[4] Thus the primacy of the brain in its psychological dimension, as the organ of subjectively experienced feelings and emotions, remains.

This is consistent, too, with the picture one gets from genetic sexual anomalies in humans. Virtually every combination of chromosomal sex, chromatin sex, and hormonal sex has now been studied, and the most accurate generalization is that, unlike the insect, in which the genetic constitution of the brain is determining regardless of either the sexual morphology of the body or of the hormonal constitution, in man the determining factor for behavior is the continuity of identification and experience as expressed by the concept of gender role.

Pseudohermaphrodites who appear to be females but who are genetically male—presumably with male chromosome complements in each and every brain cell—are psychologically female and behave as do normal women.[17] By contrast with the situation in the insect, where there is a greater hereditary predetermination and a consequent greater autonomy of each part of the organism, mammals are capable of producing a meaningfully interacting pattern under a greater variety of conditions. In a mammal, the genetically male brain can function harmoniously as part of a total complex which is female. In some insects, it goes its autonomous way, thereby preventing a harmonious functioning of the total complex.

Moving from the individual as "whole" to the social group of which he is a part, the analogy to insects is once again useful in order to underscore both similarities and differences. Social insects such as termites, bees, and ants have been thought of as superorganisms.[6] The nest built by a termite colony is characteristic of the species. Its total pattern exists as a blueprint only in the genes of the group that builds it. It is a physical record of group behavior. In this and other social roles, the "whole" is the colony and the individual is a part who can be replaced by another individual of proper genetic constitution. The entire colony can be replaced by an equivalent colony. All roles will be fulfilled, and both individual and group will function. Integration is achieved by means of behavior and social hormones, and the individual considered as a part of the system is subordinated to the total social pattern and serves its function. He is no less a component than a transient carbon atom is to the cell or than a cell within his own body is to him. The colony, in turn, is one of many exploiting similar ecological niches and having the same morphology. This is a morphology of which individuals and relations among individuals constitute a portion of the pattern, and in which a product of their joint behavior, i.e., the nest, contributes an additional portion. The rest of the pattern is extended in time. It involves the temporal replication of the pattern through the reproductive activities of those individuals specialized to perform this function—and so it goes, like a sine wave with increasing amplitude if the pattern spreads spatially in time. It may also be damped, have its period modified, or otherwise change in the course of evolution. Its potential for becoming different by giving rise to a mutated pattern that is either more or less elaborate than the pre-existing one, or that may even be different in kind, depends on the mortality of the individuals who comprise its parts. Their behavior can only be altered within narrow limits without disrupting the adaptiveness of the total complex. They cannot change their own genes, but their genetic contribution to future generations is plastic, and it is this plasticity which is the basis for the establishment of new patterns. As natural selection is the dynamic agency acting upon the variability provided by genetic mutations and recombinations to produce changing patterns in time, differential reproduction, as measured by success in having reproducing progeny, is a necessary concomitant of such change. Differential survival is involved in this, and the continued or even complete sampling of possible genetic combinations from one source, such as a given set of parents, becomes less efficient than a more limited sampling from many sets of parents distributed in space and time. The progeny, who are the vehicles by which changing patterns that usually lead to improved adaptations are brought about, require resources from the environment in order to provide the opportunity for their potentials to be actualized. Therefore, the exploitation of these resources by predecessors who have already served their evolutionary purpose becomes inimical to further adaptive change; the mortality of the previous generation within a reasonable period of time, depending on the availability of materials necessary for sustenance, becomes necessary. Even if we were to perpetuate a static situation we could not dispense with further organic change. External circumstances would force it upon us. The physical universe has not remained the same through the millenia, nor is it likely to in the future. Organisms will, therefore, have to continue to adapt, and the only means they have at their disposal is to utilize the almost infinite potential for variability that exists in the genetic mechanism, and this implies the replacement of one generation by another. Even the maintenance of existing patterns of life in the face of change in the physical environment will require the full apparatus of the evolutionary process.

We have been reasoning on the basis of populations whose responses have been rather precisely predetermined genetically. Is it valid to analogize from these to vertebrates, to mammals, and, indeed, to man? The behavior of a soldier termite within the limits usually provided by the environment is modifiable within a relatively narrow range. That of the vertebrate side of the phylogenetic tree is much more plastic. The vertebrate, too, is caught up in the pattern of social structure, and his behavior is predictably circumscribed as a result of this.

Allee has postulated a basic tendency towards sociality in all animal life.[1] The evolutionary beginnings of social behavior may be found in protozoans, whose aggregations confer a measurable degree of protection against toxic substances and other environmental fluctuations. Many unicellular forms engage in conjugative behavior for which proximity to appropriate neighbors is essential. Still others form physical aggregates of various kinds and durations. It appears that a fundamental feature of protoplasm is its tendency towards organization involving aggregations of similar units from nucleic acids to DNA molecules, to cells, tissues, organs, individuals, and societies. The major benefit to be derived from this is the more efficient exploitation of the environment. Although there is little gross morphological differentiation within a vertebrate species, directly providing for a behavioral division of labor, as in insect castes (aside from that involved in the specialization of the two sexes), it is not true that all individuals are biologically equipotential in other respects and that they depend upon environmental circumstances to impress behavioral differences upon them. From the point of view of the maintenance of certain social patterns within a given species, it may seem that individuals are interchangeable over a wide range of biological variability expressed as individual differences. It is also apparent that differences having a biological basis, such as size, intelligence, and aggressiveness, enter into the circumstance of matching a particular individual with a particular social role.

The reciprocal relations between social demands and social roles have been the subject of many studies, aspects of which will no doubt be included in other presentations at this meeting. My particular concern is to insert a genetic barrier to the almost infinite plasticity that is often assumed either by commission or omission.

There have been many studies of social hierarchies in vertebrates. There are nip orders in fish, peck orders in birds, and various forms of social dominance in mammalian groups including man.[1] On the booming grounds of the sage grouse, most of the mating is done by a few dominant males. No rebellion occurs among the subordinate males, nor do the females exercise much choice. The dominance of the alpha bird is largely maintained by demeanor, and the consequence is the behavioral castration of most other males, at least for that season.[28]

A similar but less spectacular psychological castration of long duration has been found in domestic fowl, in which the dominance hierarchy imposes an organization upon the flock that results in more food being consumed, more eggs being laid, and less energy being expended on competition and fighting once the social roles have been established, as they continue to be maintained merely by signal behavior.[1] A bird can be made to be a member of several flocks and will assume its appropriate but often different position in each.

Among laboratory mice, dominance hierarchies are established by fighting and may thereafter be maintained by social signals once members of the group have become conditioned to these. An aggressive animal can maintain his position by means of such communication long after he is physically incapable of making it stick, as shown in experiments involving severe dietary deprivation.[2] The genotype of the mouse is, however, also an important factor. As mentioned earlier, highly inbred strains react quite differently to early handling. In one series of experiments using A/Jax mice, the latency to fighting on the part of handled males increased by 63 per cent over the nonhandled controls, but the incidence of fights more than tripled. In another strain, the change in latency was comparable in direction and magnitude, but the incidence of actual fights decreased. In still another, both latency and incidence decreased. There are yet others in which the handling made no difference on these measures. Moreover, the control values for these measures were also different in the strains tested, and the critical periods during which they could most easily be altered were genotype dependent.[10,12]

A mouse population, therefore, is not equipotential with respect to its aggressiveness or with respect to ability to respond to environmental stimulation. If one were to mix the six strains used in our study and call the resulting amalgam a population, then test this population for baseline reactions and for the modifiability of these by various schedules of early manipulation, one would doubtless emerge with all the usual statistical generalizations. These are obviously meaningless in this context, since they are applied to the wrong unit. The strains are as distinct in their behavioral capacities to react to particular types of stimulation at particular times, as though they were morphologically differentiated from each other.

This situation is by no means unique either to our laboratory or to this species. Similar strain differences under behavioral stress have been encountered for rats, and breed or variety differences have been reported for dogs, deer-mice, and several other species.[20,27] In two closely related species of deer mice, the effects produced by infantile stimulation on later performance in an avoidance conditioning situation are opposite. In *Peromyscus gracilis*, performance is improved, whereas in *Peromyscus bairdii* it is impaired.[20] The reaction of an individual to external stresses is thus not merely a matter of when these are applied and how intense they are, but is also a matter of the physiological makeup of that individual as determined by his genetic potential and the way in which this potential has been actualized. The latter deserves repeated emphasis. In monozygotic twins with inherited susceptibility to sugar diabetes, for example, long-standing differences in dietary habits result in the expression of the diabetic phenotype in one twin but not in the other.[15] The recent case of the so-called Genain quadruplets also involves the variable phenotypic expression of presumably identical genotypes in the behavioral realm.[24] The tendency to generalize from average or usual behavioral responses to environmental agencies has obscured the important underlying issue of individual differences, and has tended to refer such differences to uncontrolled subtle variability in experimental history, as though the biological characteristics underlying behavior were infinitely plastic and could be molded by external forces which thereby become determining.

Returning now to an organized social group, one expects to encounter the typical species pattern even though the individuals playing particular roles will be replaced in time and will have their equivalents in other, similar groups. Within the group, not all are equally suited to a given social role, although the degree of such biological variability varies with the species and the complexity of its social organization. There is no question regarding the importance of biological determination in relation to social role in bees and termites. Analogously, sexual dimorphism in more plastic species predetermines many respects of social behavior, although experimental variables are also critical. Less obviously, genetic variance contributing to differences in behavioral outcomes in the face of similar experience also imposes limits upon which individuals may occupy a particular niche in the economy of the social organization of the group. A population normally contains a sufficient sampling of these behavioral nonequivalents to have an adequate supply of candidates for each behavioral niche, but a given individual, even before his potential has been actualized by experience, is biologically more suited for one than another.

We recognize this when it comes to the complex diversity of specialized behavioral niches that must be filled by members of our own species, but even here, we tend to avoid the obvious inferences and shrink from them when they are thrust upon us. While admitting that there is something genetic and biological about being at the extreme of a distribution on any of a variety of measures, there is a tacit assumption that the rest of the population, given appropriate environmental opportunities, could somehow be at any rank or measure represented by the remainder of the curve. Thus, we readily accept the notion that not everyone can aspire to be a musical virtuoso or a mathematician, and do not hope for normal reasoning on the part of an idiot. At the same time we deny that any "normal" individual, i.e., one not at either extreme of the distribution, cannot be shifted appreciably if exposed to proper training early enough. The same philosophy pervades our attitude towards emotional characteristics and mental health. Obviously there are biologically exceptional individuals who will be capable of coping with a large range of environments, just as some dogs reared from the preweaning period in total isolation from social contacts are able to get on if the regime is modified to include only a few minutes of social contact per day—whether positive or negative.[27] On the other hand, there are those who, no matter how they are treated, can never be normal. In between, there are all those individuals to whom the conditions of rearing are more determining, although by analogy to the animal studies we have been considering, most distinct genotypes may be expected to give a diversity of behavioral responses to similar conditions of rearing. As scientists with a deterministic philosophy, we must believe that knowledge is not only abstract understanding, but carries with it power to induce change. If the silk purse can be made out of the sow's ear in the case of the diabetic and the cretin, why not eventually with the mongoloid idiot, the autistic, and the schizophrenic? And if in these instances, certainly more easily in less extreme situations. This does not imply the hope of absolute control, as it is highly improbable that we shall ever have either absolute knowledge or the means to compensate for all the errors of development that have occurred, even if we come to understand them. However, we can have little hope of improving our control over that vast middle area of the distribution if we continue to pretend that there is biological equality within this range. It is not sufficient to realize that different points on a curve representing behavioral measures actually depict different nature-nurture interactions, but also that the same phenotype may have a variety of underlying bases, some of which may be genetic and others not.[12] When such differences exist, as in the example of the aggressiveness measures taken on inbred strains of mice, similar baseline levels will respond very differently to environmental manipulation of a particular sort, depending on the genotype. A similar situation has been demonstrated for dogs.[7]

The environmentalist position applied to human behavior, whether because of a belief that one can do nothing about biological differences and should therefore ignore them, or because of a belief that they are minor and surmountable, is now dominating educational philosophy, cultural anthropology, and some schools of psychology and psychiatry.[13] While their motives and efforts have been laudatory, they have not advanced the cause of knowledge. In animal populations, breeds, strains, and varieties obviously differ in the extent to which they represent particular morphological configurations, physiological idiosyncracies, and behavioral reactions. The Boston terrier has a peculiar pituitary;[29] the Dalmatian coach dog, a characteristic behavior with respect to slowly moving vehicles[19] and a peculiar uric acid excretion pattern.[32] Subtler examples have already been discussed. These differences among segments of interbreeding populations among which there is restricted gene flow are statistical, not absolute, but all the same they are differences. It is much more probable to encounter a given constellation of traits in one segment of the population than in another. In some cases, the probability amounts to a certainty. Although analogous situations are the rule among human populations in which gene flow is restricted by assortative mating practices, it is accepted as scientific to discuss differences between such groups when characteristics such as blood groups or sickle-cell anemia are under discussion, but not in any behavioral context. The latter is taken as "racism."

Certainly our measuring instruments for behavioral characteristics are far less perfect than those we use to classify blood groups, and most are environment dependent. The position that reliable data are difficult to obtain and even more difficult to interpret, and that there is considerable danger in making such data available because of possible misinterpretation, is widely held. However, the derivative contention that all human populations are behaviorally equipotential in identical environments because they are components of a single species is highly untenable. Human population groups do not all look alike; they have produced different cultures; the world would lose a great deal were they to be homogenized in a perfectly panmictic system of breeding, abetted by a universal language and a single set of cultural norms, and bolstered by a single system of child rearing and a universal system of education. If the human species is anything like its mammalian relatives, a successful imposition of cultural uniformity would evoke different personality profiles in individuals of different genetic composition. Panmixia, however, would tend to an equilibrium of all gene frequencies, thus leading in time to genetic uniformity. Teleologically speaking, the best strategy for trying out diverse genetic combinations and selecting the most adaptive is precisely the one we have—that is, a large number of groups comprising the species, within which there is free genetic exchange but between which there is much more limited genetic exchange.[33] Unfortunately, the naturists and nurturists do not read each other's journals, and when they do meet as humane citizens of the world they agree that we would not know what characteristics to breed for if we could; that the lack of equal opportunity makes data about the behavioral performance of different human population groups difficult to interpret; and that, in any event, there is no evidence that would lead one to conclude that any existing distribution of genetic potential within one group is better than the presumably overlapping ones to be found in other groups.[5]

The unfortunate aspect of these efforts has been that any attempt to partition individual differences within and between population samples consisting of different partial isolates or ethnic groups has been given a racist connotation, whereas our only scientific hope for understanding those differences that do exist and maximizing the biological potential of these lies in identifying and analyzing them.[13] As it stands, those data that do exist will be misused by those whose motives are questionable, and it would be far more "liberal" to try to improve our knowledge in this difficult area than to take the arbitrary position that those statistical differences that do exist are the sole result of a social structure that very largely determines the position which each individual or group will occupy in the general pattern.

This brings us full circle to the part-whole problem as exemplified in population groups. Clearly, the tighter the social organization, the more circumscribed the opportunities are for changing social roles. The potentials that an individual has for assuming a given role are partly dictated by these circumstances. If we consider a mouse population in which there are many disturbances of the nestlings due to crowding or temperature fluctuations, our "HS" mice would undoubtedly be less affected than our C57BL's.[12] These, in turn, would have their later behavior modified in a different direction than comparably stressed DBA's.[10] The mediating mechanisms for these differential effects are most likely located in the hypothalamic-pituitary-adrenal axis and/or in the sensory-neural pathways activating it, for some of these strains have been shown to respond with characteristically different steroid levels to applied stress.[21,30] The same mechanisms have been implicated in studies of later stress produced by crowding, and they are also involved in encounters leading to social dominance hierarchies.[3] It is not only the fighting that produces these effects, but also the persistence of a subordinate social role after it has been established. In mice, the subordinates respond to the aggressive signals of the dominant animal which include particular body postures, gait, and rattling of the tail.[8] These responses to the demeanor of a dominant animal also produce adrenal changes which are greater in a wild animal than in its domestic relatives.[23] The conditions of rearing interact with the genetic potential of the mouse or rat pup to determine the adult emotionality and aggressiveness. They are also important in determining the ability of the individual to withstand later stress. This results in a differentiation of levels of aggressivensss within the population that makes it much more probable for some individuals to achieve social dominance than others. These relations, in turn, intensify the neuroendocrine responses of the group and further differentiate the behavior. From the point of view of the total pattern, the social structure is maintained with different individuals playing comparable roles over a period of time. From the point of view of the individual, he begins with a range of potentials that, at each stage in development, is narrowed by the environment, including the social environment. The differentiation for social role is thus probabilistic. There are diverse phenotypes within a population that have become behaviorally differentiated for niches imposed by the social organization of the group in a series of reciprocal interactions.

In Canids, dominance develops among both males and females. Studies made on a confined population of wolves indicate that the dominant female controls the mating activity of the other females, and that the dominant male attempts to prevent other males from mating.[11] When kept in an enclosure from which they cannot escape, this control is effective enough to limit the population increase of the colony so that fewer litters are produced than are potentially possible. Evidence on the spacing out of individuals in wild populations together with observed rates of increase indicates that a comparable situation may exist in nature. Once dominance has been established, control is maintained among males largely by means of demeanor, but often includes actual attacks upon other females by the dominant female, especially during the mating season. Generally, one of the lower ranking females, who is kept at the periphery of the group during the mating season, regains social status by serving as a "baby sitter" for the litter of the dominant female. The same individuals may remain dominant for many years.[22] A given group in the wild is territorial and operates freely within its range. In Canids, as in many other forms, this is evidently dependent upon gonadal hormones, as immature animals do not appear to respect the territory of others even though they are repeatedly attacked and chased when they invade it. Within a short time after the sexually mature urination pattern appears among male dogs, they begin to recognize and avoid the territories of others and to mark and protect their own.[31] These mechanisms undoubtedly serve to space out individuals and groups out over a larger total areas. They also minimize the chance that physical encounters will occur, by signalling the occupancy of a territory. Signals serving the same function are found in other mammalian groups and in many other vertebrates as well. Communication is effected by means of chemical substances, vocalization, and postural attitudes.[25] The ability to respond to these is often hormone dependent and largely innate, although social deprivation sometimes interferes seriously with the ability to effect normal social interactions.[18]

I have speculated elsewhere on the homologies of the vertebrate communication systems, including that of man.[9] It now seems to me that the most fruitful approach is that of researching the underlying mechanisms for behavioral phenomena which are to be found in neuroendocrine systems, biochemical capacities, and dynamic morphology. The latter includes the molecular changes that are involved in coding information in the nervous system, those correlated with affect, and those events that account for the selectivity of transmission at synaptic choice points. Where genetic anomalies affecting such mechanisms occur, the process of analysis is made easier, since a gene-action approach can be used. Man may be considered a domestic and highly social species in which the evolutionary selective processes placed a high premium on effective group interaction as a means of insuring survival. The ability to develop a highly effective system of verbal communication was probably central in this process. Memory and ability to form many associations among sound values and to associate these, in turn, with perceptions derived from other senses, including inner feelings, are the derivative consequences of such a selective process. On the motor side, the development of the capacity to master the environment through the use of tools has been generally regarded as the key to the evolutionary developments that have occurred. These two evolutionary paths converged in the development of recorded thought, in which graphic representations of an oral communication system by means of the use of tools constituted the major breakthrough. These are unique specializations whose phylogenetic roots are rudimentary, consisting of such affinities as the very limited use of sticks to procure food by chimpanzees and of the simple communication systems mentioned.

The phylogenetic roots involving affect are deeper. An essential difference between a wild and a domestic form is the lower threshold of the former for reaction to environmental change, and especially to environmental novelty. The severity of the reaction, too, is much greater. A domesticated form (and man has become one by virtue of the protectiveness of his social milieu) does not need to be inordinately wary in order to survive, nor do his individual responses have to be so extreme, since he is seldom faced with the necessity to mobilize all of his physical energies in an individual struggle for survival through either combat or escape. In our experience with wild vs. domestic members of the dog family, this combination of vigilant wariness and intensity of response is the major differentiating factor. The intense response involves all autonomic signs usually associated with extreme subjective fear. Early and continued exposure to a wide variety of environmental situations, including hand-rearing by humans, will result in the "taming" of a wild Canid.[11] This is much more difficult to accomplish once the fear reactions have become established, and it is in this sense that the critical periods described for domestic dogs probably exist.[26] The socialization of older wild animals to human handling involves the gradual attenuation of the fear responses, which, until they have wholly subsided, shade into a phase of aggressive interaction with the handler who is attempting the socialization. The socialization, once accomplished, is lasting. By contrast, the fearful, aggressive, and permissive phases involved in socialization unfold very rapidly over a period of a few days under a variety of tranquilizing drugs, but the effects are not lasting once the drugs are withdrawn.[11]

If we contrast what is involved in the gradual but longlasting socialization of an adult wolf with the rapid but evanescent parallel effects obtained with chlorpromazine, librium, and reserpine, a hypothesis that suggests itself is that a new physiological balance is established in the first instance, but only temporary metabolic blocks are induced in the second. By analogy with what has been found with other wild animals and with laboratory rats, mice, and highly anxious humans, one suspects that the adrenals have enlarged, and that cholinergic responses and general easy and intense arousal have been conditioned. The habituation of the wild animal to human handling and other environmental novelty is in itself slow, and the physiological reconditioning is most likely the limiting master reaction. The quick behavioral progression to pseudosocialization under tranquilization through stages parallel to those achieved in actual socialization without drugs, suggest that:

a. the perceptions themselves may be altered by the drugs;
b. neural mediation of sensory input, which is normally perceived, may be interfered with so that arousal involving lower centers is physiologically less complete;
c. hypothalamic and limbic structures involved in determining the release of trophic hormones from the pituitary are responding at higher thresholds;
d. adrenal responses and parasympathetic mechanisms are partially blocked;
e. some combination of these and/or other of the neuroendocrine mechanisms involved in the usual intense responses of the wild animal are blocked or inhibited by a diversity of tranquilizing drugs.

Although evidence exists on the basis of which one could speculate further regarding which mechanisms are most probably affected by a particular drug, the data are not yet sufficient to provide a definitive answer. The fact that substances as different in their molecular structure and presumed modes of activity as chlorpromazine, librium, and reserpine all lead to a final common behavioral path indicates that more than one site and/or mechanism is being temporarily altered. The lack of permanence of the behavioral effects indicates that the alteration is that of a temporary block or diminution of function, and that no lasting physiological alteration, such as produced by long-term conditioning, has taken place.

On the subjective side, it would seem that the wild animal (or highly anxious person) must learn to cope with the affect of fear. Where this has been temporarily reduced, as in the case of tranquilizing drugs, the conditioning of the overt motor responses accomplishes no permanent results. If fear was not previously developed, as in the case of our wild Canids that have been hand-reared since early infancy and later placed in situations in which they have become fearful and mistrustful of human handling, they must be reconditioned.[11]

Because of the phylogenetic similarities among neurochemical mechanisms in mammals, and because alterations involving some of these mechanisms in humans involve changes in affect, the search for homologies in behavior that suggest ways in which it can be controlled and altered should more hopefully be focused in these areas. The identification of comparative differences between wild forms and their domestic relatives and the analysis of individual differences through twin studies and work with inbred strains provide methodologies for enumerating and analyzing response patterns to various environmental stresses and for researching their underlying mechanisms. As these latter may lead to the same behavioral end result via a multiplicity of paths, it is necessary to sort them out by distinguishing them biologically through the use of genetic and comparative methods.[12]

The most noteworthy evolutionary advances in the human species have been those associated with the development of the remarkable capacities of its nervous system. In order for this to have come about, great genetic variability with respect to this system must have developed and provided a basis for selective factors to act upon. By comparison with other species, we should, therefore, expect our own to be biologically the most variable in terms of the possible nature-nurture interactions open to the neuroendocrine system. Building upon this variability, environmental stresses may, by analogy to what has been found with mice, affect diverse genotypes in various ways and be differentially effective at varying times in late prenatal and early postnatal life with respect to predispositions to particular types of behavior and with respect to the mechanisms by which these predispositions are brought about. Similar syndromes may, therefore, represent the converging effects on a final common path of distinct mechanisms as well as actual identities of these. Populations vary with respect to all measurable characters that constitute ability and personality profiles. Comparative studies of other vertebrate species in which social patterns can be established and the interactions of the demands associated with these patterns, both with the nonsocial environment and with the genotypic response spectrum of the species, can be analyzed, affording a means of tracing meaningful homologies by means of which individual and group behavior may be better understood. Such homologies are already well known in the field of sexual behavior, autonomic responses, spinal reflexes, and the anatomical mapping of brain function. They are being established for other aspects of behavior as well, and they exist for many other behavior patterns per se. The genotypic parsing relative to interactions with social role is now feasible and represents an obvious next step that is already in process of being taken.

REFERENCES

1. Allee, W. C.: Cooperation Among Animals. New York, Henry Schuman, 1951.
2. Beeman, E. A., and Allee, W. C.: Some effects of thiamin on the winning of social contacts in mice. Physiol. Zool. 18:195-221, 1945.
3. Bronson, F. H.: Density, subordination and social timidity, in Peromyscus and C57BL/10J mice. Anim. Behav. 11:475-479, 1963.
4. Bush, I. E.: Chemical and biological factors in the activity of adrenocortical steroids. Pharmacol. 14:317-445, 1962.
5. Dobzhansky, Th.: Heredity and the Nature of Man. New York, Harcourt, Brace and World, 1964.
6. Emerson, A. E.: The evolution of behavior among social insects. In: Behavior and Evolution, A. Roe and G. Gaylord Simpson, Eds. New Haven, Yale University Press, 1958, pp. 311-335.
7. Fisher, A. E.: The effects of differential early treatment on the social and exploratory behavior of puppies. Ph.D. thesis, Pennsylvania State University.
8. Ginsburg, B. E., and Allee, W. C.: Some effects of conditioning on social dominance and subordination in inbred strains of mice. Physiol. Zool. 15: 485-506, 1942.
9. Ginsburg, B. E.: Genetics and social behavior—a theoretical synthesis. In: Lectures on Genetics, Cancer, Growth, and Social Behavior, Roscoe B. Jackson Memorial Laboratory Twentieth Anniversary Commemoration Lectures, 1949, pp. 101-124.
10. Ginsburg, B. E.: Causal mechanisms in audiogenic seizures. In: Psychophysiologie, Neuropharmacologie et Biochimie de la Crise Audiogene. Colloques Internationaux du Centre National de la Recherche Scientifique, No. 112, 1963, pp. 227-240.
11. Ginsburg, B. E.: Coaction of genetical and nongenetical factors influencing sexual behavior. In: Sex and Behavior. F. A. Beach, Ed. New York, John Wiley & Sons, 1965, pp. 53-75.
12. Ginsburg, B. E.: All mice are not created equal—recent findings on genes and behavior. Soc. Serv. Rev. 40:121-134, 1966.
13. Ginsburg, B. E., and Laughlin, W. S.: The multiple bases of human adaptability and achievement: a species point of view. Eugen. Quart. In press.
14. Ginsburg, B. E.: Genetic parameters in behavior research. In: Genetics and Behavior. J. Hirsch, Ed. New York, McGraw Hill, in press.
15. Goldschmidt, E., Ed.: The Genetics of Migrant and Isolate Populations. Baltimore, Williams and Wilkins Co., 1963.
16. Hamburg, D. A.: Genetics of adrenocortical hormone metabolism in relation to psychological stress. In: Genetics and Behavior. J. Hirsch, Ed. New York, McGraw Hill, in press.
17. Hampson, J. L.: Determinants of psychosexual orientation. In: Sex and Behavior, F. A. Beach, Ed. New York, John Wiley & Sons, 1965, pp. 108-132.

18. Harlow, H. F.: Sexual behavior in the rhesus monkey. *In:* Sex and Behavior. F. A. Beach, Ed. New York, John Wiley & Sons, 1965, pp. 234-265.
19. Keeler, C. E., and Trimble, H. C.: The inheritance of position preference in coach dogs. J. Hered. 31:50-54, 1940.
20. King, J. A., and Shea, N. J.: Subspecific differences in the responses of young deermice on an elevated maze. J. Hered. 50:14-18, 1959.
21. Levine, S., and Treiman, D. M.: Differential plasma corticosterone response to stress in four inbred strains of mice. Endocrinology 75: 142-144, 1964.
22. Rabb, G. B., Ginsburg, B. E., and Andrews, S.: Comparative studies of *Canid* behavior, IV. Mating behavior in relation to social structure in wolves. (Abstract of film presentation for 1962 AIBS meetings.) Amer. Zool. 2: (145) 1962.
23. Richter, C.: The effects of domestication and selection on the behavior of the Norway rat. J. Nat. Cancer Inst. 15:727, 1954.
24. Rosenthal, D., Ed.: The Genain Quadruplets. New York, Basic Books, 1963.
25. Schenkel, R.: Ausdrucks—studien an Wölfen. Behaviour 1:81-130, 1948.
26. Scott, J. P.: Critical periods in behavioral development. Science, 138:949-958, 1962.
27. Scott, J. P., and Fuller, J. L.: Genetics and the Social Behavior of the Dog. Chicago, University of Chicago Press, 1950.
28. Scott, J. W.: Mating behavior of the sage grouse. Auk 59:477-498, 1942.
29. Stockard, C. R.: The Genetic and Endocrine Basis for Differences in Form and Behavior. Philadelphia, Wistar Institute, 1941.
30. Thiessen, D., and Nealey, V.: Adrenocortical activity, stress response and behavioral activity of five inbred mouse strains. Endocrinology 71: 227-232, 1962.
31. Tinbergen, N.: Curious Naturalists. London, Country Life, 1958.
32. Trimble, H. C., and Keeler, C. E.: The inheritance of "high uric acid excretion" in dogs. J. Hered. 29: 280-289, 1938.
33. Wright, S.: Statistical Genetics in Relation to Evolution. Paris, Herman and Cie, 1939.

The Presidental Address for 1965, which would ordinarily appear in this volume of proceedings of the American Psychopathological Association, was not delivered, owing to the illness of the speaker, Franz J. Kallman, M.D. The title of the intended address was "Genetics as a Unifying Concept of Behavioral Variability." "In Memoriam, Franz J. Kallman" appears on page 322.

DISCUSSION

ARI KIEV, M.D.*

I appreciate the privilege of opening the discussion of these interesting papers. I am particularly interested in the value they have for increasing our understanding of human behavior. These papers emphasize the importance of a variety of environmental factors in the development of a wide range of normal and abnormal behavioral patterns ranging from stereotyped motor acts found among monkeys and apes reared in isolation, to population crashes among lemmings exposed to ecological traps. Furthermore, behavioral factors have been seen to influence the environment, as Cumming has noted in his remarks about the response of social systems to deviant members and as Etkin has noted in his remarks about the stabilization of social groups as a consequence of the ritualization of behavior.

At a time when we in psychiatry are tending to follow the direction of the molecular biologists, and perhaps even the ethologists as typified by Lorenz and Tinbergen, in searching for underlying mechanisms or reductionist principles through our biochemical, psychopharmacological, and psychoanalytic studies, the ecological view which in the past, according to René Dubos, has been productive of Darwin's theory of evolution, Bernard's concept of the constancy of the internal milieu, and Cannon's concept of homeostasis is of particular value. Such an approach can help us to understand how both the level of organization of function and the changing environmental requirements they must meet influence the way in which animals and humans behave.

Berkson's observations, for example, are pertinent to an understanding of the behavior of caged animals and mental patients hospitalized in total institutions where space and arousal are also limited. Zoo animals have long been known to exhibit stereotyped movements when chained or too narrowly confined. Thus, bears will constantly nod, elephants move their heads back and forth, tigers trot back and forth, and hyenas make figure 8's. Coprophagia, which is seen in certain monkeys under certain conditions of captivity, is an example of another type of regressive response. Similar behavior has been seen in

---

*Columbia University, College of Physicians and Surgeons, New York, N.Y.

some hospitalized patients, especially such symptoms as deep emotional regression, infantilism, pseudo-dementia, and catatonic gestures. Recent studies have suggested that these symptoms are situationally determined and not attributable to the underlying disorder. The study of animal behavior may help to enlarge our perspective along these lines and perhaps to assist us in distinguishing elements of illness from elements produced by exogenous factors.

Animal studies are of relevance to other human problems, such as the population explosion. The world's population is increasing by more than 100,000 people per day or fifty million a year, a rate which will lead to six to seven billion people by the year 2000, or several billion beyond the upper limits of the world population set by those pessimistic about expanding technological resources.

It seems not unreasonable to ask whether this rate of increase will be controlled through the operations of factors similar to those which limit population in the animal world. There are species that automatically reduce their reproductive and sexual activity when conditions of crowding develop. I would also think that some of the patterns of animal behavior such as territoriality and pecking order help animals in some way to regulate their numbers. Regulation of population size in human groups depends, I would think, not only on social patterns of behavior but on biochemical and physiological regulatory mechanisms as well. Insofar as man's ability to control his population appears to be failing, it is important to study what it is about other species that regulate their behavior which distinguishes them from the lemmings and man. It would also be valuable to know what ecological factors account for differing responses in the same species, as is shown by the lemmings who variously disperse, die from a stress syndrome, or migrate to the sea.

Whether or not humans behave more like lemmings than other species, the concept of ecological traps has much heuristic value in examining human situations. One need only turn attention to the crowded urbanizing areas of the developing countries to see such traps being set up daily, where migration from rural areas to cities depletes the rural working force and produces large overcrowded urban slums. These slums are effectively behavioral sinks with their high rates of morbidity, delinquency, and technological unemployment, and they invariably parasitize the economy of the country and slow its development.

Concepts such as that of ecological traps and ritualization are of value in providing additional dimension and perspective and useful ways to organize contrasting data. While Etkin has stressed the species-specific character of behavior and learning capacities he is too wont to acknowledge a fixed view of learning capacities and perhaps minimizes the role of environment. While there is much value in the concept of ritualization as an important way in which certain behaviors become more effective signals, thereby contributing to the adaptation of the animal, as in the grooming of monkeys helping to maintain their ingroup socialization, I wonder whether the learning capacities are in fact genetically determined and whether the social behavioral system is, as he suggests, confined within limits yielding usually only one effective pattern of life. This view tends to minimize the fact that the same species of animal may learn different things at different times in the course of its development. The kind of learning an animal does and the role it plays for the animal is in part dependent on the situation in which the animal learns. Thus, Calhoun's notion of a learned self-cycling mechanism in lemmings emphasizes that environmental influences operate in progressive stages and that previous experiences play a role in determining how the behavior of an animal will develop. Such a mechanism may not only not operate for all species, but even for all of a given species. The fact that lemmings in different locales adjust to population densities by different behaviors supports this view.

Etkin's evolutionary view of culture may also be subjected to the same criticism, since it is unlikely that the various social patterns seen throughout the world have developed as automatically as he has suggested. Cumming's formulation of Erikson's theory of personality development through crisis resolution, which emphasizes how strengths develop on the basis of current and past experiences, is, I believe, in line with this criticism. So, too, I believe is Berkson's paper. He has been careful to delineate the species-specific aspects of a behavior pattern similar in man and animal. He has pointed to differences in the variety of responses, the frequency of their expression, and their mode of expression. Furthermore, his experiments show that stereotypy levels were influenced by novelty, spatial restriction, and arousal level, as well as by other environmental factors which affected the likelihood of performance of other behaviors in the animal's response repertoire.

In summary, I would say that these papers have been of value in focusing attention on the relationship between living beings and environment, particularly as living beings change through time in responses to their environments, and on stressing the fact that similarity of behavioral pattern does not necessarily imply similarity of underlying mechanisms between animal and man. They have, I believe, suggested several ways in which such studies are particularly relevant to an understanding of human behavior.

Part II: Genetics, Internal Environment, and Brain Function

6

WITHDRAWAL AND FIXATION REACTIONS IN RODENTS

by W. T. LIBERSON, M.D., PH.D.*

THE NUMBER OF INVESTIGATIONS following Pavlov's discovery[1] of conflict-driven experimental animal neuroses is such that an account of this work would be clearly beyond the scope of this paper, even if only the studies on rodents were reviewed for this purpose. We shall be limited here by the more modest goal of reviewing the work of my colleagues or associates and me concerning two experimental situations resulting in characteristic behavioral changes.

1. *Fixation* of the rat's spatial response induced by the conflict-generating technique of Maier,[2] modified in our laboratories.

2. *Prolonged "hypnotic"* states of guinea pigs induced by a conflictual situation previously described by the author.[3]

While the first behavioral deviation involves behavior vaguely resembling human compulsions, the second seems to illustrate a behavioral complex involving withdrawal, depression, and agitation. Both have been used for the study of interaction of drugs, brain enzymes, and behavior.

BEHAVIORAL FIXATION IN RATS

A. Techniques

Maier's Technique of Inducing Fixation in Rats

The animal is placed on a Lashley jumping stand (Fig. 1) and is taught to jump to either of two windows (or doors) of the stand. If

This work has been supported by the Institute of Living, Hartford, Conn.; University of Connecticut, Storrs, Conn.; University for Massachusetts, Amherst, Mass.; Veterans Administration Hospitals, Northampton, Mass. and Hines, Ill.; and by the following grants: National Institute of Health, MY-1061, MH-06210 and the National Association of Mental Health.

*Veterans Administration Hospital and Loyola University Stritch School of Medicine, Hines, Ill.

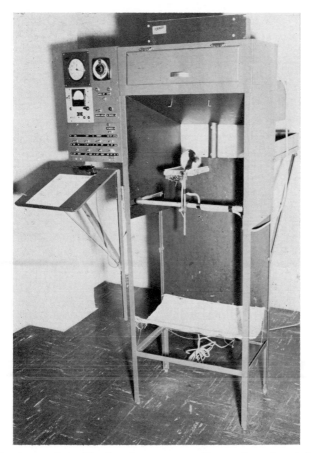

Fig. 1.—Automatic Lashley jumping apparatus. The rat faces the windows and jumps from the stand through the windows to reach the platform in the rear.

it does not jump within a 30 second period, an electric shock is applied to its feet. During the first stage of the experiment (insoluble problem phase) one of two windows is lighted during each trial. The resulting bright window shifts from side-to-side (left or right) at random, so that on each side the bright window appears 50 per cent of the time. In addition, during the insoluble period, one window at a time is locked, also at random (left or right). When the window is locked, the jumping animal bumps its head against the window pane and falls down into a net. Thus, this becomes a punishing or negative window. When the window is not locked, the hungry animal will jump through and find food on the platform behind the window. The unlocked window becomes, therefore, a rewarding or positive one.

Thus, during the first insoluble problem phase, the bright window shifts from side to side and may be either locked or unlocked at random. The animal has no cue at that point as to whether the window to which it decides to jump is going to be a rewarding or a punishing one. Whatever it does, it will be punished or rewarded 50 per cent of the time. Under these experimental conditions, the animal develops a spatial preference. It always jumps to either the right or the left window only, thus developing either a right or left "stereotyped response."

After 16 daily sessions (10 trials each day), the condition is changed and the problem becomes soluble, since the experimenter always locks the window which is bright. Now the animal has a cue to which window will be rewarding (dark) and which will be punishing (bright). The solution of this problem consists, obviously, in jumping always to the dark window whether it appears on the right or on the left side. However, less than 5 per cent of the rats solve this problem under standard conditions. They seem to be unable to "break" fixations and to abandon their spatial preference, despite the obvious fact that, on the fixated side, they discriminate the dark from the bright window. Indeed, their latency time ("decision time") becomes progressively shorter for the dark positive window and longer for the bright negative window as the soluble problem is repeated during the successive remaining 20 days of the experiment (Fig. 2, top). If the animal is actively pushed toward the nonfixated window ("guidance"), or even if the latter is wide open showing food, the animal still manifests considerable resistance to jumping to that window and prefers the punishment of bumping its head against the locked window on the fixated side.

Fixation Induced by Other Techniques

We have shown that fixation may be induced without the presence of a preliminary insoluble problem phase.[4] Thus, when the animal acquires a stereotyped spatial response (open window always on the left or the right), under conditions of a soluble, simple discrimination problem, it still manifests reluctance to be guided to the opposite side.

Fixation is a Result of a Situation Implying a Choice

If the animal is taught to jump always to the left window, the

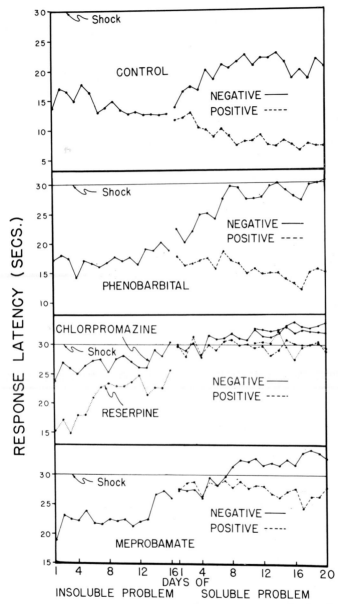

FIG. 2.—Comparisons of response latency changes among control, phenobarbital (25 mg./Kg.), reserpine (0.4 mg./Kg.), chlorpromazine (4 mg./Kg.), and meprobamate (80 mg./Kg.) treated rats (from Liberson, Feldman and Ellen.[10] Reprinted by permission of the International Journal of Neuropsychiatry).

right window being concealed by a black paper (or vice versa), during a 16 day period and consequently is presented with a bright, locked window now shifting at random from left to right (with the right window now uncovered), the incidence of solutions is higher than when Maier's technique is used.[5] Forcing the animal to make a choice at the beginning of the experiment seems to favor fixation; if the choice is made for the animal, the compulsive behavior is less rigid.

Simplification of the Motivational Field

In the original Maier's technique, which was followed by my associates and me for many years, the animal facing a bright window on the fixated side (during the soluble phase) is motivated to jump by an impending electric shock to its feet and is motivated *not* to jump by the anticipated punishment at the window. The duration of decision time is influenced by this double avoidance drive. As the animal almost always jumps before the onset of the electric current, obviously the drive to avoid the latter is stronger than that of avoiding punishment at the window.

When the animal faces the dark window on the fixated side, the motivational field in Maier's technique is as follows: The rat is motivated to jump (1) to avoid the impending electric shock and (2) because of the food reward. Inasmuch as there is no motivation not to jump, decision time is relatively quick. We found that the presence of food, although increasing motivational drive, is not necessary in order to induce fixation or to elicit a progressive decrease of the decision time to jump to the dark window on that side. Therefore, during recent experiments, the rats were not fed on the stand.[4,6,7]

B. Psychotropic Drugs and Perception

One of the basic goals of this study has been to determine the effects of different psychotropic drugs on the behavior of rats on the jumping stand in order to contribute to the understanding of drug effects in patients. Chlorpromazine (4 mg./Kg.) was found particularly effective in prolonging different phases of the animals' behavior, in particular the "decision time." It was, therefore, essential to ascertain that this drug does not change the perceptual thresholds in discriminating between the bright and dark windows. Indeed, it was found that the latter were not affected.[8]

C. Psychotropic Drugs and "Decision Time"

Chlorpromazine (4 mg./Kg.) and reserpine (0.4 mg./Kg.) prolong to a considerable degree the "decision time" in the case of either the rewarding or punishing windows (Fig. 2).[9,10] Phenobarbital (25 to 75 mg./Kg.) has the same effect.[6,11] However, when this drug is administered in a dose which is effective from this point of view, a great number of rats are so sedated that they are unable to jump (Figs. 2, 3, and 12). Monoamine oxidase inhibitors (Catron, Marsilid) usually do not affect significantly the latency times; occasionally a slight decrease of the "decision time" may be observed (Figs. 4 and 5) —cf. Feldman.[12] Amphetamine may slightly decrease the decision time. Imipramine may also slightly decrease the latency time (Fig. 6). Meprobamate (80 mg./Kg.) increases the decision time (Fig. 2).[10] Ethoxybutamoxane (Table 1) increases the decision time. Flexin may slightly increase or decrease latency time (Table 1). Chlordiazepoxide 5 to 15 mg./Kg.) decreases decision time.[4,14-18] This effect is clearly a function of the dosage (Table 1, Fig. 7).[4,15]* Feldman,[12,18] as well as Lewis and Feldman,[17] found this to be true not only for chlordiazepoxide but also for diazepam. LSD-25 (1 mg./Kg.) completely disrupts behavior.[19]

It is remarkable that these effects outlast the period of their admin-

TABLE 1.—Effects of Muscle Relaxants on Latency Times

Drug	Average in Seconds	
	Bright	Dark
Control	30	12
Flexin (10 mg./Kg.)	30	25
Flexin (20 mg./Kg.)	30	25
Librium (15 mg./Kg.)	12	5
Ethoxybutamoxane (.25 mg./Kg.)	32	30
Ethoxybutamoxane (2.5 mg./Kg.)	>30	>30

*Recently it was found that pemoline magnesium hydroxide (Cylert) at doses of 5 mg/kg duplicates the effects of chlordiazepoxide on decision time. This drug, which increases the synthesis of RNA, did not have any effect on fixation. (Liberson and Karczmar, in press, Conf. American College of Neuropsychopharmacology, Puerto Rico, Dec. 1966).

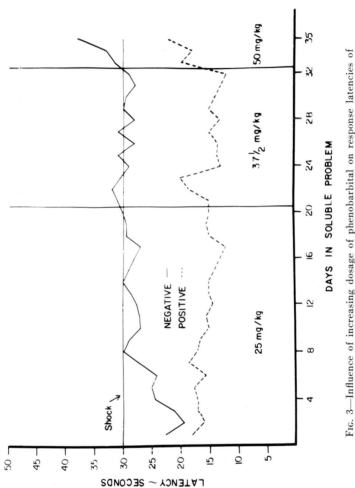

Fig. 3—Influence of increasing dosage of phenobarbital on response latencies of fixated rats (from Liberson, Ellen and Feldman.[21] Reprinted by permission of the International Journal of Neuropsychiatry).

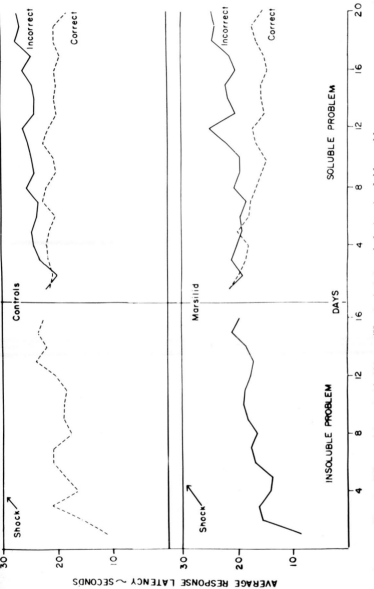

FIG. 4.—Effects of iproniazid (20 mg./Kg. i.p.) injected during insoluble problem on response latencies during insoluble and soluble problems (from Liberson et al.[19] Reprinted by permission of the International Journal of Neuropsychiatry).

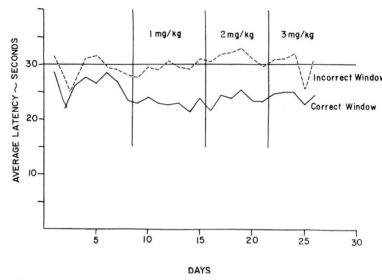

Fig. 5.—Effects of JB-516b (Catron) on response latencies of fixated rats during soluble problem. (from Liberson et al.[19] Reprinted by permission of the International Journal of Neuropsychiatry).

istration by several weeks.[4,7,15] A behavioral habit once formed under the influence of a drug, which modified it in one or another direction, is retained for a considerable time (more than 6 months in the case of Librium).

D. Psychotropic Drugs and Discrimination Problems

Under conditions of the "soluble problem" phase, the animal learns to discriminate between the dark and the bright window generally within the first two sessions. Almost all the drugs we have used so far prolong this "differentiating time" to a certain degree. Chlorpromazine and reserpine prolong it to 10 to 20 days, meprobamate to an average of 8 days (Fig. 2). Even librium, which shortens the decision time, may increase the differentiating time by one day or two.

E. Psychotropic Drugs and the Variability of Behavior

Drugs may induce a change in the variability of the physiological effects. It was shown, for instance, that monoamine oxidase inhibitors may greatly increase the range of recorded amplitudes of evoked responses in the hippocampus.[20] In the case under consideration, if the animal is particularly variable in its spatial responses (to the right or to the left), opportunities are provided for finding out that the dark window on the nonfixated side may be rewarding. Indices of behaviorial variability were, therefore, determined in the insoluble problem phase under the influence of different drugs. Moreover, these indices were determined separately for the solvers and "nonsolvers." These studies have not as yet given clear-cut answers, although in one study involving librium and high incidence of solutions, the variability was unusually high. However, the solvers were not more variable than the nonsolvers.

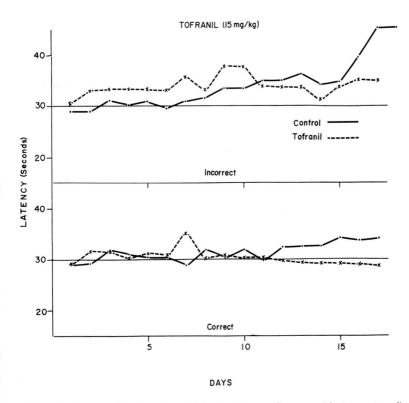

Fig. 6.—Effects of imipramine (Tofranil, 15 mg./Gg.) on "decision times." Most of these rats did not manifest avoidance and showed only escape reactions. After two weeks of the drug administration, the percentage of rats showing an avoidance reaction increased, particularly in the case of a rewarding (correct) window.

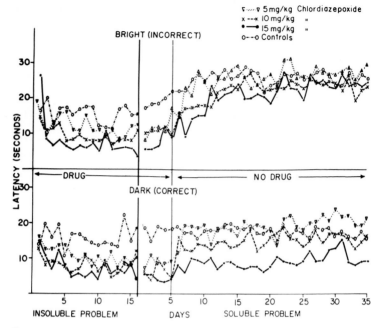

Fig. 7.—Effect of different dosages of chlordiazepoxide (Librium) on latency times during a fixation experiment. (From Liberson et al.[4] Reprinted by permission of the International Journal of Neuropharmacology).

F. Somatic Therapies and Motivation

The strength of avoidance or approach behavior is obviously a function of the total motivational field. It can be manipulated by changing experimental conditions. For instance, the current level of electric shock to the feet will determine the incidence of the avoidance reaction and the duration of "decision time." The duration of the preshock period also influences the "decision time."

The latter may also be manipulated by the drugs, or by convulsive electric shock "treatments."[21] It has been shown that the same somatic treatment will affect behavior differently in the presence of different motivational drives. Thus, daily convulsive treatments applied 10 to 15 minutes prior to the trial completely suppress the avoidance behavior of the rat when it faces a punishing window on the fixated side (Fig. 8). When the same rat, during the same session, faces a rewarding window, the same electric convulsive shock is ineffective in suppressing the animal's avoidance after the first "treatment" day.

As a matter of fact, the animal increasingly resists the effects of convulsive treatments during the subsequent sessions. The same observation may be made if, instead of the overt convulsions a "convulsive EEG pattern" is elicited in the hippocampus of the animal. Such differences in the effect of the somatic treatments of the animal facing either the rewarding or the punishing window on the fixated side were found for most of the drugs tested. Thus, with the highest doses of chlorpromazine and reserpine (respectively, 4 mg./

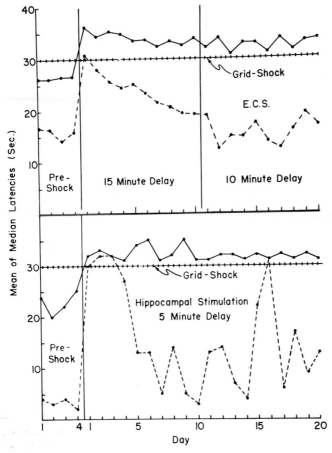

Fig. 8.—Comparison of the effects on response latency of ECS and hippocampal stimulation administered daily before testing in a soluble problem situation in fixated rats (from Liberson, Feldman, and Ellen[10]).

Kg. and 0.4 mg./Kg.) the avoidance in the case of the punishing window was suppressed (Fig. 2). It was preserved in half of the animals in the case of the rewarding window. In the case of meprobamate (80 mg./Kg.) the avoidance was either suppressed or preserved under the same conditions for all the animals tested (Fig. 2). In the case of imipramine (Fig. 6), avoidance was recovered only in the case of the rewarding window. For the chlordiazepoxide (Fig. 7), the effects of the drug on decision time persisting beyond the period of administration of the drug were progressively dissipated in the case of the punishing window; they remained the same for two months in the case of the rewarding window for the same rats.

A study which is being reported in detail elsewhere[6] demonstrates that the rat's behavior on the stand may be subdivided into at least three periods: (1) orienting period; (2) "decision making" period; and (3) jumping period. There is no correlation between the total latency time and either the "orienting" time or the "jumping" time. The individual differences in the duration of decision-making processes are entirely responsible for those of the total latency time (Fig. 9). Both the orienting and decision-making periods are almost eliminated by the action of librium when the animal faces the rewarding window (Fig. 10). The effects are much less pronounced when the punishing window is on the fixated side.

The mode of action of librium remains obscure. A hypothesis was

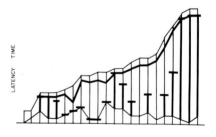

FIG. 9.—A group of rats, some of which had in the past librium or flexin and others of which served as control, were ranked according to the increasing latency (decision) times during the soluble problem phase. On the left, therefore, are represented the fastest and on the right the slowest rats. The total latency is subdivided into three phases: orienting period (below the lower dividing line); jumping period (above the upper dividing line), and "decision-making time" (between the two dividing lines). Moreover, the latter period is subdivided in two subperiods by a short horizontal bar. Below the bar: time spent looking away from the window to which the rat is going to jump. Above the bar: time spent looking at the fixated window to which the animal is going to jump (Liberson, Karczmar, and McMahon[6]).

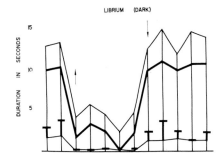

Fig. 10.—Average latency time for the librium rats. Arrows indicate the beginning and the end of librium (15 mg./Kg.) injections (Liberson, Karczmar, and Mc-Mahon[6]).

tested as to whether librium reduces the effects of extraneous stimuli, causing the rat to "concentrate" on the jumping activity. In order to test this hypothesis, intermittent lights were activated on both sides of the Lashley jumping stand, and also auditory stimuli were presented to the animal at random. This experiment will be described in detail elsewhere.[6] Table 2 shows that the control animals had a slight increase in the latency time when the stimuli were present; however, the librium animals were less affected by such stimuli. This may be one of the factors involved although it does not explain all the observed facts.

An analysis has been made to determine the percentage of time the animal spends looking at the window to which it jumps and the percentage spent looking away from it. It was found that in the case of a dark rewarding window, the animal looks at that window for a longer time than in the case of the bright punishing window (respectively, 64 per cent for the dark window and 54 per cent for the bright window). In the case of the librium rats, the corresponding figures are 74 per cent and 54 per cent. However, when these figures are compared to a group of fast rats not receiving librium, they

TABLE 2.—Effects of Distracting Stimuli on Latency Times

Group	Bright Trials Stimulus		Dark Trials Stimulus		All Trials Stimulus	
	Present	Absent	Present	Absent	Present	Absent
Librium	17.95	18.32	9.86	9.80	13.50	13.56
Control	28.36	26.06	19.70	18.00	22.90	20.30

prove to be of the same order (respectively, 73 per cent and 59 per cent).

Finally, the analysis of the jumping behavior indicated that when the rat jumps to the rewarding window, it does it head on, and when it jumps to the punishing window, its long axis becomes parallel to the window so as to avoid a painful blow (Fig. 11).

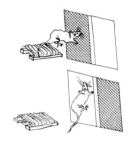

Fig. 11.—Adaptation of jumping behavior to the experimental conditions (Liberson, Kaczmar, and McMahon[6]).

G. Environmental and Pharmacological Manipulation of Behavior

One important finding during this investigation was the persistence of the effects of psychotropic drugs on behavior. Thus, if librium or chlorpromazine was suspended, the animals continued to behave as if they were still under the influence of these drugs (Fig. 7).[4] In the case of librium, the behavioral effects persisted several months after the suspension of the drug. On the other hand, the type of conditions under which the behavior is trained also has a profound effect on the behavior reactions. As mentioned previously, the motivational factors interact continually with the pharmacological action. In view of this, an experiment was set up in the following way (details of this experiment will be reported[6]: A group of rats (Fig. 12A) were trained to jump on the Lashley stand. They were then divided into three groups so that the average of their latency time (decision time) was the same for each of these groups. One group of 12 rats received chlorpromazine (4 mg./Kg.), a second group of 12 rats received Librium (15 mg./Kg.), and the third group (6 rats) served as control (saline injections). The animals were run for 16 days under conditions of the insoluble problem. At the end of this time, the librium and chlorpromazine groups were subdivided into two subgroups. One continued under

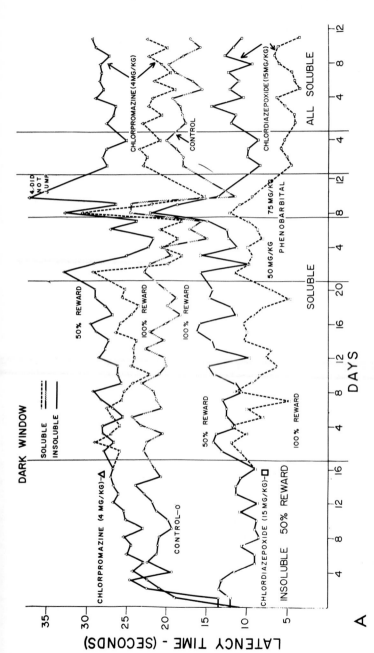

Fig. 12a.—Manipulation of behavior by drugs and variable rewarding rate: beginning of experiment (see text; Liberson, Karczmar, and McMahon[6]).

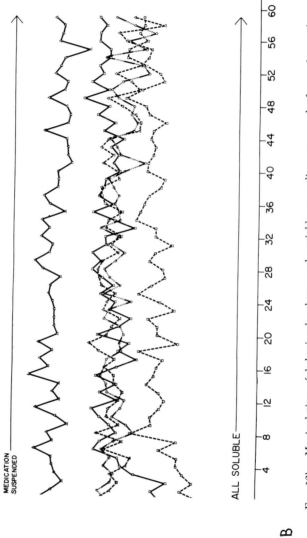

FIG. 12b.—Manipulation of behavior by drugs and variable rewarding rate: end of experiment (see text; Liberson, Karczmar, and McMahon[6]).

the conditions of the insoluble problem; while the other was run under soluble problem conditions. The control group also was run under the soluble problem conditions. At the end of the second stage (20 days), all previous medication was suspended and all rats were given phenobarbital (50 mg./Kg. for 7 days and then 75 mg./Kg. for another 3 days). During this period, the rats that had a history of chlorpromazine injection and had 50 per cent reward (in the case of the dark window) reacted to this drug more than those who had a history of chlorpromazine and had 100 per cent reward with that window. Similarly, the group of rats who had a history of librium injections and had 50 per cent reward reacted to the same drug (phenobarbital) more than those who had a history of librium and had 100 per cent reward. The latter subgroup practically did not react to this drug. Therefore, the previous pharmacological history of the rats that originally constituted an homogenous group now permitted us to subdivide this group by behavioral and pharmacological manipulation into five different subgroups in terms of their reactions to a new drug (phenobarbital). In the later part of the experiment, the animals were put back on the same medications as originally (chlorpromazine, librium, and saline). This time, however, they were all placed in the same behaviorial conditions—namely, 100 per cent reward for jumping to the dark window (soluble problem). Despite this, for a period of several weeks, the rats still behaved as though subdvided in the same five subgroups according to the duration of their decision times. Thus, the chlorpromazine rats that were rewarded in the past only 50 per cent of the time jumping to the dark window were slower than those rewarded 100 per cent of the time in the past. Similarly, the librium rats, who have all had 100 per cent reward but previously had 50 per cent reward, jumped with a latency time more than twice as long as that found for the librium rats jumping under the same conditions but who also in the past had 100 per cent reward.

Therefore, by combined behavioral and pharmacological manipulation we could succeed in dividing our rats into five distinct groups.

Then all drugs were suspended for six months (Fig. 12B). The difference between some of the subgroups progressively diminished. However, even at the end of this experiment, chlorpromazine rats which experienced six months prior to this time 50 per cent reward for jumping to the dark window remained by far the slowest and librium rats with a continuous history of 100 per cent reward remained the fastest.

H. Psychotropic Drugs and Behavioral Polarization

Maier showed that the fixated animal violently resists "guidance" through the window on the "nonfixated" side, and we have demonstrated that this effect may be found even in the case of a simple learning problem with a spatial cue.[4,7] In the case of fixation, this aversion of the animal, manifested toward the "other window," is all the more surprising in that the animal does not jump through this window for several weeks and therefore has no recent experience of being punished on that side. Never in its past was the rat punished on that side more than on the side of "fixation."[7] In other words, the adverse effects of the "other window" are all "in the mind of the animal" without any experiential justification. One is led to conclude that the choice of the animal to jump to one side leads it automatically, without experiential control, to persistently avoid the nonpreferred window. In other words, the behavior of the animal becomes strongly polarized; the preference of one window automatically signifies the aversion to the other.

It was of interest to test whether psychotropic drugs reduce avoidance to the "other window" under conditions of active guidance. The latter remains the most effective way to break the rat's fixation ("psychotherapy"). Repeated trials to guide the animal through the other window leads the rat to solve the problem subsequently. It was interesting to see whether psychotropic drugs (chlorpromazine, meprobamate, librium, and amphetamine) would foster this "psychotherapy." Chlorpromazine, mebrobamate, and amphetamine did not seem to have any definite effects on guidance, although librium[4] seemed to reinforce its effects (Fig. 13).

I. Psychotropic Drugs and Problem Solution

What is going on in the "black box" of the animal during the decision-making processes? As mentioned, when the animal faces the rewarding window on the fixated side, he spends more time looking at that window than when it faces the punishing window on the fixated side; instead, the animal looks at the dark window on the other side. This suggests that consideration of the "other dark window" is a factor in the decision-making process, which is prolonged at that time.

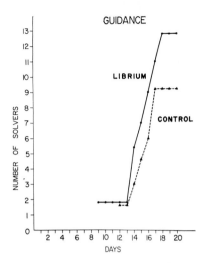

Fig. 13.—Effect of librium on "therapy" by guidance. Horizontal axis: number of guided trials. The solutions occur earlier under the influence of this drug (modified from Liberson et al.[4]).

Another important observation has been made in our laboratory concerning those rare animals that solved the problem either spontaneously or following somatic "treatments." This investigation has been made on the basis of the study of several hundred rats. However, only about 30 of these rats spontaneously solved the problem. Very few of the solvers were not under the influence of somatic treatment. A number of them were given electric convulsive treatments and solved the problem under experimental conditions quite different from the standard one. Eighteen solvers received various drugs.

In order to solve the problem, the rat has to (a) differentiate the dark from the bright window; (b) break its fixation and jump toward the "other window"; (c) start to jump always to the dark window wherever it is found (right or left side). Each drugged rat that solved the problem was given differentiation, breaking, and learning scores.

1. *Differentiating score* is defined by the number of days of the soluble problem phase preceding the day when the rat started to consistently differentiate the dark from the bright window, the difference of the corresponding latency times being at least 2 seconds.

2. *Breaking score* is defined by the number of days of the soluble problem preceding the day when for the first time the animal broke his fixation and jumped to the other window.

3. *Learning score* is defined by the number of days of the soluble problem phase preceding the day when the animal started to consistently jump only to the dark

window on both sides, making no more than one mistake a day for three consecutive days.

The examination of daily protocols of the rats that solved the problem shows the presence of two classic types of problem solution: "trial and error" and "insightful solution" (Fig. 14).

Solution by "insight" is truly a remarkable finding. Corresponding rats always jumped to the same window for more than 30 days in a row, 10 times each day, being satisfied to be rewarded only 50 per cent of the time; then one day, the rat started to jump to the rewarding windows on both sides, making no mistake.

The use of different drugs, influencing to a different degree the decision times and the differentiating scores, provided an opportunity to investigate the effects of these time parameters on the incidence of "insightful solutions."

Librium rats have a relatively short differentiation time. The solution is reached after breaking fixation, as a rule, after several days of "trial and error." Chlorpromazine prolongs the differentiation time. The breaking time is also delayed, but as a rule the animal solves the problem the same day that it breaks the fixation or sometimes the next day. In other words, the chlorpromazine rats that solve the problem generally show "insightful solutions." Meprobamate rats show an intermediate behavior. These findings are illustrated in Figure 15. Here, the time spent between breaking fixation and solution of the problem is represented as a function of the differentiation score. This time reflects presence and duration of the "trial and error" period. When reduced to 1 to 2 days it indicates the insightful behavior which seems to require a relatively large number of days spent in a process of differentiation. Moreover, inasmuch as the long differentiation times are found for the rats showing long "decision times," Figure 15 leads to an inescapable conclusion: If the drugged animal is going to solve the problem, the more it sits on the stand looking at the windows prior to the breaking of fixation, the higher will be the incidence of insightful behavior. Therefore, the prolonged latency time appears to correspond to an active mental state.

Analogous data were obtained in the case of rats submitted to guidance procedures. Figure 16 shows that there is a trend indicating that fewer trials are required to solve the problem for the animals who required a relatively larger number of trials to break fixation.

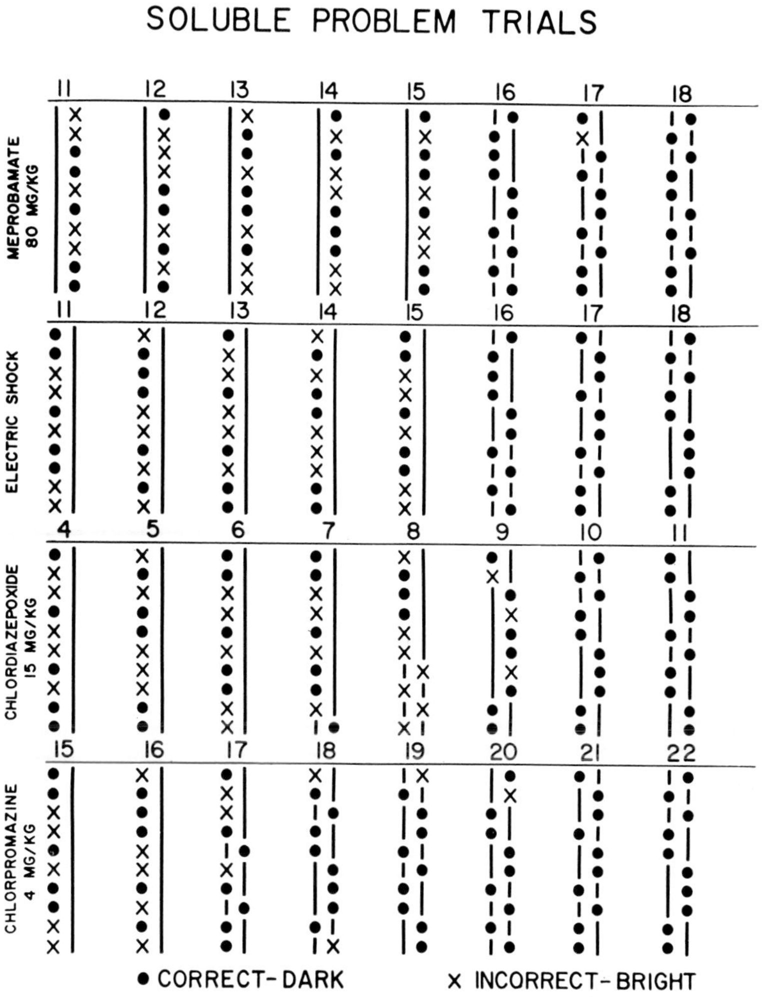

SOLUBLE PROBLEM TRIALS

● CORRECT–DARK   X INCORRECT–BRIGHT

Fig. 14.—This figure shows examples of solution of the problem by meproba-
mate-, electroconvulsive-, chlordiazepoxide- and chlorpromazine-treated rats. The
programming of each session is indicated by two vertical columns, one for the left,
one for the right window. The serial number of the experiment during the soluble
problem phase is indicated above each dual column. The x's represent the
incorrect (bright) and the dots represent the correct (dark) windows to which
the rat jumped. The vertical lines cover the windows to which the rat *did not*
jump. Thus, for instance, the first session on this graph symbolizes a right-window
fixation for meprobamate and the left-window fixation for electroshock, chlorpromazine, and chlordiazepoxide rats. When the vertical lines leave uncovered only
dots (as in the case of the last experiments for each of the rats), the solution of
the problem is obvious (modified from Liberson[7]).

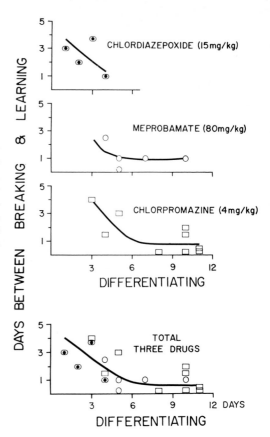

Fig. 15—This figure shows the relationship between the duration of differentiation processes and the period between breaking and solving fixations (see text; modified from Liberson[7]).

PROLONGED HYPNOTIC STATES IN GUINEA PIGS

A. Techniques

"Animal hypnosis," which consists of a "tonic immobility," of an animal placed on its back can be demonstrated in a great number of domestic animals. It is generally assumed that this behavior is a protective mechanism in that the animal pretends to be dead, and presumably becomes a less desirable prey for its enemies. This phenomenon may be easily observed in the guinea pig. However, the hypnotic condition is not very effective as a defensive mechanism in this animal, inasmuch as a slight noise or a touch of the animal is sufficient to interrupt the hypnotic immobility. We showed[3] that by repeatedly stimulating the animal and replacing it on its back each

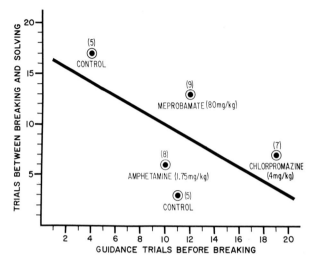

FIG. 16.—Number of trials between breaking and solution of fixation under the influence of guidance. Number of animals is indicated for each group (modified from Liberson, Ellen, and Feldman[11]).

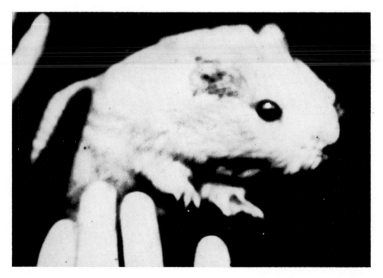

FIG. 17.—This figure shows the animal in a prolonged hypnotic state. Note the animal expression in response to hand clap. Note also marked exophthalmus (from Liberson, Smith, and Stern.[22] Reprinted by permission of the International Journal of Neuropsychiatry).

time it gets up, the duration of the animal hypnosis increases in a step
like fashion. In time it becomes very prolonged, reaching, in some
animals, a duration of four hours or more. Figure 17 shows an hypnotized guinea pig. Figure 18 shows increases of the hypnotic state
by training.

It is possible to train the guinea pig to stand in an erect position,
propped up by a stand or books, by replacing the animal in this position each time it tries to escape (Fig. 19). At the end of the training
period, the animal will pull itself up spontaneously as soon as it slips
down under the influence of its own weight and fatigue.

B. Behavior Characteristics

When the animal is trained to lay on its back, it remains in the
"hypnotic" state for minutes or hours despite external stimuli. When
the latter are too intense, the animal may show exopthalamos, dilated
pupils, and tremor. In response to a clap of the hands, it may jump

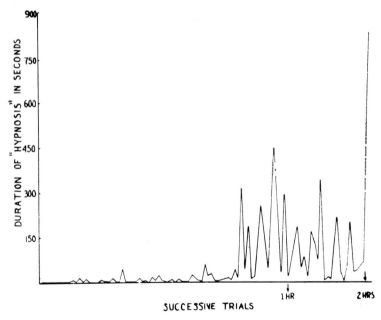

Fig. 18.—This figure shows a sudden onset of prolonged reactions after about
45 minutes of intensive training. At the end of 2 hours, the animal remains in a
state of tonic immobility for almost 14 minutes (from Liberson, Smith, and
Stern.[22] Reprinted by permission of the International Journal of Neuropsychiatry).

FIG. 19.—This animal was placed against a pile of books during a two-day training session. It remained in an upright position from the second day, despite sensory stimuli, for more than ten minutes (from Liberson[7]).

into the air with its legs up and let itself fall down on its back.[3] The animal appears much calmer when trained to stand erect.[7] Some of the animals died from cerebral hemorrhage when the stimulus was too intense.

C. Cage Effect

At the beginning, the animal has to be retrained to remain immobile when novel stimuli are applied. However, later in the training even the novel stimuli may not interrupt prolonged hypnotic states. The exception to this rule is demonstrated by the effect of the animal cage. If a hypnotized guinea pig is placed on its back or side in its own cage, the animal immediately rights itself and a new prolonged training in the cage becomes necessary. This experiment suggests that the handling of the animal in his own cage is the strongest stimulus.

D. Individual Differences

Marked individual differences are found. Some of the animals remain hypnotized for hours; others can barely be trained. So far, we have had one animal who without any intercurrent training for six months retained his ability to remain immobile.

E. Behavioral Polarization

If the animal is trained to remain on one side, it will exhibit a prolonged hypnotic state when placed on this side only. Conversely, if placed on the other side, it will right itself much quicker and more violently than it did prior to training on the opposite side. Thus, here again, the behavior is polarized: The training of the animal to remain immobile on one side automatically induces the opposite type of behavior when placed on the opposite side.

F. EEG Studies

EEG studies may be conducted on individual hypnotized animals or on several animals simultaneously, each of them connected to one channel of an 8-channel EEG machine. It has been claimed that animal hypnosis is a kind of induced sleep. EEG's derived from the hippocampus showed that the prolonged hypnotic states may be associated with various EEG patterns[22] such as increased fast activity, suggesting a state of excitation; theta activity, suggesting an attentive state; and different patterns of relaxation or slow wave sleep (Fig. 20).

It is true that when the clicks are repeated during the process of training hypnotic states, a progressive decrease in amplitude of the evoked potentials may be recorded, the minimal amplitude observed with the occurrence of a particularly long period of immobility.[22] However, high amplitude evoked potentials may be recorded while the animal is still unable to right itself.

G. Drug Effects

Chlorpromazine and particularly reserpine prolong the hypnotic states and facilitate training (Fig. 21).[22]* When an animal on reserpine is forcibly replaced on its back after righting itself, paroxysmal dis-

---

*These findings were recently confirmed by Klemm. (Klemm, W. R., Electroenceph. Clin. Neurophysiol., 15:163-167, 1965; 21:365-72, 1966.

WITHDRAWAL AND FIXATION

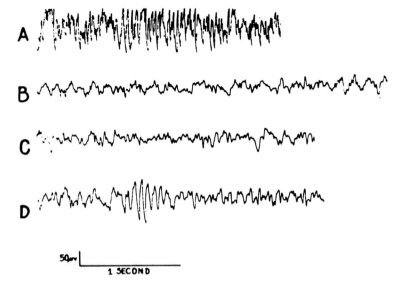

FIG. 20.—This figure exemplifies different hippocampograms found during the state of prolonged immobility. (A) State of excitement; (B) synchronized 6 per second activity; (C) poorly synchronized tracing; (D) a spindle (14 cps) (from Liberson, Smith, and Stern.[22] Reprinted by permission of the International Journal of Neuropsychiatry).

charges may be recorded from the hippocampus followed by a postictal spike discharges,[22] apparently resulting from an intense emotional state. Monoamine oxidase inhibitors reduce the duration of the induced hypnotic state and impede training (Fig. 22).[19] LSD-25 makes the training impossible.[19] Studies in progress[23] suggest that DOPA alone is relatively ineffective unless given in very high dosages (about 150 mg./Kg.). It becomes effective if a monoamine oxidase inhibitor is added to it. However, the latter alone is practically as effective. An agent inhibiting catecholamine synthesis (alpha-methyl-meta-tyrosine, 20 to 40 mg.) does not counteract the effect of monoamine oxidase inhibitors.

H. Brain Serotonin Content

The effect of reserpine (favoring hypnotic states) and of monoamine oxidase inhibitors (shortening the hypnotic states) suggested that serotonin and/or catecholamines are involved in animal resistance to being hypnotized.[24] Several experiments were performed to see how serotonin and catecholamine brain content changes during training.[24] No consistent changes were found as far as catecholamine were concerned. However, we could not be certain of these results, since the techniques used were not sufficiently sensitive.

Consistent findings were observed as to the serotonin content. It was found that experimental animals showed a lower serotonin content in the cortex and hippocampus combined. This was particularly so in animals who were resisting the training (see Table 3).

The animals' brain serotonin content was also determined in animals either remaining in cages (never used for any experiments) or placed in front of the experimenter in a sitting or an erect position (see Table 4). The brain serotonin content tended to be lower in all experimental animals. However, there was no difference between those remaining sitting and those standing erect. The serotonin content of those animals who were "fighting" hypnosis, being placed on their backs, remained the lowest.

Thus, serotonin content in the cortical regions seems to be definitely lowered by the repeated resisted induction of hypnotic states.

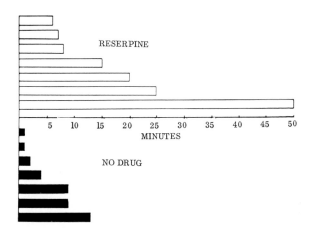

Fig. 21.—Horizontal rectangles indicate the maximum duration of the hypnotic state during a 2 hour initial training period with reserpine (white rectangles) and without reserpine (black rectangles). Each rectangle corresponds to an experiment carried out on a different animal (7 animals in each series—from Liberson, Smith, and Stern.[22] Reprinted by permission of the International Journal of Neuropsychiatry).

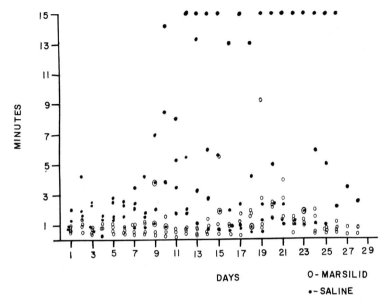

Fig. 22.—Effects of iproniazid (Marsilid) on maximal duration of hypnotic immobility (from Liberson, Smith, and Stern.[22] Reprinted by permission of the International Journal of Neuropsychiatry).

Discussion

A. General Findings

Conflict-driven Behavior Disorders

It is obvious that no attempt should be made to equate the previously described behavioral deviations with human mental illness. Yet it is reasonable for an investigator interested in psychopathology to try to derive lessons from animal observations which may be of help in clinical research. The previously described behavior of rats so closely resembles compulsions that it may be profitable to consider this analogy. The guinea pig behavior described, on the other hand, bears the marks of withdrawal—the giving up of fighting and the abandonment of normal essential reactions for survival. The first general observation which may be made is that both of these behavior deviations are generated by a conflict imposed by the experimenter on the animals. This extends the original insight of Pavlov concerning the genesis of experimental animal neuroses.

Polarization of Behavior

The other observation of interest is that resulting behavior is strongly polarized. The rats under stress were presented with experimental conditions which offered a choice of jumping to the window on one side. They did not have any experimental knowledge of the other window which would cause them to be adverse to it. Yet the very fact of a choice of one solution between two possible ones, made under stress, automatically leads to an extremely adverse reaction to the opposite solution. Translated in human terms, it might signify that a strong belief (prejudice?) automatically generates an aversion for

TABLE 3.—Mean Values of Brain Serotonin Content for Guinea Pigs

Brain Structure	γ/Gm. West Tissue			
	Controls	Experimentals	Best Trained*	Resistant to Training*
Cortex and Hippocampus	.23	.13 (P < .01)	.19	.13 (P < .10)
Brain Stem and Cerebellum	.28	.23 (P < .20)	.27	.19 (P < .30)

*These data were obtained only in two experiments.

an opposite belief. This animal notion might be considered in a new light in relation to human psychopathology. The concept of such behavioral polarization may be recognized when manifested in a different form by the guinea pig trained to remain immobile when placed on one side of its body. Without any training, the animal automatically acquires an exaggerated righting response when placed on the opposite side, even though at no time during the training period was the animal placed on that side. The same interpretation may be extended to the polarization of the environment outside of the cage as contrasted with the cage of the hypnotic animal.

Effects of Guidance

The remarkable effects of guidance, allowing the experimenter to "cure" fixations, may also be discussed. This procedure consists in overcoming the fear and resistance of the animal and giving the rat the opportunity to experience the passage through the other window without additional trauma. After a few trials, the animal submits to the will of the "therapist" (as shown by the guinea pig experiments) and solves the problem. In this particular case the addition of drug therapy seemed to be effective only in the case of librium. However, the whole process is so short that one wonders whether the experimental conditions were adequately designed to test the action of the other drugs in this situation. Tranquilizers other than librium prolong the learning period, which makes the negative results of this experiment less convincing than the positive ones.

Insightful Behavior

The increased incidence of insightful behavior in the animal as a function of the duration of the decision-making process is truly remarkable, as is the complexity of the adjustments of the animal to the experimental situation. Here again, the cerebral processes responsible for these findings largely escape present-day experimental capabilities. Yet a method used by John and Killam[25] and Liberson and Ellen[26] seems to be particularly adaptable to further analysis of the decision-making processes. We have found in the past that the traces of the flickering signal persist in the hippocampus of the animal (images signal? See reference 27) after the trials when the conflictual situation is particularly active; they disappeared when the avoidance conflict was resolved by training (Fig. 23). Parallel to that was the development and the subsidence of the driven rhythm during stimulation. This method seems to be particularly adaptable to the presently described

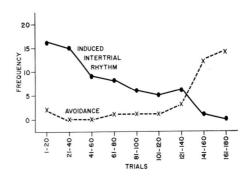

Fig. 23.—Frequency occurrence of induced-intracerebral wave frequency as a function of solving avoidance problem in rats (modified from Liberson and Ellen[25]).

experiment. We have recently succeeded in recording through the scalps of the rodents, using averaging devices, evoked potentials to light, clicks, and stimulation of the sciatic nerve* (Fig. 24).

Variability

The drug-induced changes in variability of the rat's behavior affecting the incidence of solutions has been as yet uncertain. It will have to be reinvestigated in future experiments.

All in all, the rodents' ability to intelligently adapt to circumstances, their trainable submissiveness, their differentiation of the general environment from that of their own cage, and many other facts reported previously illustrate once more the remarkable level of the behavioral achievements of these animals.

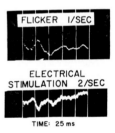

FIG. 24.—Evoked potentials from scalp of guinea pig. Left: Transcranial recording of summated evoked potentials to flashes. Right: Same to electrical stimulation of the sciatic nerve.

B. Pharmacological Implications

Preventive Effects

No drug administered *after* the formation of fixation could "cure" the animal. On the other hand, drugs administered during the formation of the behavioral deviation may alter the course of this behavior. This calls attention to the desirability of more systematic human research on preventive administration of psychotropic drugs.

The major pharmacological finding which can no longer be ignored is the presence of a continuous drug interaction with a motivational field. Another finding is the remarkable persistence of drug-induced behavioral changes if appropriate motivational drive are present

---

*Recently we showed that different components of this "global" evoked potential to visual stimuli changes during the latency period. While its early negative component (peak latency 140 msec) is increased just before jumping, its second negative component (peak latency 140 msec) is depressed as the animal is about to jump. (Liberson and Karczmar, in press, Conf. American College of Neuropsychopharmacology, Puerto Rico, 1966.)

(see also references 28, 29 and 30). The above described possibility of predetermining different "personalities" in rats, with respect to the rapidity of their decision-making processes, by the combined behavioral and pharmacological manipulation is truly remarkable. A practical suggestion derived from this experiment involves the possible benefit to the patient of interrupted pharmacological treatment. In one experiment with librium, which resulted in a high number of solutions, the drug was not given in the soluble problem phase. The reported efficacy of this and other drugs by Feldman[18] may be related to his technique of administering the drug only during the isoluble problem. It is of interest to investigate a method of treatment which would consist of successive periods of administration and withdrawal of psychotropic drugs.

From the general point of view, our findings of a persisting change of rapidity in the performance of the animals placed under similar conditions by a history of either 100 per cent reward or 50 per cent reward suggests far-reaching implications with respect to the importance of high-reward regimen for forming an efficient performance habit.

Serotonin and Catecholamines

The role of serotonin versus catecholamines involved in drug treatment of depressive states may be related to our findings in the hypnotic states. So far, the role of serotonin appears as more important than that of catecholamines in the animal's resistance during the processes of the formation of animal hypnosis. This observation could be explained if during repeated frustrations involved in guinea pig

TABLE 4.—Brain Serotonin Content or Guinea Pigs in the Normal and Vertical Position

| Brain Structure | γ/Gm. Wet Tissue | | |
| | Experimental Animals | | |
	Natural	Vertical	Controls
Cortex and Hippocampus	.23	.27	.32
Brain Stem and Cerebellum	.32	.36	.42

training, serotonin became depleted. If serotonin is depleted by reserpine, hypnosis is favored. If it is protected by monoamine oxidase inhibitors, the animal becomes more resistant to training.

In the case of rats, no biochemical testing was done. However, in addition to the preventive effects of the drug described above, the pharmacological influences upon the decision-making processes were investigated. Most of the classical tranquilizers (reserpine, chlorpromazine, meprobamate) prolonged the decision-making processes and retarded learning. The antagonistic action of the monoamine oxidase inhibitors was found, but only to a relatively slight degree.

Effects of Librium

A remarkable finding of the effect of librium shortening decision-making processes in rats should generate appropriate experiments in humans. This drug might be effective in neurotics because it may shorten periods of rumination, hesitation, and indecisiveness found in certain patients.

Effects of LSD-25

LSD-25 disrupts completely both types of behavior, illustrating confused states produced in animals by this drug.

SUMMARY

Two trained behavioral deviations of rodents were studied: Fixations of spatial reactions (rat) and prolonged hypnotic states (guinea pigs). This study reveals:

A. Findings of General Interest

These reactions result from induced conflicts. They are behaviorally polarized: An animal trained to behave in a certain way automatically resists behavior directed in the opposite way. A remarkable relationship between the duration of "decision-making processes" and the incidence of insightful behavior is reported. On the other hand, the training done under conditions of 100 per cent reward leads to faster performances than training done under conditions of 50 per cent reward. These findings, as well as significant adjustments of the animal to the experimental situations, illustrate again the behavioral achievements of rodents.

B. Pharmacological Findings

Drugs, as well as other somatic treatments, seem to be continually interacting with the motivational field of the animal. Also, the behavioral drug effects persist several months longer than the time of their actual administration, given a favorable motivational field. This suggests the advisability of exploring the efficacy of interrupted treatment by psychotropic drugs in humans.

Drug research and biochemical studies seem to be consistent with the hypothesis of a depletion of serotonin during the resisted training of prolonged hypnotic states. There is a suggestion that serotonin is "used" by the animal during successive inductions of the hypnotic states. Reserpine, which depletes brain serotonin, favors the development of hypnosis. Monamine oxidase inhibitors protecting serotonin increase the resistance of the animal to hypnosis. Cortical serotonin falls by about 40 per cent during training of animals initially resistant to hypnosis. Results concerning catecholamines are less consistent and as yet are not convincing. The remarkable effects of librium in shortening decision-making processes in rats should stimulate appropriate research in humans. LSD-25 given in high dosage disrupts both reported types of deviant behavior in rodents.

ACKNOWLEDGEMENTS

The collaboration and help of the following colleagues and associates is acknowledged: Drs. Joseph Bernsohn, Robert S. Feldman, Paul Ellen, Alexander Karczmar, Edward Schwartz, Alex Stern and Messrs. Arthur Wilson, Vincent Daly, John McMahon, Aaron Kafka, Joan Robins, Virginia P. Gagnon, Priscilla Gagnon, Brone Motusis, Louis Pedigo, Robert Smith, Russel Smith, Jack Stansbeary.

REFERENCES

1. Pavlov, I. P.: Conditional Reflexes: An Investigation of the Physiological Activity of the Cerebral Cortex. Translated by G. V. Anrop. New York, Oxford University Press, 1927.
2. Maier, N. R. F.: Frustration: The Study of Behaviour Without a Goal. New York, McGraw-Hill, 1949.
3. Liberson, W. T.: Prolonged hypnotic states with "local signs" induced in guinea pigs. Science 108:40-41, 1948.
4. Liberson, W. T., Kafka, A., Schwartz, E., and Gagnon, V.: Effects of chlordiazepoxide (librium) on fixated behaviour in rats. Int. J. Neuropharmacol. 2:67-78, 1963.

5. Liberson, W. T., and Ellen, P.: Unpublished observations.

6. Liberson, W. T., Karczmar, A., and McMahon, J.: In preparation.

7. Liberson, W. T.: Interaction of motivational and drug effects in animal behavior research. J. Nerv. Men. Dis. 138:131-140, 1964.

8. Feldman, R. S., Liberson, W. T., Ellen, P., and Robins, J.: The effects of chlorpromazine on brightness discrimination of rats with habits or fixations. J. Comp. Physiol. Psychol. 52:322-326, 1959.

9. Feldman, R. S., and Liberson, W. T.: The effect of reserpine on behavior fixations in rats. J. Comp. Physiol. Psychol. 53:483-487, 1960.

10. Liberson, W. T., Feldman, R. S., and Ellen, P.: The behavioral analysis of the effects of meprobamate as compared with other tranquilizers and electroconvulsive shock. In: Neuropsychopharmacologica, Vol. I, 1959, pp. 351-357. Amsterdam, Elsevier Pub. Co., 1959

11. Liberson, W. T., Ellen, P., and Feldman, R. S.: Effect of somatic vs. "guidance" therapies on behavior rigidity in rats. J. Neuropsychiat. 1:17-19, 1959.

12. Feldman, R. S.: Comparisons of the benzodiazepines with other tranquilizers during conflict and chronic anxiety states. In: Neuropsychopharmacology, Vol. 3. Bradley, Flugel, and Hoch, Eds. Amsterdam, Netherlands, Elsevier Publishing Co., 1964.

13. Feldman, R. S.: The prevention of fixation with chlordiazepoxide. J. Neuropsychiat. 3:254-259, 1962.

14. Liberson, W. T., Kafka, A., and Schwartz, E.: Effects of chlordiazepoxide (librium) and other psychopharmacological agents on "fixated behavior" in rats. Biochem. Pharmacol. 8:15-16, 1961.

15. Liberson, W. T.: Analysis of the effects of psychotropic drugs on rigid behavior in rodents. Trans. 6th VA Research Conf. Cooperative Chemotherapy Studies in Psychiatry and Broad Research Approaches to Mental Illness, March, 1961, Vol. VI, pp. 159-166. Washington, D.C., Veterans Administration.

16. Feldman, R. S., and Lewis, E.: Response differences of psychotropic drugs in rats during chronic anxiety states. J. Neuropsychiat. (Suppl. 1) 3:1962.

17. Lewis, E. M., and Feldman, R. S.: The depressive effect of chlordiazepoxide on a negative incentive. Psychopharmacologia 6:143-150, 1965.

18. Feldman, R. S.: Further studies on assay and testing of fixation-preventing psychotropic drugs. Psychopharmacologia 6:130-142, 1965.

19. Liberson, W. T., Ellen, P., Schwartz, E., Wilson, A., and Gagnon, V. P.: Further studies of the effects of psychotropic drugs on the behavior of guinea pigs and rats. J. Neuropsychiat. 3:298-303, 1962.

20. Liberson, W. T., Karczmar, A., Schwartz, E., and Ellen, P.: Synaptic transmission in the hippocampus and psychopharmacological agents. Int. J. Neuropharmacol. 2:291-302, 1964.

21. Liberson, W. T., Feldman, R. S., and Ellen, P.: Effects of electroshock on discriminative processes in rats. J. Neuropsychiat. 1:108-111, 1959.

22. Liberson, W. T., Smith, R. W., and Stern, A.: Experimental studies of the prolonged "hypnotic withdrawal" in guinea pigs. J. Neuropsychiat. 3:28-34, 1961.

23. Liberson, W. T., and Karczmar, A.: In preparation.

24. Liberson, W. T., Bernsohn, J., Wilson, A., and Daly, V.: Brain serotonin content and behavioral stress. J. Neuropsychiat. 5:363-365, 1964.

25. John, E. R., and Killam, K.: *In:* The Central Nervous System and Behavior. Brazier, Mary A. B., Ed., New York, Josiah Macy, Jr. Foundation, 1959, p. 33.

26. Liberson, W. T., and Ellen P.: Conditioning of the driven brain wave rhythm in the cortex and the hippocampus of the rat. *In:* Recent Advances in Biological Psychiatry. New York, Grune & Stratton, 1960, pp. 156-171.

27. Beritoff, J. S.: Neural Mechanisms of Higher Vertebrate Behavior. Translated from Russian and edited by W. T. Liberson. Boston, Little, Brown and Co., 1965, 384 pages.

28. Rushton, R., and Steinberg, H.: Modification of behavioral effects of drugs by past experience. *In:* Animal Behaviour and Drug Action, Boston, Little, Brown and Company, 1964, pp. 207-223.

29. Bindra, D., and Mendelson, J.: Transaction of habit strength and drug effects. J. Comp. Physiol. Psychol. 55:217-219, 1962.

30. Ross, S., and Schnitzer, S. B.: Further support for a placebo effect in the rat. Psychol. Rep. 13:461-462, 1963.

7

BEHAVIORAL ASPECTS OF
CIRCADIAN RHYTHMS

by CHARLES F. STROEBEL, PH.D.*

T HE SUBJECT OF THIS PAPER—the role of 24 hour rhythms in the
acquisition, "memory," and extinction of learned responses—has
not been widely studied.[1] Several reasons come to mind.

First, the diverse range of adaptive behavior exhibited by higher
organisms has encouraged a natural and widespread interest in the
more reactive mechanisms of central and autonomic nervous system
control (e.g., EEG or GSR correlates of behavior). This interest, along
with an attempt to simplify experimental designs, leads many investigators to assume a background of relative constancy in the less reactive
mechanisms which control the ongoing metabolic functioning of the
body (e.g., biologic rhythms; see Fig. 1). Thus, if a behavioral scientist
is aware of the possible relevance of biologic rhythms, he attempts to
hold their role invariant by maintaining subjects on a rigid lighting
regimen and by presenting experimental trials at the same clock hour
in the lighting cycle. (Awareness of this control is apparently rare,
since it is reported in fewer than 5 per cent of the reports in the
experimental psychology, neuropsychology, and neurophysiology literature between 1960 and 1964, by actual tabulation.)

A second reason for neglect stems from a confusion of the distinction
between circadian (*circa*, about; *dies*, day) and diurnal rhythms. Diurnal rhythms may be viewed as "autonomous systems whose oscillations
decay if the inevitable losses of energy are not restored periodically
from outside the system."[2] Circadian rhythms then, are "autonomous
systems capable of auto-oscillation" (self-sustained oscillations which
persist even in a *constant* environment). Under normal environmental
conditions, the correlation among an adaptive organism's circadian

This research was supported by grant MH-08552 from the National Institute of
Mental Health and by the Gengras Foundation.

*Director, Laboratories for Experimental Psychophysiology, Institute of Living,
Hartford, Conn.

rhythms and light-dark, eating, drinking, sleeping, and reproductive times is very high; the circadian versus diurnal confusion occurs when these correlations are (erroneously) assumed to be causal.[3,4]

Virtually every physiologic variable (component) which has been sampled longitudinally has demonstrated a 24 hour periodicity. The orderly sequence of crest and trough of these component rhythms (not all in phase) creates a unique succession of internal physiologic states which is repeated once every 24 hours. This orderly sequence—a kind of internal temporal coordination or interlocking of metabolic functioning—can be viewed as the body's own timing mechanism or biologic "clock." In the normal organism the overall sequence of internal rhythms may be synchronized with laboratory clock time my means of a light-dark cycle. In the experiments which follow, the real dependent variable is biologic clock time; the operational dependent variable is laboratory clock time. By sampling component rhythms (e.g., core temperature or blood eosinophils) longitudinally, the synchrony of biologic and laboratory times can be ascertained, as shown in Figure 2.

Conditioned Fear and Circadian Rhythms

We initiated these experiments after recognizing that because circadian rhythms could operate independently of the usual environmental

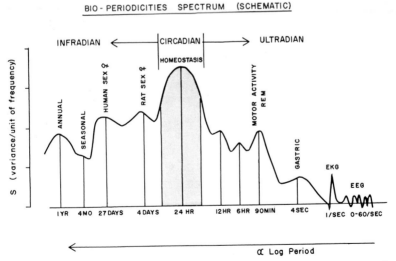

Fig. 1.—Schematic spectrum of biologic periodicities along a continuum with more reactive rhythms to the right.

stimuli specified by psychologists, they represented a potentially important source of error variance in behavioral studies. An initial hypothesis was that if an organism's metabolic functioning changed predictably with time over a 24 hour period, optimal acquisition or extinction of responses should occur if trials were always presented at the same biologic clock time.

To test this hypothesis and its generality the circadian dependency of six common learning paradigms (see Table 1) was examined in a series of experiments. The basic design for each study was balanced (see Table 2), contrasting groups which received trials at the same time each day (biologic clock time relevant) or at random times (biologic clock time irrelevant).

For each experiment, 32 naive male, Sprague-Dawley rats, approximately 100 days old, were randomly allocated into 4 groups of 8 animals each. For three weeks prior to an experiment, all animals were synchronized with a 12 on-12 off laboratory lighting cycle; food and

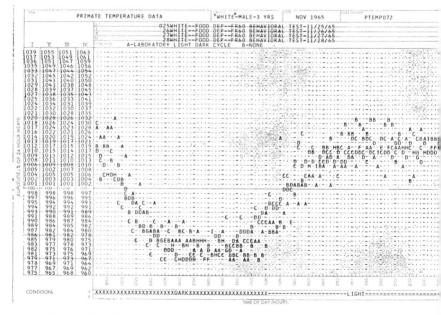

Fig. 2.—Four days of monkey brain temperature data recorded from a chronic extradural thermistor have been overlayed on a 24 hour abscissa to compare the equivalence of biologic clock time and laboratory time. Plots such as this are produced automatically by an IBM 1440 computer.

water were *ad libitum*. During each experiment all subjects were maintained in a constantly lighted environment and were permitted to drink water *ad libitum* except for the 24 hour period preceding an experimental trial. Trials were presented on alternate days to minimize the possibility that deprivation stimuli would assume the role of a rhythm

TABLE 1.—Six Learning Paradigms Tested for Circadian Dependency

Conditioned Emotional Response (CER)[6]:

During adaptation (A) and all other trials, Ss may lever press for a periodic (VI = 1.0) water reinforcement. During conditioning (C) trials, a clicking noise is presented during the middle three minutes, terminated by a 30 msec. shock to the feet. During extinction (E) trials, the clicker is presented without the shock.

$$\text{Measure: Inflection ratio} = \frac{\text{presses during clicker} - \text{presses before clicker}}{\text{presses before clicker}}.$$

A ratio of -1.0 indicates complete suppression of bar pressing during the clicker period. A ratio of zero indicates no suppression during the clicker period.

Punishment[6]:

A and E trials and "measure" are same as for CER. During conditioning (C) trials, lever presses are punished by shock to the feet while the clicker is on.

Sidman Avoidance[7]:

Lever presses postpone a shock to the feet for 20 seconds during a nine minute trial. Measure: Number of shocks received and average R-R interval.

Classical Avoidance:

Random presentations of a warning tone precede shock to feet by 5 seconds. A lever press during the tone represents successful avoidance. Measure: Number of successful responses and response latency during a nine minute trial of 18 presentations.

Escape:

Randomly presented shocks to the feet may be terminated by a lever press. Measure: mean latency of 3 escape trials during a nine minute period.

Discriminative Lever Pressing:

Ss responds to a fixed ratio ($= 5$) vs. variable interval (.30) differential reinforcement schedule with a stimulus light as discriminative stimulus for the VI condition. Measure: Latency for adopting an appropriate response pattern for 4 discriminations during a 12 minute trial.

synchronizer. Random trial times were assigned for appropriate groups from a random number table. "Same" trial times were given within two hours of the time corresponding to onset of the dark cycle in the pre-experimental phase. A five day rest separated acquisition and extinction trials; a three week rest period preceded extinction trial E_f. When conditioned stimuli were used, they consisted of a tone or clicking noise of about 85db. Shock to the body, when used, was an unscrambled 0.65 ± 0.15 ma. a.c. shock applied to alternate floor grids. Floor grids were wiped clean after each experimental trial.

Results for two of the paradigms studied, CER (Conditioned Emotional Response) and punishment, are shown in Figure 3, contrasting results for the only significant study (CER) versus one of the clearly nonsignificant ones. We can draw the following conclusions from differences, significant at the $p = .05$ level or better, in the CER Study:

1. Acquisition was significantly slower when trials were presented at random times. This observation, coupled with the unusual resistance to extinction of the (random-random) group, suggests that the CER was conditioned to a wide variety of internal physiologic states[5] corresponding to differing clock-memories available at the many trial times.
2. This finding is supported by the rapid extinction of the (same-same) group, in which the memory substrate associated with only one biologic clock time was involved.
3. Further substantiation derives from the significant spontaneous recovery shown by the (random-same) group; i.e., extinction of the CER memory at the same time each day did not significantly affect CER memory linked to biologic clock variables at other points in the 24 hour cycle which had become conditioned under the random acquisition sequence.

TABLE 2.—Balanced Design for Treatment Assignments for each Study

Group	Acquisition	Extinction	Spontaneous Recovery
1	Same	Same	Same
2	Same	Random	Same
3	Random	Same	Same
4	Random	Random	Random

*Groups 1 and 2, and 3 and 4 were pooled for analysis of acquisition data.

TABLE 3.—Probabilities of Circadian Rhythm Dependency for Six Learning Paradigms

Paradigm	Biologic Clock Effect?	Best Probability
CER	Yes	.001–.05
Escape	No	.07
Sidman Avoidance	No	.11
Classical Avoidance	No	.30
Punishment	No	.45
Discriminative Lever Pressing	No	.50

4. In contrast, none of the results shown for the punishment study remotely approach significance.

Table 3 indicates the results for each of the six experimental procedures studied. Since significance was achieved in only the CER

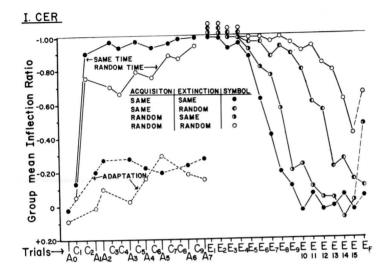

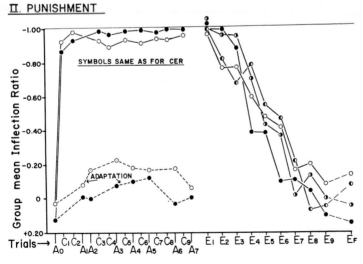

Fig. 3.—The effect of random versus same daily trial times for I—conditioned emotional response and II—punishment.

study, the table has been made more informative by ranking the experiments on the basis of the best probability values actually obtained. It is possible that refinements in experimental technique, such as delivery of shocks to chronically implanted subcutaneous electrodes, might improve the precision of the escape or the Sidman avoidance experiments.

Thus, if we repeatedly train a subject to an unavoidable fear stimulus at 8 a.m. each day and then test him for fear strength at random times, he shows the strongest response at the time of training and the weakest 12 hours earlier or later. This relationship persists even though the experiment is conducted under constant environmental conditions, indicating that the subject's only time cue is his system of internal clocks. This hypothesis has been verified by recognizing that biologic clock time could be set ahead or behind 12 hours by inverting the light-dark cycle (though full adjustment requires 8 to 16 days in rodents).[8] In this experiment, subjects on an 8 p.m.-8 a.m. light cycle were trained for 10 days with a CER presented at 8 a.m.; for days 11 to 25, subjects were permitted to rest while the light cycle was inverted so that night became day and vice versa; thereafter, the lights were "on" continuously. Tests trials at random times on the 30th day revealed the strongest fear response now at 8 p.m. and the weakest at 8 a.m. If memory of the fear response were not linked to the biologic clock system, the opposite results would presumably have been observed. An analogy might be the "memory" of a bank vault, which is programmed to display its contents at a preset time.

What is unique about the CER which makes it, and not the other procedures tested, sensitive to biologic clock time?

1. The conditioned fear associated with Sidman avoidance, classical avoidance, and punishment is *avoidable* under criterion learning conditions.
2. The conditioned fear associated with the CER is *unavoidable* under criterion learning conditions. Hunt and Brady[6] have labeled this unavoidable fear "intercurrent anxiety." It should be noted that a greater degree of sympathetic nervous system activation (piloerection, micturition, defecation, freezing) is also observed with the CER than in the other procedures.
3. The cognitive cues associated with avoidance become progressively more clear in the rank sequence of escape, Sidman, classical, and punishment, as indicated in Table 3. The discriminative lever pressing task is almost entirely cognitive with little or no conditioned fear component.

In summary, circadian dependency has been observed in the learning, "memory", and extinction of unavoidable conditioned fear. Such dependency may be present in other learning situations, but not at a statistically significant level in carefully controlled laboratory experiments.

Conditioned Emotionality and Light Cycle Inversion

Having had success in carrying the memory of a CER* through one inversion of the light-dark cycle, we wondered how far we could carry this procedure without a significant decrement in response strength. Halberg[8] reported that the component phase relationships are "scrambled" during the time required for resynchronization, since component rhythms vary in their rate of adjustment to the new lighting regimen. Hence, five groups of 16 rats each were subjected to a varying number of light cycle inversions ("treatments") after they had been trained to criterion on a CER. Training trials for all animals were administered shortly after the onset of the dark cycle. The groups were treated as follows after they had achieved criterion learning:

Group A (Control)—No inversions

Group B—Single inversion 10 days prior to extinction

Group C—Two inversions at 10 and 20 days prior to extinction

Group C′—Two inversions at 30 and 40 days prior to extinction

Group D—Four inversions at 40, 30, 20, and 10 days prior to extinction.

The remainder of the design is illustrated in the top panel of Figure 5. Group C′ was included to test the possibility that resynchronization would not be complete in 10 days; as an additional check on this, all groups were tested for spontaneous recovery three weeks after the last extinction trial. If Group C′ extinguished more slowly than did Group C, or if either Group C or D showed significant spontaneous recovery, it would indicate that part of a memory decrement observed during extinction trials had been a temporary one. (A temporary decrement could be attributed to failure of component rhythms to entirely resynchronize before extinction trials were initiated.) Group C and C′ may also be viewed as controls for a possible memory consolidation effect.

Several conclusions (p < .05 level) may be drawn from the results presented in Figure 4.

1. The faster extinction of Group C′ compared to controls demonstrates a permanent decrement in memory as a result of two inversions, since little spontaneous recovery was observed on the E_r trial.

---

*Using the inflection ratio (Table 1) as a measure of CER response strength, the acquisition criterion was two successive trials with an I.R. = —.90 or better. The extinction criterion was two successive trials with an I.R. = —.30 or poorer.

2. Similarly, the accelerated extinction of Groups C and D reflects both permanent and temporary decrements in memory, since both groups showed significant spontaneous recovery.

3. Four successive inversions at ten day intervals (Group D) appear equivalent to 10 electroconvulsive shock treatments in reducing the CER in albino rats.[9]

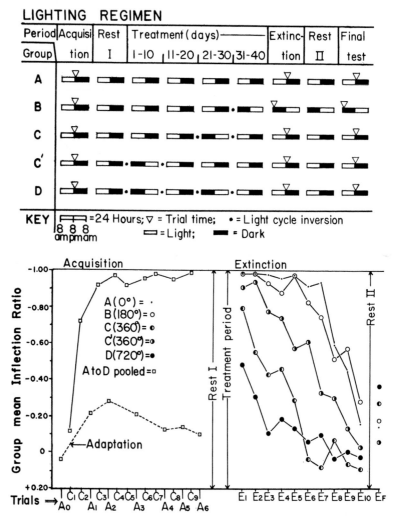

Fig. 4.—Treatment procedure and results, indicating the effect of successive light cycle inversion on CER extinction.

DRUG SUSCEPTIBILITY RHYTHMS

Halberg[10] and his co-workers have demonstrated a large number of susceptibility rhythms to noxious agents and drugs. We have verified his general results with a number of phenothiazine drugs. Figure 5 illustrates the results of a susceptibility study in which the same dose of TPS-23‡ was given i.p. to four independent groups of rats at the times indicated by arrows in the figure. The response variable was hours for return of normal activity. Whereas this dose was lethal for 75 per cent of the animals receiving it at a time corresponding to the onset of the light cycle, it was totally nonlethal for the three groups injected at the other times.

CER SUSCEPTIBILITY RHYTHM

Upon finding that the CER could be linked to the internal timing system, we wondered if, by analogy with the drug studies, certain biologic clock times might be more favorable than others for acquiring a CER. Pilot experiments substantiated this possibility, showing most rapid learning at a time corresponding to onset of the dark cycle and slowest learning at onset of the light cycle. Because this susceptibility rhythm for CER acquisition paralleled the rhythm reported for blood steroids,[11] we designed an experiment to test for a possible relationship.

Ninety-six naive rats were maintained on a pre-experimental, 12 on-12 off lighting regimen. The experiment was performed under constant light conditions in 24 specially constructed isolation Skinner boxes. Within each group of 24, sets of 6 animals were randomly allocated to one of 4 testing times: 800, 1400, 2000, 200. Groups were treated as follows:

Group 1: (control) sham adrenalectomy.[12]

Group 2: adrenalectomized two weeks prior to the experiment.[12]

Group 3: 100 mg./Kg. methopyropone i.p., 1½ hours before trial time. This drug blocks the synthesis of 11-beta corticosteroids.*

Group 4: sacrificed at trial times for blood samples to assay for blood eosinophils and blood corticosterone (Silber fluorogenic material; see reference 19).

---

‡TPS-23 was kindly supplied by Dr. R. Bircher of Sandoz, Inc., Hanover, N.J. TPS-23 is similar to Mellaril in action with approximately three times the potency and with fewer side effects.

*Generous quantities of methopyropone (SU-4885) were supplied by Dr. J. J. Chart of Ciba Pharmaceuticals. Aqueous tartaric acid, in concentrations of 1.0 to 2.0 per cent, was used as the vehicle. See: Chart, J. J.: *Experientia* 14:151, 1958.

In addition, the motor activity of randomly chosen members of groups 1 and 2 was monitored prior to CER trials with a Peacock-Williams ultrasonic activity device.[13] Figure 6 shows a common time scale with the behavioral results above and the corresponding physiologic data below. Physiologic data are plotted as per cent of the 24 hour mean, which permits meaningful comparison of measurements with different units. The following conclusions seem relevant:

1. The susceptibility of rats to CER conditioning shows a circadian rhythm; i.e., rats learn a CER faster at certain biologic clock times than at others.
2. Adrenalectomy reduces the amplitude of the susceptibility curve.
3. Methopyropone administered prior to trials virtually eliminates the susceptibility rhythm. This drug affects adrenal cortical and possibly other sources (gonadal) of steroid production.
4. The CER susceptibility rhythm closely parallels the measured levels of blood corticosterone.

In conclusion, the rate of CER acquisition is positively correlated with levels of blood steroids. It is interesting to note that no significant difference would be observed among adrenalectomized, sham operated, and methopyropone-dosed animals if trials had been given at 8 a.m. exclusively.

Discussion

These studies suggest an explanation for many of the apparently contradictory or nonreplicable findings in the experimental psychopathology and psychopharmacology literature;[20] namely, failure to consider the role of circadian susceptibility rhythms for either the drug and/or the conditioned "anxiety" paradigm against which the drug is tested. It would seem advisable that future research in these fields include controls for the dominant synchonizer (a specified light-dark cycle) and time of testing (for possible pitfalls in this control, see reference 18).

Although caution is always warranted in making inferences from animal data, the following clinical applications can be noted:

1. The drug susceptibility rhythm data suggest that the phasing of treatments with a patient's own susceptibility rhythm would permit us to maximize the effective drug principle and minimize undesirable side effects with *minimal drug doses*.[14] In contrast, drugs are currently administered on a ceiling basis, supplemented by additional drugs to counteract undesirable side effects. This "massive" approach usually makes a patient more amenable to psychotherapy, but simultaneously debilitates him as he attempts to reintegrate his social

functioning. An analogy to the present clinical procedure might be an automobile with its throttle jammed wide open, with exotic polymers added to the fuel mixture to control speed. With a biologic rhythm approach to treatment, the throttle would operate in the usual fashion, being opened or closed as one ascended or descended hills, represented by the patient's own susceptibility rhythms.

2. The circadian rhythm differential between avoidable and unavoidable fear appears to be an interesting one, insofar as one goal of psychotherapy is to teach patients to gain cognitive control (i.e., avoidance control) over what has been termed "nonspecific anxiety." Our evidence indicates that from a physiologic point of view, effective psychotherapy with neurotics may operate by removing unavoidable fear from the domain of biologic rhythm functioning. Further, the random-same experiments imply that if anxiety or conditioned fear is learned under random conditions, it must be unlearned under similar conditions. Hence, for patients with diffuse anxiety syndromes, maximally effective psychotherapy would take place at random times rather than at the same time each day—a proposal which has not endeared us to some of our psychotherapist colleagues who enjoy a good night's sleep.

3. The findings that four inversions of the light-dark cycle (or social regimen) at ten day intervals is roughly equivalent to 10 electroconvulsive shock treatments suggests that, conceivably, inversion could itself be used as a psychiatric treatment. One possibility for accomplishing such inversions clinically has particularly delighted those members of staff who might be involved; namely, shuttle patients between Hartford and Tokyo once every ten days.

4. This research suggests a possible link among circadian rhythms, anxiety similar to that specified in many psychodynamic formulations, and the abnormal "longer than 24 hour rhythms" noted by Richter,[*15] Gjessing,[16] and others[17] in psychiatric patients suffering from manic depressive illness, periodic catatonia, and cyclical schizophrenic remissions.[18]

Finally, several comments may serve to relate this work to that presented by Dr. Richter in the Hamilton Award Lecture at this Symposium. First, in his elegant studies of rat activity rhythms, Richter seems to imply that biologic clocks operate in a dichotomous

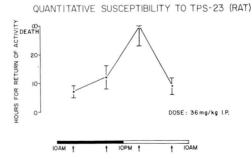

Fig. 5.—Circadian susceptibility rhythm for the same dose of a phenothiazine drug administered to independent groups of rats. Injections were made under constant light conditions and are indicated at times noted by arrows.

fashion, emitting "go" or "no go" signals. For example,[15] "It must be pointed out again that none of the clocks that we know about at present can be consulted at any time of the day or night. Thus, they do not serve as chronometers as do our watches and clocks. These clocks signal only at the beginning of each phase or at the maximum or minimum of sinusoidal curves." The studies reported here would favor an analogue interpretation, particularly when we view these

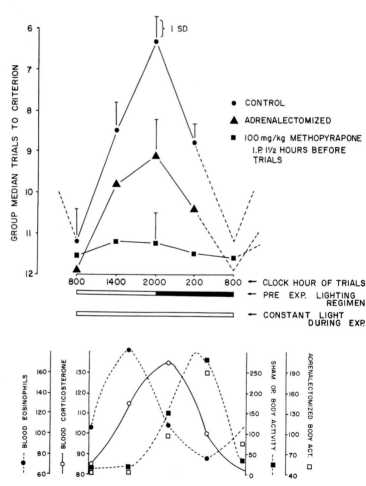

Fig. 6.—Adrenal steroid rhythm and susceptibility to CER conditioning (rat). The upper panel presents behavioral data. The lower panel presents physiologic measures at corresponding time points.

results from the perspective of human functioning. An analogue model would not, of course, preclude the possibility that an analogue sensor in the body is operating in a "go, no go" mode as a basis for rat activity. Second, Richter implies that many different "clocks" may exist in the body with different time periods, particularly in pathological disease states. A more parsimonious explanation requires only that several "about 24 hour rhythms" produce *beat frequency effects* with beat periods significantly longer than 24 hours. For example, if two biologic variables can produce additive effects, and the first remains circadian while the second begins to lag 30 minutes behind per day (as a result of infection, or a reduced secretory cell population), one additive beat of substantial magnitude would be produced once every 48 days. Operationally, this beat period could be viewed as a 48 day "clock."*

REFERENCES

1. Sollberger, A.: Biologic Rhythm Research. New York, Elsevier Publishing Co., 1965.
2. Aschoff, J.: Comparative physiology: diurnal rhythms. Ann. Rev. Physiol. 25:581-600, 1963.
3. Quay, W. B.: Circadian and estrous rhythms in pineal and brain serotonin. *In:* Progress in Brain Research. Vol. 8. New York, Elsevier Publishing Co., 1964, p. 61.
4. Axelrod, J., Wartman, R. J., and Snyder, S. H.: Control of hydroxyindole O-methyltransferase activity in the rat pineal gland by environmental lighting. J. Biol Chem. 240:949, 1965.
5. Miller, N. E.: Learnable Drives and Rewards. *In:* Handbook of Experimental Psychology. S. S. Stevens, Ed. New York, John Wiley & Sons, 1951.
6. Hunt, H. F., and Brady, J. V.: Some effects of punishment and intercurrent "anxiety" on a simple operant. J. Comp. Physiol. Psychol. 48:305, 1955.
7. Sidman, M.: Avoidance conditioning with brief shock and no exteroceptive warning signal. Science. 188:157, 1953.
8. Halberg, F.: Temporal coordination of physiologic function in Cold Spring Harbor Symposia on Quantitative Biology. 25:289-310, 1960.
9. Hunt, H. F., Jernberg, D., and Brady, J. V.: Effects of ECS on a CER. J. Comp. Physiol. Psychol. 45:589, 1952.
10. Savage, I. R.: Test of peak values in a physiopathologic time series. Exp. Med. Surg. 20:309, 1962.

*The author is indebted to the following individuals who assisted in this research: B. C. Glueck Jr., M.D., G. T. Heistad, Ph.D., Douglas Scott, Jay Starr, Stephanie Norman, Ned Cochorane, Joyce Brilliant, and R. Peter Ericson. Acknowledgement is also made of the generous assistance given by the Advanced Medical Systems Group of IBM.

11. Ungar, F., and Halberg, F.: Circadian rhythm in the in vitro response of mouse adrenal to ACTH. Science 137:1058-1060, 1962.
12. Ferris, E. J., and Griffith, J. Q.: The Rat in Laboratory Investigations. New York, Lippincott, 1949.
13. Peacock, L. J., and Williams, M.: An ultrasonic device for recording activity. Amer. J. Psychol. 75:648, 1962.
14. Stroebel, C. F.: Models for drug interaction effects. *In:* Proceedings of the Fifth International Congress of Neuropsychopharmacology. New York, N.Y., Excerpta Medica Foundation, 1967.
15. Richter, C. P.: Biologic Clocks in Medicine and Psychiatry. Springfield, Ill., Charles C Thomas, 1965.
16. Gjessing, R.: Beitrage zur Kenntins der Pathophysiologie des Katatonen Stupors. Arch. Psychiat. 96:319, 1932.
17. Fleeson, W. B., Glueck, B. C., Jr., and Halberg, F.: Persistence of daily rhythms in eosinophil count and rectal temperature during "regression" induced by intensive electro-shock therapy. Physiologist 1:28.
18. Stroebel, C. F.: A biologic rhythm approach to psychiatric treatment. *In:* Proceedings of the Seventh Medical Symposium. Yorktown Heights, N.Y., IBM Corp. Procedure for Estimation of Corticosterone on Hydrocortisone, 1967.
19. Silber, R. H., et al.: Clin. Chem. 4:278, 1958.
20. Stern, J. A., and McDonald, D. G.: Physiologic correlates of mental disease. *In:* Annual Review of Psychology, Vol. 16. Palo Alto, Calif., Annual Reviews, Inc., 1965.

8

PRENATAL GONADAL HORMONES AND BEHAVIOR IN THE ADULT*

by WILLIAM C. YOUNG, Ph.D.†

I N 1958 at the time of a symposium on animal behavior organized for the American Psychiatric Association by Dr. Eugene Bliss we presented the results from what I believe was the first study devoted to a test of the possibility that gonadal hormones secreted prenatally act on the developing mammalian brain in such a way that the predominant pattern of behavior displayed during the juvenile period and after the attainment of adulthood is masculine or feminine.[1] The results we announced at that time are summarized in Table 1. Their significance, as we envisaged it, extended beyond the organization of sexual behavior.

Having reached this point by a path which had passed through the periphery of experimental embryology and the physiology of reproduction, we were impressed by the apparent analogy between the role played by the gonadal hormones in the differentiation of the genital tracts and in their functioning in the adult[2,3] and the role of prenatal gonadal hormones in the differentiation of the neural tissues mediating mating behavior and their functioning in the adult. We were excited too by the possibility that not only differences in the mating behavior of males and females are determined by the action of prenatal hormones, but also other behavioral differences not instrumental to mating are also determined or established by actions of the same substances.

Since that meeting in 1958 a rapid succession of experiments by graduate students and associates has enabled us to confirm these concepts, to obtain a wider view of what is involved, and to sense some-

---

*The work reported has been supported for a number of years by grants from USPHS. Current support continues under Grants MH 08634 and FR 00163.

†Deceased, 1965. Dr. Young was at the Oregon Regional Primate Research Center and at the University of Oregon Medical School.

TABLE 1.—Hormonal Effect During Embryonic and Fetal Periods on the Patterning
of Mating Behavior Displayed During Adulthood

*When guinea pigs are given testosterone propionate from day 10
(5 mg.) to day 68 (1 mg. daily, days 11 to 68) of pregnancy:*

1. All females become hermaphroditic with masculinized external
genitalia, hypertrophied Wolffian ducts, failure of Müllerian duct-uro-
genital sinus fusion, and ovarian dysfunction.

2. Supression of feminine measures of behavior and intensification of
masculine components.

3. Increased responsiveness to androgen.

4. Effects are permanent.

5. No striking effects on male siblings.

thing of their significance for psychiatric thought. All this will be the
substance of what I will say in the time left to me this morning.

A chance observation that adult females injected with testosterone
propionate during pregnancy do not display malelike mounting
behavior until after parturition led to the demonstration by Milton
Diamond[4] that during pregnancy, while the mother is carrying the

TABLE 2.—Responsiveness of Pregnant and Nonpregnant Guinea
Pigs to Testosterone

Subjects		Malelike Mounting Behavior (5 tests)			Clitoris (50 days of treatment)	
	N	Mean mounts per animal	Mean mounts per test	N	% with some modification	% with full modification
Pregnant	33	1.3	0.26	42	2.4	0
Pregnant receiving testosterone	27	1.7	0.34	39	56.4*	7.7*
Nonpregnant	20	2.9	0.58	20	5.0	0
Nonpregnant receiving testosterone	17	23.0*	4.60*	17	100*	94.0*

* = P < .001.
By courtesy of Dr. Milton Diamond.

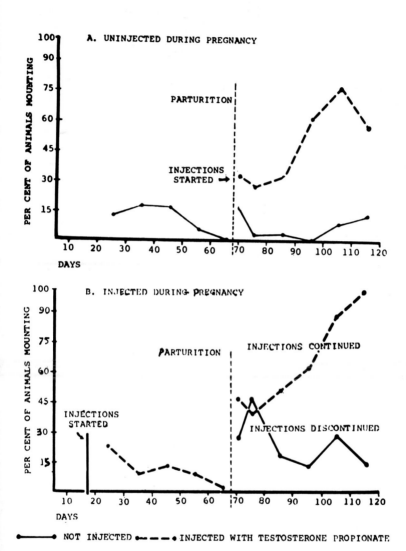

FIG. 1 (A AND B).—Proportion of female guinea pigs mounting in successive 10 minute tests with diestrous female partners. A. Uninjected during pregnancy. Following parturition one subgroup was injected with testosterone propionate and one subgroup remained uninjected. B. Injected during pregnancy. After parturition one subgroup was maintained on daily testosterone and the injections were discontinued for the other.

female fetuses that are undergoing masculinization, she is relatively unaffected and is protected by progesterone (Table 2, Fig. 1). This demonstration and other data I will not present here[5] suggested that, as in the case of the genital tracts, there is for the brain a period of maximal susceptibility to the action of the prenatal gonadal hormones.[6,7] In the guinea pig this period appears to lie between the 25th and 35th days of the 67- to 71-day gestation period (Table 3).

Leaning again on the model established by the experimental embryologists[2,3,8] we have been able to demonstrate the primacy of the testicular hormone for the organizing action our work has revealed. When this androgen is present, the brains of genotypic males and females are masculinized; when this androgen is absent, the brains of genotypic males and females remain feminine. Not only are estrogens not involved

TABLE 3.—Morphologic and Behavioral Measures for Gonadectomized Female, Female Pseudohermaphroditic, and Male Guinea Pigs.

		N	% with "male" urethra	Mean length of phallus (mm.)	Mean no. of mounts w/o hormones	% seldom in heat
	Untreated females	11	0*	11.7*	1.6	0
Females treated prenatally with androgen during postcoital days	15-30 days	9	0*	10.9*	2.3	0
	15-40 days	8	0*	12.2*	1.8	12.5
	15-45 days	11	18.2*	13.8*†	3.5	36.4
	15-60+ days	10	10.0*	13.6*†	5.1	30.0
	20-65 days	10	10.0*	14.1*†	6.4	50.0
	25-40 days	13	84.6†	17.2*†	5.0	23.1
	30-45 days	6	66.7†	15.8*†	8.8	66.7
	30-55 days	6	66.7†	18.3*†	6.3	83.3
	30-65 days	11	81.8†	20.0*†	10.1	90.9
	35-65 days	9	22.2*	14.3*†	5.4	55.6
	40-65 days	9	0*	13.6*†	3.6	33.3
	50-65 days	3	0*	12.7*†	3.3	0
	Untreated males	7	100.0†	23.7†	8.6	85.7

*Significantly different from males (all P_1s $<$.005).
†Significantly different from control females (all P_1s $<$.05).
By courtesy of Dr. Robert W. Goy.

in feminization, but their action is inimical to a normal feminization.[9-11] Feminization therefore is attributed to an absence of androgen, not to the presence of an estrogen.

In our hands, demonstrations of these points on the long-gestation guinea pig has not been possible because 25- to 35-day fetuses did not survive our attempts at gonadectomy. The gap was filled by the use of the rat in which masculinization is not completed until 5 to 10 days after birth.[12] Dr. Kenneth Grady castrated male rats at 1, 5, 10, 20, 30, 50, and 90 days of age and, after they reached adulthood, tested their ability to display masculine behavior in response to testosterone, and their ability to display feminine behavior in response to estradiol benzoate and progesterone. Without exception the males castrated on day 1 and day 5 displayed relatively weak masculine behavior and a conspicuous feminine behavior, whereas those castrated day 10 and later displayed a reasonably normal masculine behavior and little or no feminine behavior (Tables 4 and 5).

Harvey Feder, a graduate student, has completed an experiment in which the behavior of male rats castrated the day of birth and given estradiol dipropionate was compared with that of males castrated and not treated further. The behavior of the latter group was more strongly feminine than was that of the subjects castrated and given the estrogen (Table 6). He stated in his article, written with Dr. Richard E.

TABLE 4.—Means of the Mean Copulatory Quotients of Castrated Male Rats Receiving Estradiol Benzoate and Progesterone.

Groups	N. Ss	3.3 μ	N. Ss	6.6 μg
Spayed females	9	.452 (97)*	7	.787 (100)
1 Day males	8	.301 (88)	7	.572 (100)
5 Day males	8	.253 (78)	6	.183 (96)
10 Day males	5	.000 (75)	6	.028 (88)
20 Day males	7	.003 (79)	7	.056 (89)
30 Day males	7	.000 (71)	7	.085 (89)
50 Day males	8	.000 (84)	7	.053 (96)
90 Day males	7	.000 (78)	7	.038 (100)

*Numbers in parentheses are the per cent of tests during which the experimental Ss were mounted.

By courtesy of Dr. Kenneth L. Grady.

TABLE 5.—Mean Rates of Mounting and Intromission in 30 Minute Tests Given Ss Castrated at Various Ages, Having Been Injected with Testosterone Propionate as Adults, and the Percentage of Ss in Each Group Ejaculating During at Least One Test

Group	N	Mean Mts./Min.	Mean Intro./Min.	% Ejaculating
Day 1	6	2.44	.01	0
Day 5	8	1.85	.18	25
Day 10	9	1.59	.59	88
Day 30	8	1.46	.53	88
Day 90	7	1.98	.76	86

By courtesy of Dr. Kenneth L. Grady.

Whalen,[13] that estrogen injected neonatally does not enhance the ability of the castrated male rat to display feminine behavior; on the contrary, such treatment interferes with the development of the ability to display feminine behavior. The finding that it is the absence of androgen during the period of neural differentiation rather than the presence of estrogen which induces female behavior completes the demonstration of the analogy between the role of the prenatal gonads in the differentiation of the genital tracts and the brain.

TABLE 6.—Female Behavior of Male Rats Castrated Neonatally (1A), Castrated and Given Estradiol Dipropionate Neonatally (2A), Given Estradiol Dipropionate Neonatally (3A), or Not Treated Neonatally (4A)

Group	N	Mean Latency to Lordosis Induced by Males (hrs.)	Tests Positive for Crouching, Ear wiggling (%)	$\frac{\text{Lordoses}}{\text{Mounts}} \times 100$ (%)
IA	8	6.1*	70.8*	40.0*
2A	9	11.2	0	6.0
3A	9	9.9	0	14.0
4A	8	9.6	8.3	6.6

*Significantly different from all other groups by Mann-Whitney U test ($p < .05$). Groups 2A, 3A, and 4A did not differ significantly from one another.

By courtesy of Dr. Harvey H. Feder.

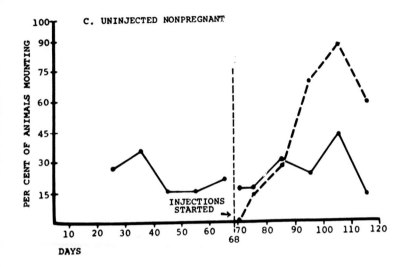

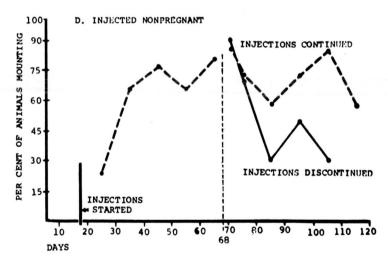

Fig. 1 (C and D).—C. Uninjected nonpregnant females. No injections given for the period corresponding to normal gestational interval (68 days). Following this period, injected and uninjected subgroups were formed. D. Injected nonpregnant females. Injections of testosterone for 68 days. After day 68, injections were continued for one subgroup and terminated for the other. In all cases the injection procedure consisted of 5 mg. testosterone propionate in oil on the 1st day and 1 mg. daily thereafter (by courtesy of Dr. Milton Diamond).

For several reasons we feel that the story that has unfolded in our laboratory is essentially correct and accounts for the sexual differentiation of the brain which heretofore has only been assumed to exist except for the role of the hypothalamus in gonadotrophin secretion.[14-18] For one thing, the results from every experiment have conformed to those we predicted on the basis of the model provided by the experimental embryologists. Furthermore, the statistically significant differences found in each of the experiments were calculated from the first data to be collected in that experiment.

Second, and more important, colleagues elsewhere—Geoffrey Harris at Oxford, Seymour Levine at Stanford, Richard Whalen at U.C.L.A., Arnold Gerall at Tulane—who have become interested in the role of neonatal gonadal hormones in the patterning of behavior in the rat and guinea pig, have obtained comparable results and are reaching the same conclusions. Today, moreover, evidence is being accumulated in our own laboratories and those of the colleagues mentioned to indicate that the early actions of the androgens influence the individual's functional characteristics beyond those that are purely sexual. There is increasing reason to believe that androgens participate in the establishment of those differences between the sexes in social behavior and play described for primates by Yerkes,[19] Hebb,[20] and Erikson.[21] Many of those traits which are sexually dimorphic for a given species appear to be influenced in the masculine direction by appropriate treatment with androgen and in the feminine direction by the absence of early steroid hormones. The range of such traits, which have already received at least beginning experimental attention, includes the social behavior of rhesus monkeys,[22] cyclic running behavior,[16] and emotional responses in rats,[23] metabolic rates and oxygen consumption in guinea pigs,[24] and micturitional behavior patterns in dogs.[25,26]

In a few sentences I will state the possible contribution of this work to psychiatric thought. What we have found in the guinea pig, and what we seem to be finding in the rhesus monkey, not only supports the Freudian view of a bisexuality at birth, but reveals something of the manner in which this differentiation is brought about. If we re-examine the incongruities called to our attention by Dr. John Money and the Hampsons approximately 10 years ago and which served as the basis for their conclusion that psychologic sex is undifferentiated at birth,[27-31] we find that these incongruities may not be incompatible with the hypothesis of a psychologic bisexuality at birth. Our analysis, which provides an alternative explanation for the incongruities they described, is presented in relatively recent summaries of our work.[22,32,33] The development of the male gender role by hermaphrodites with ambiguous or masculinized external genitals and with a female sex chromosome pattern may have been helped along by a concurrent masculinization of their nervous tissues. The female gender role of the cryptorchid hermaphrodites with a male sex chromosome pattern may have been acquired more easily because of the deficiency in testicular function. The gender role of the "females" born with gonadal dysgenesis and the XO or XY chromosome pattern seen in these Turner's syndrome patients may have been feminine, not because they were sexually neutral at birth and brought up as girls but rather for the reason that their brains were never masculinized.

The conclusions reached by John and Joan Hampson and by John Money were consistent with much that was a part of psychiatric thought when their analyses were made. The suggestions we are making do not imply criticism in the narrower sense, but rather that a re-examination be made against the background of the newer information investigators from anatomy, endocrinology, and psychology are providing.

REFERENCES

1. Young, W. C.: Patterning of sexual behavior. *In:* Roots of Behavior, E. L. Bliss, Ed. N. Y., Hoeber-Harper, 1962, 115-122.
2. Burns, R. K.: Hormones and the differentiation of sex. *In:* Survey of Biological Progress, Vol. I. New York, Academic Press, 1942, pp. 233-266.
3. Burns, R. K.: Role of hormones in the differentiation of sex. *In:* Sex and Internal Secretions. W. C. Young, Ed. Baltimore, Williams & Wilkins, 1961, pp. 76-158.
4. Diamond, M., and Young, W. C.: Differential responsiveness of pregnant and nonpregnant guinea pigs to the masculinizing action of testosterone propionate. Endocrinology 72:429-438, 1963.
5. Phoenix, C. H., Goy, R. W., Gerall, A. A., and Young, W. C.: Organizing action of prenatally administered testosterone propionate of the tissues mediating mating behavior in the female guinea pig. Endocrinology 65: 369-382, 1959.
6. Goy, R. W., Bridson, W. E., and Young, W. C.: Period of maximal susceptibility of the prenatal female guinea pig to masculinizing actions of testosterone propionate. J. Comp. Physiol. Psychol. 57:166-174, 1964.
7. Goy, R. W., Phoenix, C. H., and Young, W. C.: A critical period for the suppression of behavioral receptivity in adult female rats by early treatment with androgen. Anat. Rec. (Abstr.) 142:307, 1962.
8. Wells, L. J., Cavanaugh, M. W., and Maxwell, F. L.: Genital abnormalities in castrated fetal rats and their prevention by means of testosterone propionate. Anat. Rec. 118:109-133, 1954.

9. Wilson, J. G.: Reproductive capacity of adult female rats treated prepuberally with estrogenic hormone. Anat. Rec. 86:341-363, 1943.

10. Whalen, R. E., and Nadler, R. D.: Suppression of the development of female mating behavior by estrogen administered in infancy. Science 141:273-274, 1963.

11. Levine, S., and Mullins, R., Jr.: Estrogen administered neonatally affects adult sexual behavior in male and female rats. Science 144:185-187, 1964.

12. Grady, K. L., Phoenix, C. H., and Young, W. C.: Role of the developing rat testis in differentiation of the neural tissues mediating mating behavior. J. Comp. Physiol. Psychol. 59:176-182, 1965.

13. Feder, H. H., and Whalen, R. E.: Feminine behavior in neonatally castrated and estrogen-treated male rats. Science 147:306-307, 1965.

14. Everett, J. W., Sawyer, C. H., and Markee, J. E.: A neurogenic timing factor in control of the ovulatory discharge of luteinizing hormone in the cyclic rat. Endocrinology 44:234-250, 1949.

15. Harris, G. W.: Neural Control of the Pituitary Gland. London, Arnold, 1955.

16. Harris, G. W.: Sex hormones, brain development and brain function. Endocrinology 75:627-648, 1964.

17. Barraclough, C. A., and Gorski, R. A.: Evidence that the hypothalamus is responsible for androgen-induced sterility in the female rat. Endocrinology 68:68-79, 1961.

18. Gorski, R. A., and Barraclough, C. A.: Effects of low dosages of androgen on the differentiation of hypothalamic regulatory control of ovulation in the rat. Endocrinology 73:210-216, 1963.

19. Yerkes, R. M. Chimpanzees. A Laboratory Colony. New Haven, Conn., Yale University Press, 1943.

20. Hebb, D. O.: Behavioral differences between male and female chimpanzees. Bull. Canad. Psychol. Assoc. 6:56-58, 1946.

21. Erikson, E.: Sex differences in the play configuration of preadolescents. Amer. J. Orthopsychiat. 21:667-692, 1951.

22. Young, W. C., Goy, R. W., and Phoenix, C. H.: Hormones and sexual behavior: Broad relationships exist between the gonadal hormones and behavior. Science 143:212-218, 1964.

23. Gray, J. A., Levine, S., and Broadhurst, P. L.: Gonadal hormone injections in infancy and adult emotional behaviour. Anim. Behav. 13:33-45, 1965.

24. Goy, R. W., Mitchell, J. C., and Young, W. C.: Effect of testosterone propionate on O_2 consumption of female and female pseudo-hermaphroditic guinea pigs. Amer. Zool. (Abstr.) 2:525, 1962.

25. Berg, I. A.: Development of behavior: The micturition pattern in the dog. J. Exp. Psychol. 34:343-368, 1944.

26. Martins, T., and Valle, J. R.: Hormonal regulation of the micturition behavior of the dog. J. Comp. Physiol. Psychol. 41:301-311, 1948.

27. Money, J.: Hermaphroditism, gender and precocity in hyperadrenocorticism: Psychologic findings. Bull. Johns Hopkins Hosp. 96:253-264, 1955.

28. Money, J., Hampson, J. G., and Hampson, J. L.: Hermaphroditism: Recommendations concerning assignment of sex, change of sex, and psychologic management. Bull. Johns Hopkins Hosp. 97:284-300, 1955.

29. Money, J., Hampson, J. G., and Hampson, J. L.: An examination of some basic sexual concepts: The evidence of human hermaphroditism. Bull. Johns Hopkins Hosp. 97:301-319, 1955.
30. Money, J., Hampson, J. G., and Hampson, J. L.: Sexual incongruities and psychopathology: The evidence of human hermaphroditism. Bull. Johns Hopkins Hosp. 98:43-57, 1956.
31. Money, J., Hampson, J. G., and Hampson, J. L.: Imprinting and the establishment of gender role. A.M.A. Arch. Neurol. Psychiat. 77:333-336, 1957.
32. Young, W. C.: The hormones and behavior. In: Comparative Biochemistry, Vol. 7, M. Florkin and H. S. Mason, Eds. New York, Academic Press, 1940, pp. 203-251.
33. Young, W. C.: The organization of sexual behavior by hormonal action during the prenatal and larval periods in vertebrates. In: Sex and Behavior. F. A. Beach, Ed. New York, John Wiley & Sons, 1965, pp. 89-107.

9

ALCOHOL PREFERENCE IN MICE

by DAVID A. RODGERS, Ph.D.*

THE EXPRESSION "DRUNK AS A MOUSE" occurs in Old English literature from the time of Chaucer. However, systematic exploration of alcohol preference in mice as a possible analogue to human alcoholism is more recent. Kurt Richter's studies associated with his thesis that animals make wise choice of foodstuffs are a convenient point of departure for the current tradition, even though Richter was working with rats rather than with mice. He popularized the two-bottle, voluntary choice situation for assessing differential preference for alcohol,[24] and documented that self-selection of foodstuffs, including alcohol, is often appropriate to nutritional needs. Mardones and Onfray used Richter's preference technique to show that rats increased alcohol consumption when placed on a diet deficient in thermolabile elements of the vitamin B complex.[15] They thus demonstrated in this and subsequent work[14] (see also Brady and Westerfeld[3]) that increased alcohol consumption of rats is associated with a presumed nutritional deficiency. Soon after, Williams and co-workers began reporting their studies on effects of different foodstuffs on voluntary consumption of alcohol by rats and mice. These studies led to and grew out of their genetotrophic theory of alcoholism,[39] the theory that the appetite for alcohol is stimulated by nutritional deficiencies but that the alcohol does not correct the deficiency which stimulates the appetite for it. Indeed, by substituting for other nutritional substances, the alcohol may prevent the correction of such deficiency and may therefore perpetuate and even aggravate the alcohol craving.[39] These investigators emphasized the importance of genetic constitution in determining which nutritional factors might be relevant for a particular subject and what the effects of these would be on alcohol preference.

*The Cleveland Clinic Foundation, Cleveland, Ohio.

This paper was granted the Henry M. and Lillian Stratton Award for 1965.

The work was supported in large part by Public Health Research Grant MH-06139 from the National Institute of Mental Health and earlier by National Science Foundation Research Grants G 9936 and G 4574.

While Williams' concept of perverted appetite would tend to be directly contradictory to Richter's concept of wise choice of food-stuffs, a theoretical basis for reconciling these two points of view was provided by Westerfeld and Lawrow. Mardones and colleagues, Williams and colleagues, and Westerfeld and colleagues had all em-phasized the importance of the B vitamins in alcohol preference. Westerfeld and Lawrow[37] called specific attention to the fact that thiamin, vitamin B_1, was utilized less per unit calorie release when the initial food substance was alcohol than it was with sugar or fat, the alternative common sources of calories. Specifically, a given thiamin utilization yields 79 per cent more calories from alcohol than from glucose and 12 per cent more than from stearic acid. Thus, an animal deficient in thiamin would place less strain on thiamin reserves by consuming alcohol for calorie needs than by consuming fats or sugars. Richter and Barelare had already shown, for example, that thiamin-deficient rats would consume olive oil in preference to sugar,[25] a reversal of usual preference but one that conserves thiamin. While placing minimal demand on thiamin already present, alcohol as a food does not replenish thiamin supplies. Thus, the alcohol appetite presumably associated with thiamin deficiency would be perverse in Williams' sense of not correcting the deficiency that gave rise to the appetite. The studies already cited lent support to the validity of this hypothesis or a closely parallel one involving other vitamins or essential foodstuffs.

As alcohol clinics are aware, however, merely restoring good nutri-tional balance to the alcoholic unfortunately does not solve the problem of his alcoholism. While nutritional factors may be involved in the physiological damage that results from heavy alcohol use or in the terminal drinking of the alcoholic, there is little evidence that good nutrition alone protects one from heavy consumption of alcohol. More specific, or at least different, mechanisms would seem to be critical for the full explanation of the alcoholic syndrome. The critical problem appeared to be one of determining what mechanisms stimulate high alcohol intake under conditions of essentially normal nutrition. The most common theory was (and still is) that animals and/or people drink to reduce anxiety or the impact of stressful situations. Except for highly suggestive work by Diethelm and Fleetwood with humans[8] and by Clark and Polish with monkeys,[7] evidence for this hypothesis is not compelling.[31,36] Two characteristics of research in this area have complicated investigation. One is the inevitable problem of subject control and potential damage that limits work with humans, and the other is the physiological variability of the human as well as most subhuman subjects investigated.

The possibility of gaining genetic control over physiology that underlies alcohol preference had been demonstrated by Williams, Berry, and Beerstecher[39] in strain comparisons in mice as well as rats, by Mardones, Segovia, and Hederra[16] in selective breeding for high- and low-alcohol-preference strains of rats under conditions of nutritional deficiency, and by Reed[23] in comparisons of different strains of rats. In addition, Mirone[20-22] had used different strains of inbred mice in her studies of nutritional effects of alcohol consumption, her results suggesting the possibility of mouse strain differences in preference even though she did not measure this directly.

WORK PREVIOUSLY SUMMARIZED

In 1959, McClearn and I demonstrated clear and pronounced strain differences in alcohol preference of highly inbred groups of mice.[18] The primary data that I will report today concern attempts to identify precisely factors underlying these strain differences and phenomena associated with them. Our early joint work on this problem has been summarized elsewhere.[27] We found differences in alcohol preference under standard conditions to be under pronounced genetic control (e.g., McClearn and Rodgers[19]). First generation crosses showed alcohol preference intermediate between that of parent strains. Pups cross-fostered on mothers of other strains showed preference patterns consistent with the genetic rather than the foster line. A variety of environmental manipulations failed to obscure the strain differences in preference. In one analysis of sources of variance in alcohol preference, strain differences accounted for over 97 per cent of total variance, even though sex differences, litter effects, and the usual errors of bottle leakage and experimental procedure were additional sources of variance.[28] Segregation for alcohol preference was demonstrated in selective breeding from four-way cross animals derived from high- and low-preference parent strains. We thus were able to establish a highly consistent and reproducible relationship between genetically standardized physiology and alcohol consumption.

Figure 1 illustrates the range of stabilized preferences, measured under standard conditions, that can be found among different groups of inbred strains of mice. The data in Figure 1 provide further highly convincing evidence of the importance of genetic factors in alcohol preference of the mice. Note that all sublines of C57BL and the closely related sublines of C57BR, C57L, and C58 mice show high preference

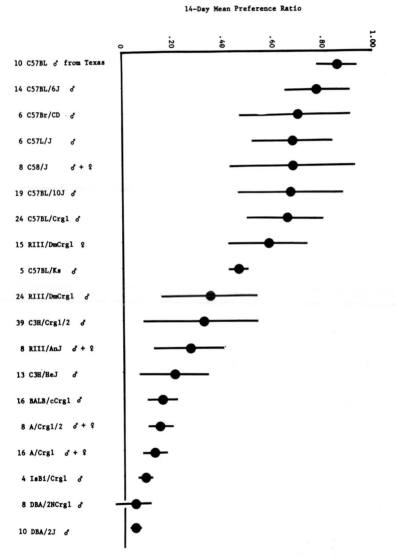

FIG. 1.—Ethanol preference of mouse sublines. (Limits are shown for one raw-score standard deviation.)

for alcohol. The C57BL, C57BR, and C58 strains separated in 1921, prior to close inbreeding of any of the lines.[4] The C57 sublines have been maintained on independent breeding schedules since the mid 1930's, some having separated earlier. Thus, the common base for alcohol preference is not a recent one. These data suggest that the number of genes involved in alcohol preference in these sublines is rather limited, such that subline divergence through selective segregation has not occurred. Our previous attempts to assess gene frequency have not led to usable estimates, however.[19] Fuller[9] has suggested an alternative method of measuring alcohol preference that might prove more satisfactory for estimation of gene frequency.

We identified a relationship between strain differences in alcohol preference and differences in amount of activity of liver alcohol dehydrogenase enzyme,[17,30,32] the primary factor determining initial rate of oxidation of alcohol in the system. Genetic control of this enzyme could account for the marked genetic effect in alcohol preference, since strain differences accounted for 92 per cent of the variance in enzyme activity as measured across several strains known to differ in preference for alcohol.[30] Increase in enzyme activity following prior alcohol ingestion has been demonstrated.[17,32] Thus, some increase in capacity to metabolize alcohol occurs as a result of experience with alcohol. While more animals must be studied to establish reliability, Trujillo, of Scripps Clinic and Research Foundation, found suggestively different Michaelis constants for alcohol dehydrogenase enzyme from the C57BL and DBA/2 strains, 2.9×10^{-4} and 4.1×10^{-4}, respectively. These data suggest the possibility that strain differences in enzyme activity are due to differences in nature of the enzyme rather than differences in amount.

Using the Lester and Greenberg technique[11] of comparing alcohol preference to preference for a sugar solution, we have demonstrated that alcohol preference of the mice is not marked as compared to preference for sweetened water. By adding sugar to the alcohol instead of the water, we have also demonstrated that aversion to alcohol of the low preference strains was not sufficient to overcome their preference for sugar water, since all strains drank moderately of an adequately sweetened alcohol solution.[29]

In brief summary of background data, then, it has been demonstrated that highly reliable differences exist in alcohol preference among different inbred strains of mouse, that these preference differences seem to be related to difference in alcohol dehydrogenase enzyme activity, and that the "craving" or "aversion" of the mice for alcohol is not great as compared to their preference for a sucrose solution. Subsequent data have further clarified some of the similarities and differences between alcohol consumption by the mice and alcohol consumption by the human "alcoholic." In material to follow, I shall primarily report data collected by Thiessen and me, often in association with other colleagues at Scripps Clinic and Research Foundation. We have especially focused on four apparently relevant areas: (1) effects of long-term voluntary alcohol ingestion on general health and behavior; (2) effects of liver damage on amount of alcohol consumed; (3) relationship between ability to metabolize alcohol and amount of alcohol consumed; and (4) effects of stress on amount of alcohol consumed.

Long-term Voluntary Ingestion

A brief consideration of what precisely is meant by "alcoholism" is appropriate at this point. Mere consumption of alcohol, even in large quantities, is not equivalent to alcoholism if it is not acccompanied by negative social or physiological consequences. Similarly,

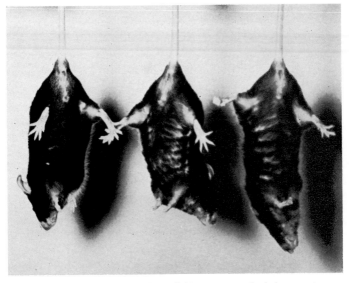

Fig. 2.—Effects of 1 year ingestion of 10 per cent alcohol on appearance of mice. (From left to right, animals are water control, voluntary ingestion, and forced ingestion.)

no characteristic tissue pathology can exclusively identify the presence of alcoholism, since all known pathologies can be induced by agents other than alcohol or by nutritional deficiencies in the absence of alcohol. Alcoholism, by conventional definition, is the development of a nonspecific physiological or sociological pathology that is aggravated by, and presumed to be the consequence of, a chronic history of alcohol ingestion.

The analogous condition in the mouse would be physiological or behavioral deficit, following prolonged voluntary alcohol ingestion, that would not have resulted had the animals not previously ingested the alcohol. We have maintained C57BL/Crgl animals on voluntary choice of 10 per cent alcohol or water for a one year period, matched against controls with no access to alcohol and other controls with access to only 10 per cent alcohol as a drinking fluid. Standard laboratory chow was concurrently available ad lib. After one year of such treatment, we can differentiate without exception all of the water controls from both the "forced alcohol" and the voluntary ingestion animals (Fig. 2). The sleek coat and generally healthy appearance of the animal on the left in Figure 2 are characteristic of the water controls, whereas the two remaining animals show the thin, nonglossy coat and wrinkled belly skin characteristic of the alcohol-ingestion groups. We thus conclude that we have demonstrated a close analogue to the condition of human alcoholism: specifically identifiable physiological changes of an undesirable sort, resulting from prolonged voluntary ingestion of alcohol by animals with alternative access to adequate diet, who continue their level of ingestion following the physiological changes. Much caution is still warranted in considering the parallel to human alcoholism to be complete, however. Autopsy and histological examination of organ morphology of two randomly selected animals of each group revealed no clearly demonstrable pathology. Specifically, liver cirrhosis, inflammatory cells, and fatty infiltration of the livers were not demonstrable. Examination was by Peter Ward, M.D., of the Division of Experimental Pathology, Scripp Clinic and Research Foundation. To date, there has been no mortality (except for sacrificed animals) in any of the groups, so that physiological changes apparently are not of a life-threatening nature at the one year stage. After two days away from alcohol, the voluntary ingestion group was not distinguishable from the water controls on activity in an open field arena or on rate of learning to escape from an electric grid. On these measures, at least, we therefore have not demonstrated changes in behavior as a result of prolonged voluntary alcohol ingestion. In some contrast to the water controls and voluntary-ingestion animals, the forced-alcohol group showed reduced activity in the open field arena but was comparable to the other two in rate of learning to escape from an electric grid.

Recent data on rate of alcohol metabolism in the mouse demonstrate a striking difference between mice and humans in the extent to which alcohol can be utilized to provide total daily caloric needs. An adult human can essentially meet his caloric needs through alcohol, whereas a mouse can satisfy only about 30 per cent of its caloric needs, and probably less than that in some strains, the rest presumably coming from additional consumption of a normal diet. Thus, the human is far more vulnerable to the nutrition-deficiency effects associated with high alcohol consumption than is the mouse. To enable the mouse to con-sume a larger proportion of daily caloric needs that are free of vitamins and other foodstuffs, we have provided groups of animals with long-term ad lib access to 10 per cent alcohol solutions containing 16 Gm. sucrose per 100 cc. of alcohol solution, thereby approximately doubling the vitamin- and protein-free calorie content of the solution. We have maintained other animals with ad lib access to water containing 16 Gm. refined sugar per 100 cc., and other animals with access to only a normal diet. Normal food and water have been available ad lib in addition to the sugar and alcohol solutions. On such schedules, animals consume large quantities of the sweetened water or sweetened alcohol and correspondingly reduce other food intake. These runs are still continuing for several strains. However, the following data from the C3H/HeJ strain are indicative of results to date. After six months of differential treatment, one out of ten animals on water had died, three out of ten on sweetened water had died, and five out of ten on sweetened alcohol had died. Causes of death were not determined but apparently were not due to any highly specific factor, since they occurred over a long and apparently random period of time. Three of the remaining animals of each group were subsequently sac-rificed, and liver sections were examined following hematoxylin and eosin staining. Histological examination was by Charles Cochrane, M.D., of the Division of Experimental Pathology, Scripps Clinic and Research Foundation. In one of the alcohol animals, mononuclear and polymorph inflammatory cells were found in the liver. In another, cytoplasmic clumping, characteristic of human alcoholics, was found. Similar changes were not observed in any of the control animals. However, in two of the three sugar water controls, abnormalities thought to be glycogen droplets were observed in the liver cells. These results appear to demonstrate the possibility of inducing pathological changes through voluntary ingestion of alcohol solutions or vitamin-free sugar solutions, and thus provide a close parallel to nutritional-deficiency effects associated with human alcoholism.*

The sugar-water and sweetened alcohol runs call somewhat into question the Lester and Greenberg conclusion that, since alcohol preference is not as high as preference for sugar water, the alcohol consumption of the mouse is not as "pathological" as is the consumption of the human alcoholic.[11] Specifically, our data suggest that the preference for sugar water is sufficiently pathological in itself to raise rate of mortality in a six month interval. This would seem to exceed considerably human preference for sugar solutions and to suggest the possibility that preference for alcohol could be at a pathological level even though it did not exceed this "pathological" preference for sucrose.

An incidental observation of possible importance in the long-term alcohol-ingestion groups concerns infestation with parasites. I have had parasitic infestations of mice in my colonies only twice (this is twice more than I intended to have them), and both started this past year, in cages on long-term alcohol consumption. The first was with lice and the second was with mites, so that the second infestation did not result from failure to eradicate the first parasite. Other animals in the colony, even those on adjacent shelves, did not show evidence of the parasites. We infer, but of course are not sure, that long-term alcohol ingestion markedly reduced resistance and contributed to the infestation, which occurred in spite of careful attention to colony hygiene.

LIVER DAMAGE AND ALCOHOL PREFERENCE

Sirnes's early work[33] on effect of liver damage on preference of rats, recently confirmed by Campos and co-workers[6] in conjunction with the Westerfeld-Lawrow hypothesis of the thiamin-sparing action of alcohol,[37] has suggested that liver damage may play a key role in high levels of alcohol consumption. We have induced liver damage in mice both by surgical removal of portions of the liver and by

---

*In more recent work, C57BL males have developed liver pathology suggestive of human alcoholism, following long-term access to sweetened alcohol. The pathology consisted of pronounced vacuolar changes in the middle chord cells of the liver and scattered foci of mixed inflammatory cells.[26]

periodic fuming with carbon tetrachloride for long periods of time. While these data are too complex to present in detail, our findings in general suggest that liver damage induced by these methods does not markedly increase alcohol consumption in the strains of mice we have tested. Thus, we do not confirm previous suggestions that high alcohol intake of animals results from liver damage. The fact that our normally high-consuming strains will abandon alcohol in favor of sugar solutions is further evidence that the alcohol is not consumed as a thiamin-sparing measure, since sucrose places more demand on the thiamin system but is preferred consistently over the alcohol solutions. Our data on liver damage do indicate that amount of alcohol consumed is not markedly decreased following our fuming or surgical procedures, even though metabolic capacity of the liver may be impaired to an unknown degree (although cf. Lieberman,[12] who found no decline in ability of cirrhotic humans to metabolize alcohol unless their liver disease was very advanced, to the point of jaundice, and Sirnes,[33] who found that liver damage had little effect on capacity of rats to metabolize alcohol). Our data with the mice would appear to parallel the human experience, in which heavy alcohol consumption normally occurs before observable liver damage, if at all, and frequently is not reduced following evidence of liver impairment.

In a more direct assessment of the Westerfeld-Lawrow hypothesis as it applies to mice, we have placed animals on thiamin-free diets while concurrently measuring alcohol preference. As with liver damage, amount of alcohol consumed does not markedly change, either up or down, over control levels, even when most other foodstuffs have been abandoned and the animal is manifesting severe deficiency. Figure 3 shows the effects of such thiamin deprivation on alcohol consumption of ten mice of the RIII/DmCrgl strain. The decline of consumption over time, shown by the control as well as experimental group, is apparently a normal characteristic of this subline.

RATE OF METABOLISM AND PREFERENCE

When drinking, the human alcoholic may consume each 24 hours almost as much alcohol as he can metabolize; and, in general, such heavy consumption is not characteristic of the nonalcoholic. Our estimate of probable maximum rate of metabolism of the mouse, using data from in vitro assay of liver alcohol dehydrogenase activity, ranged from a low corresponding to 1.9 cc. of 10 per cent (vol./vol.) alcohol solution per animal per 24 hours for A/Crgl/3 animals to a high of 4.2 cc. 10 per cent alcohol per animal per 24 hours for one group of C57BL/Crgl mice.[29]

More recent data on rate of metabolism of alcohol by the live mouse are consistent with results from these in vitro assays. Using Carworth Farms albino stock. Kinard[10] reported rates of metabolism ranging from 240 to 740 mg. alcohol per Kg. per hour for mice weighing between 19 and 25 Gm. each. This corresponds to approximately 1.6 to 4.8 cc. of 10 per cent (vol./vol.) alcohol per 22 Gm. mouse per 24 hours. Using breath-line apparatus and rate of CO_2 production following injection of radioactively labeled ethanol, Bennett and Hebert[2] found maximum rate of metabolism of the C57BL/Crgl and DBA/2Crgl mice to be comparable and to be approximately equivalent to 5.4 cc. 10 per cent alcohol per day per 25 Gm. mouse. Using the same technique, Schlesinger[32] found rate of metabolism of the C57BL/Crgl strain to be about 11 per cent above that of the DBA/2Crgl, equivalent to about 3.5 cc. of 10 per cent alcohol per day 25 Gm. mouse. In collaborative work with Dr. Eiduson, of UCLA, we have estimated maximum live-animal rate of metabolism of alcohol of the C57BL/10J strain, following certain simplifying assumptions, to be approximately 3.8 cc. 10 per cent alcohol per animal per day. In this same study, rate for C3H/HeJ mice was estimated to be 6.5 cc. 10 per cent alcohol per mouse per day; for BALB/cJ, to be 6.7 cc. 10 per cent alcohol per mouse per day; and for DBA/2J, to be 3.5 cc. 10 per cent

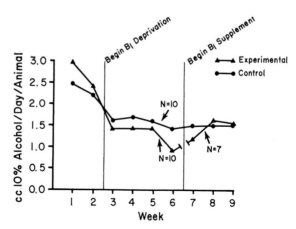

Fig. 3.—Effects of thiamin deprivation on alcohol consumption of RIII/DmCrgl mice.

alcohol per mouse per day. This assay involved intraperitoneal injection and subsequent serial sacrifice of animals, with blood alcohol level determined by enzymatic techniques. More recently, in serial blood sampling from the same animals, through the orbital sinus, following intravenous injection of the initial alcohol load, we have estimated rates of metabolism of the C57BL/Crgl, C3H/2Crgl, and DBA/2Crgl strains to be highly similar, corresponding to approximately 4.9 cc. 10 per cent alcohol per animal per day.

These estimates of rate of metabolism indicate that the C57BL strain normally voluntarily ingests alcohol at a rate close to its maximum capacity to metabolize it. Average daily voluntary ingestion of 10 per cent alcohol of one group of 8 male C57BL/Crgl, for example, was 3.4 cc. per day over a 14 day interval. Other groups of C57BL have shown even higher average consumption. Recall that the estimated maximum rates for this strain varied from 3.8 to 5.4 cc. This voluntary ingestion of a large percentage of total daily metabolic capacity of alcohol thus represents another close analogue to human alcoholic consumption.

If voluntary ingestion does indeed approach metabolic capacity, then this relationship would account for our previously reported correlation between such capacity and alcohol preference.[30] Factors that affect metabolic capacity should, then, affect alcohol preference. One circumstance in which general metabolic capacity increases is pregnancy and postpartum lactation of a female, during which food for the pups, as well as for the mother, is processed. Bade and Llanas, for example, report a 70 per cent increase in liver size of lactating mice.[1] When tested for alcohol consumption from premating to weaning of the pups, 10 C57BL/Crgl females increased alcohol intake from a premating level of 3.8 cc. of 10 per cent alcohol per mouse per day to an average of 7.6 cc. per day by days 10 to 14 postpartum.[38] These data thus strongly support the inference that metabolic capacity is a primary factor in amount of alcohol consumed by the C57BL strain.

Some anomalies still exist concerning the relationship between alcohol preference and metabolic capacity. When mice have voluntary access to 10 per cent alcohol containing 16 Gm. sucrose per 100 cc. of solution, in addition to normal food and water, preference for the sweetened alcohol solution is high. Average daily consumption has been measured to be 3.4 cc. for DBA/2J, 4.8 cc. for BALB/CJ, 6.7 cc. for RIII/J, and 8.1 cc. for C57BL/10J. Three factors are of interest in these data. First, the strain order of preference for the sweetened alcohol solution is identical to that for unsweetened alcohol solution, with the DBA's lowest, BALB's next, RIII's next, and C57's highest (see Fig. 1). Second, when sugar is added to the alcohol, all strains drink amounts approaching maximum capacity to metabolize alcohol. Third, the average consumption of the C57BL strain is higher than any estimated maximum rate of metabolism for this strain (see previous paragraph). This third anomaly clearly requires further exploration and clarification. Two alternatives are possible. First, a high sucrose load may facilitate alcohol metabolism and may therefore enable the C57BL to drink more sweetened than unsweetened alcohol. This possibility seems unlikely to account for as much apparent excess consumption as was observed. A second, more likely, possibility is that stress reduces rate of metabolism in the mouse, as reported by Lykke, Robertson, and Kosche.[13] Experimental determination of rate of metabolism almost invariably involves some procedures that are somewhat stressful to the animal, such as initial injection of the alcohol, and that might therefore lead to lower measured rates of metabolism than would exist in the unstressed animals ingesting alcohol voluntarily.

Supporting the inference that stress may reduce rate of metabolism of alcohol are data from our collaborative work with Eiduson, in which blood alcohol levels were measured 75, 105, and 135 minutes after intraperitoneal injection of a 10 per cent alcohol solution, blood samples being taken only once from each animal. In all four strains tested (DBA/2J, BALB/cJ, RIII/J, and C57BL/10J), rate of metabolism during the 75 to 105 minute interval was lower than rate during the 105 to 135 minute interval (Figure 4). The effect was most pronounced in the C57BL strain, previously shown to be the most vulnerable to stress effects.[34-36] A reasonable inference would be that the stress effects of the initial injection and absorption of the concentrated alcohol solution would exert more effect over the first time interval than the second and that the effect would be such as to reduce rate of metabolism. Additional data of a similar nature, from both our laboratory and the published literature (e.g., Kinard[10] and Schlesinger,[32] already cited), can be reinterpreted to support the conclusion of reduced rate of metabolism in the mouse as a result of stress. More definitive studies are needed, however.

STRESS AND ALCOHOL CONSUMPTION

As already mentioned, we find no compelling evidence in the published literature on the rodent to confirm the common assumption that differences in alcohol preference are associated with differences in susceptibility to stress effects (Rodgers and Thiessen;[31] Thiessen and Rodgers[36]). Calhoun, Pryor, and Schlesinger have recently rank-ordered six inbred mouse strains as to emotionality.[5] The rank-order correlation between their rating and our assessment of alcohol preference of the strains is 0.01. Clearly, our strain differences in alcohol preference cannot be explained on the basis of strain differences in emotionality.

The possibility still exists that within-strain variability in alcohol preference would reflect general level of stress. However, we have characteristically found stress to leave unaffected or to reduce (Rodgers and Thiessen[31]; Thiessen and Rodgers[36]) voluntary ingestion. The strain differences in this effect are pronounced, and the C57 appears to be the most vulnerable to stress effects on preference, just as it is the most vulnerable to stress effects in general. The stressors used have been population density and intraperitoneal injection of various materials. Specifically, population density sufficient to produce significant changes in adrenal size and in behavioral activation has failed to alter alcohol

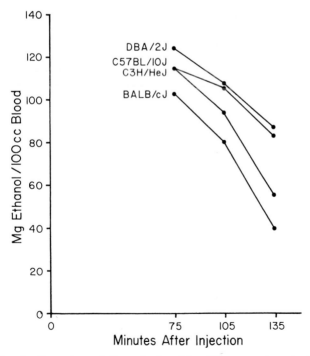

Fig. 4.—Rate of metabolism of ethanol by different strains of mice.

consumption of C3H/Crgl/2 mice. Grouping (Fig. 5) and intraperitoneal injections of such various materials as saline, progesterone,
alcohol, and 6-mercaptopurine have all reduced alcohol preference of
C57BL/Crgl mice and failed to alter significantly the preference of
RIII/DmCrgl mice. If our inference is correct that stress reduces
capacity to metabolize alcohol, then these data would be consistent with
our other evidence that metabolic capacity is an important determiner
of amount of alcohol consumed by the high-preference C57BL mice.
Our data to date provide no support for the hypothesis that stress
increases alcohol intake in any of the strains.

SUMMARY

In summary, a pronounced genetic component has been demonstrated
in alcohol preference of mice. Prolonged voluntary ingestion of alcohol has been shown to lead to obvious differences in gross appearance
of the animals, although specific organ pathology has not yet been
demonstrable. Metabolic capacity limits possible caloric yield from
alcohol to somewhat less than half of daily caloric need, such that
voluntary ingestion does not reduce alternative food intake by more

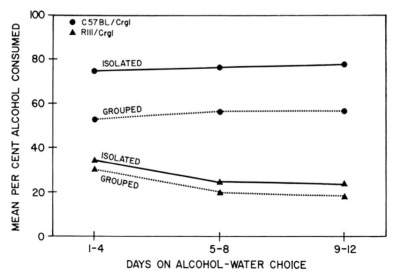

Fig. 5.—Effect of population density on alcohol preference of C57BL/Crgl and
RIII/DmCrgl mice (alcohol preference expressed as per cent of total fluid intake
consumed as 10 per cent alcohol).

than 30 per cent. When supplemented with adequate refined sugar, sweetened alcohol solutions will be ingested in sufficient quantity to reduce markedly other food intake. Present data indicate that voluntary consumption of such sweetened alcohol results in increased mortality rate over a six month interval and development of liver pathology suggestive of conditions associated with human alcoholism. Increased mortality also occurs when refined sugar not containing alcohol is provided. Voluntary ingestion of the high preference C57BL strain approaches metabolic capacity of the strain. Tentative evidence suggests that stress somewhat reduces capacity to metabolize alcohol. Much evidence suggests that metabolic capacity is an important factor in determining the alcohol consumption of mice. Strains showing highest preference for alcohol have correspondingly highest activity of alcohol dehydrogenase enzyme as assessed from in vitro liver studies. Amount of alcohol consumed increases during lactation, when metabolic capacity increases. Amount consumed under stress conditions remains constant or decreases. Liver damage from surgical section and from carbon tetrachloride fuming leaves relatively unaltered the amount of alcohol consumed. Thus, genetically influenced alcohol preference of the mice appears related to capacity to metabolize alcohol and appears capable in the high-preference strain of resulting in prolonged voluntary ingestion sufficient to produce deleterious physiological changes, possibly associated with nutritional deficiencies as a result of the unenriched calorie yield. The alcohol consumption is not a result of stress and is not stimulated or attenuated by moderately severe liver damage.

ACKNOWLEDGMENT

The author is indebted to many for assistance on the work reported here, most of which was done in collaboration with colleagues, who are all too briefly mentioned in the report.

REFERENCES

1. Bade, E. G., and Llanas, J. M. E.: Increase in weight of the liver and of the kidney during lactation. Influence of previous hepatectomy. Acta Physiol. Lat. Amer. 13:193-194, 1963.
2. Bennett, E. L., and Hebert, M. Investigation of possible biochemical differences correlated with ethanol preferences in mice. Univ. Calif. Rad. Lab. Quart. Rep. No. 9208, April, 1960.
3. Brady, R. A., and Westerfeld, W. W.: The effect of B-complex vitamins on the voluntary consumption of alcohol by rats. Quart. J. Stud. Alcohol 7:499-505, 1947.

4. Burdette, W. J. (Ed.): Methodology in Mammalian Genetics. San Francisco, Holden-Day, 1963.
5. Calhoun, W. H., Pryor, G. T., and Schlesinger, K.: Brain serotonin and emotionality in mice. Amer. Psychol. (Abstr.) 19:498, 1964.
6. Campos, I., Solodkowska, W., Muñoz, E. Segovia-Riquelme, N., Cambrano, J., and Mardones, J.: Ethanol metabolism in rats with experimental liver cirrhosis. I. Rate of combustion of labeled ethanol and rate of decrease of blood ethanol level. Quart. J. Stud. Alcohol 25:417-422, 423-426, 1964.
7. Clark, R., and Polish, E.: Avoidance conditioning and alcohol consumption in rhesus monkeys. Science 132:223-224, 1960.
8. Diethelm, O. (Ed.): Etiology of Chronic Alcoholism. Springfield, Ill., Charles C Thomas, 1955.
9. Fuller, J. L.: Measurement of alcohol preference in genetic experiments. J. Comp. Physiol. Psychol. 57:85-88, 1964.
10. Kinard, R. W.: Changes in the rate of metabolism following administration of ethanol in the mouse. Nature (London) 200:852-854, 1963.
11. Lester, D., and Greenberg, L. A.: Nutrition and the etiology of alcoholism. The effect of sucrose, fat, and saccharin on the self-selection of alcohol by rats. Quart. J. Stud. Alcohol 13:553-560, 1952.
12. Liberman, F. L.: The effect of liver disease on the rate of ethanol metabolism in man. Gastroenterology 44:261-266, 1963.
13. Lykke, A. W. J., Robertson, J. S., and Kosche, E. R.: The effect of traumatic shock on experimental blood ethyl alcohol levels in mice. Aust. J. Exper. Biol. Med. Sci. 41:275-280, 1963.
14. Mardones, R. J.: On the relationship between deficincy of B vitamins and alcohol intake in rats. Quart. J. Stud. Alcohol. 12:563-575, 1951.
15. Mardones, R. J., and Onfray, B. E.: Influencia de una substancia de la levadura (elemento del complejo vitamínico B) sobre el consumo de alcohol en ratas en experimentos de antoselección. Rev. Chile Hig. Med. Priv. 4:293-297, 1942.
16. Mardones, R. J., Segovia, M. N., and Hederra, D. A.: Heredity of experimental alcohol preference in rats: II. Coefficient of heredity. Quart. J. Stud. Alcohol 14:1-2, 1953.
17. McClearn, G. E., Bennett, E. L., Hebert, M., Kakihana, R., and Schlesinger, K.: Alcohol dehydrogenase activity and previous ethanol consumption in mice. Nature (London) 203:793-794, 1964.
18. McClearn, G. E., and Rodgers, D. A.: Differences in alcohol preference among inbred strains of mice. Quart. J. Stud. Alcohol 20:691-695, 1959.
19. McClearn, G. E., and Rodgers, D. A.: Genetic factors in alcohol preference of laboratory mice. J. Comp. Physiol. Psychol. 54:116-119, 1961.
20. Mirone, L.: The effect of ethyl alcohol on growth, fecundity, and voluntary consumption of alcohol by mice. Quart. J. Stud. Alcohol 13:365-369, 1952.
21. Mirone, L.: Dietary deficiency in mice in relation to voluntary alcohol consumption. Quart. J. Stud. Alcohol 18:552-560, 1957.
22. Mirone, L.: The effect of ethyl alcohol on growth and voluntary consumption of alcohol by successive generations of mice. Quart. J. Stud. Alcohol 19:388-393, 1958.

23. Reed, J. G.: A study of the alcoholic consumption and amino acid excretion patterns of rats of different inbred strains. Univ. Texas Publ. No. 5109: 144-149, 1951.

24. Richter, C. P.: Alcohol as food. Quart. J. Stud. Alcohol. 1:650-662. 1941.

25. Richter, C. P., and Barelare, B.: Further observations on the carbohydrate, fat, and protein appetite of Vitamin B deficient rats. Amer. J. Physiol. 127: 199-210, 1939.

26. Rodgers, D. A.: Factors underlying differences in alcohol preference among inbred strains of mice. Psychosom. Med. 28:498-513, 1966.

27. Rodgers, D. A., and McClearn, G. E.: Alcohol preference of mice. In: Roots of Behavior. Bliss, E. L., Ed. New York, Hoeber, 1962.

28. Rodgers, D. A., and McClearn, G. E.: Mouse strain differences in preference for various concentrations of alcohol. Quart. J. Stud. Alcohol. 23:26-33, 1962.

29. Rodgers, D. A., and McClearn, G. E.: Sucrose versus ethanol appetite in inbred strains of mice. Quart. J. Stud. Alcohol 25:26-35, 1964.

30. Rodgers, D. A., McClearn, G. E., Bennett, E. L., and Hebert, M.: Alcohol preference as a function of its caloric utility in mice. J. Comp. Physiol. Psychol. 56:666-672, 1963.

31. Rodgers, D. A., and Thiessen, D. D.: Effects of population density on adrenal size, behavioral arousal, and alcohol preference of inbred mice. Quart. J. Stud. Alcohol 25:240-247, 1964.

32. Schlesinger, K.: Genetic and biochemical determinants of alcohol preference and alcohol metabolism in mice. Ann Arbor, Mich., Univ. Microfilms, 1964.

33. Sirnes, T. B.: Voluntary consumption of alcohol in rats with cirrhosis of the liver: a preliminary report. Quart. J. Stud. Alcohol 14:3-18, 1953.

34. Thiessen, D. D.: Population density, mouse genotype and endocrine function in behavior. J. Comp. Physiol. Psychol. 57:412-416, 1964.

35. Thiessen, D. D., and Nealey, V. G.: Adrenocortical activity, stress response and behavioral reactivity of five inbred mouse strains. Endocrinology 71: 267-270, 1962.

36. Thiessen, D. D., and Rodgers, D. A.: Alcohol injection, grouping, and voluntary alcohol consumption of inbred strains of mice. Quart. J. Stud. Alcohol 26:378-383, 1965.

37. Westerfeld, W. W., and Lawrow, J.: The effect of caloric restriction and thiamin deficiency on the voluntary consumption of alcohol by rats. Quart. J. Stud. Alcohol 14:378-384, 1953.

38. Whitworth, N., Thiessen, D. D., and Rodgers, D. A.: Reproductive variables in alcohol consumption of the C57BL/Crgl female mouse. Amer. Psychol. (Abstr.) 19:504, 1964.

39. Williams, R. J., Berry, L. J., and Beerstecher, E., Jr.: Biochemical individuality. III. Genetotrophic factors in the etiology of alcoholism. Arch. Biochem. 23:275-290, 1949.

DISCUSSION

MURRAY GLUSMAN, M.D.*

In opening the discussion of the papers presented this morning I would like to direct my remarks chiefly to the papers presented by Drs. Young and Rodgers.

In a paper Dr. Young published in *Science* in January, 1964, he noted that "during a lull at Brown University, Drs. Young, Hugh Myers and Edward Dempsey, while waiting for what turned out to be the disapproval of an application for a small amount of money for work on the function of the epididymis, fell into a discussion of the abrupt and dramatic change that occurs in the behavior of the female guinea pig when she comes into heat. They wondered whether this change is associated with any structural change in the ovaries. Continuous day and night observation of the laboratory animals was rewarded by the information Young and his co-workers were seeking. The beginning of heat was found to coincide closely with the beginning of the preovulatory growth phase of the Graafian follicle." Young commented that the three investigators had stumbled on the only spontaneously occuring macroscopic structural change associated with the alteration of a behavioral state in a mammal.

As far as I can determine, Young's discussion with Myers and Dempsey occurred approximately 30 years ago and certainly was one of the most productive bull sessions about sex on record, because since then Dr. Young has been working day and night in his laboratory, producing a highly important, systematic series of studies elucidating the relationship between gonadal hormones and sexual behavior.

His most recent work—which he summarized today—deals with some remarkably interesting and important findings which support a very exciting concept which endocrinologists have been moving toward gradually: namely, that part or parts of the c.n.s. may be masculine or feminine depending on the sex of the individual. Young's work not only supports this view but provides some information concerning the way in which masculinity or femininity is conferred on the nervous system. Utilizing as his model the work of experimental

---

*Columbia University, College of Physicians and Surgeons, New York, N.Y.

embryologists, which indicated that fetal gondal hormones play a crucial role in the anatomical differentiation of the genital tract, he has found an analogous effect of prenatal gonadal hormones on differentiation of masculine and feminine patterns of mating behavior and other forms of behavior. The behavioral differentiation is attributed to an organizing action of androgen on the portions of the brain and c.n.s. which are destined to mediate sexual behavior. Briefly, it is known that when androgen is present in the fetus, the genital tract of genotypic males and genotypic females is masculinized; when androgen is absent, genital tract development tends to be of the female type. Dr. Young has observed analogous effects on behavior; when androgen is present in the fetus, genotypic males and females display masculinized behavior, attributed to masculinization of the c.n.s. When androgens are absent, genotypic males and females display feminine behavior, attributed to feminization of the c.n.s. Feminization is attributed to an absence of androgen and not to the presence of estrogen.

The maximal susceptibility of the brain to the organizing action of androgen is 25 to 35 days postconception in the guinea pig, and therefore in the prenatal period; 21 to 28 days postconception in the rat, and therefore in the neonatal period; and 40 to 50 days postconception in the monkey, in the prenatal period.

Dr. Young's findings are supported by Geoffrey Harris' work. Harris also believes that the secretions of fetal and immature gonads influence sexual differentiation of the c.n.s., as manifested by the type of control the c.n.s. exerts over (1) the pattern of secretion of gonadotrophic hormone of the anterior pituitary, whether cyclic, as in the female, or acyclic, as in the male; and (2) the pattern of sexual behavior displayed by the individual. Harris says that the evidence indicates that both male and female rats are born with an undifferentiated nervous system capable of regulating the release of gonadotrophic hormone in a cyclic female fashion, and that this is normally differentiated in the male by the action of testosterone from the testes. The administration of testosterone to the new-born female results in a male pattern of gonadotrophic release, absence of female behavior patterns, and enhancement of masculine behavior. Administration of estrogen to the new-born male produces a female behavior pattern (cyclical) of gonadotrophic release and often loss of all sexual behavior.

The implications of this work are of course very great. Dr. Young suggests that at birth the organism is bisexual and that sexuality is then differentiated. I wonder if it wouldn't be more correct, in view of the profound differentiating and organizing effects of androgen, to view the organism as basically feminine and then differentiated by androgen. For the neurologist and the student of brain function there is the important indication that the transient application of an endocrine to the c.n.s. can produce a profound and permanent alteration in complex behavior patterns. The question of course arises whether other endocrines—e.g., thyroid and other chemicals—applied in the fetal or neonatal period can similarly produce durable behavioral alterations. For the psychiatrist the implications for psychosexual development, both normal and pathologically distorted, are highly important. Hopefully, new possibilities will be opened for understanding the genesis of homosexuality and psychosexual aberrations.

Dr. Rodgers has presented a very interesting and systematic study of alcohol preference in mice, seeking in this phenomenon a possible analogue with human alcoholism. I believe he has drawn attention to a number of interesting similarities between alcohol preference in mice and alcoholism in humans, but important differences do remain. Thus he has noted that the preference of mice for alcohol is not as great as the preference for a sucrose solution. In humans it is precisely of the converse that we have a major problem with alcoholism: The human prefers the rum in his drink to the "coke"; if he were like the mouse and preferred the "coke" we would have few problems with alocholism.

Dr. Rodgers in his definition of alcoholism noted that "alcoholism, by conventional definition, is the development of a nonspecific physiological or sociological pathology that is aggravated by and presumed to be the consequence of a chronic history of alcohol ingestion." This of course is true for the consequences of alcoholism. It seems to me, however, that alcoholism in man involves not just the consequences of long-term voluntary ingestion but the craving which is at the basis of this long-term ingestion. I would like to ask Dr. Rodgers if he has directed any of his investigations at measuring the strength of the drive in his mice for alcohol—e.g., will food and water-satiated mice work for, or press a lever for, an alcohol reward? Will such activity be greater for alcohol than for example for a brain-stimulus reward? Will food- and water-satiated mice cross an electrified grid for an alcohol reward? Certainly we know that in the human alcoholic the drive for alcohol is so overwhelming as to override all other conventional rewards—money, family, job, etc.

10

PSYCHOPATHOLOGY OF PERIODIC BEHAVIOR IN ANIMALS AND MAN

by CURT P. RICHTER, M.D.*

C LAUDE BERNARD[1] AND WALTER CANNON[2] described many of the
devices that maintain the various conditions of the body at fixed
levels—in spite of great changes in the external environment. Bernard
spoke of the "fixity of the internal environment"; Cannon of "homeostasis." These concepts have come to play an all-important part in our
thinking about the operations of almost every organ of the body and
also about factors underlying behavior of the whole organism.

I bring this up because in studies made during the past 44 years
on biological clocks in animals and man, a number of timing devices
or clocks were found that exert definite control over functions of
organs and behavior of the whole organism in the complete absence
of any homeostatic controls. These clocks operate free of any feedback
from organs or from autonomic, emotional and mental functions that
they regulate.

To illustrate the functioning of such biological clocks, I shall offer
only one example—the 24 hour clock—which has been found by
various workers—biologists, physiologists, and zoologists—in mammals, birds, insects and plants, and even in unicellular organisms.
This clock is one of the most remarkable of all biological phenomena;
and, if our interpretations are correct, it may play as important a part
as homeostatic mechanisms in the lives of animals and man.

To make clear the nature of this clock and its relation to the rest
of the organism it will be necessary to present in some detail records
of our experiments—carried out intensively over the past ten years
almost exclusively on the common laboratory or Norway rat.

*Johns Hopkins Medical School, Baltimore, Md.

The Samuel W. Hamilton Memorial Award Lecture, presented at the Fifty-fifth
Annual Meeting of the American Psychopathological Association, February, 1965.

These studies were supported by the National Science Foundation (1956 to
present) and the National Institutes of Health (1953 to present) and the Commonwealth Foundation.

FIG. 1.—Photograph showing five stands of activity cages (16 to each stand).

Results of these studies were reported in part in my Salmon Lecture in Psychiatry in 1959* and in a paper read before the 2nd International Congress of Endocrinology in London in 1964[4]; they will be reported in full in a monograph (on the "24-Hour Clock in Rats and Man") that should appear in 1966.

I shall begin with a brief summary of our observations on the 24 hour clock in rats, and then sketch in how I believe this clock operates in man.

Observations on the 24 Hour Clock of Rats

The rat lends itself very well to studies on periodic phenomena because of its high amount of spontaneous activity and the ease with which this activity can be recorded and measured. This is important since spontaneous gross bodily activity is one of the best tools for the study of functioning of biological clocks. Furthermore, the rat is a stable animal whose general physiology closely resembles that of man.

Figure 1 shows a view of five stands of cages used in recording spontaneous activity of the rat. Each stand holds 16 individual cages,

*These lectures have been published under the title "Biological Clocks in Medicine and Psychiatry."[3]

each one consisting of a small living compartment with a nonspillable food cup, a graduated inverted water bottle, and a revolving drum. A cyclometer attached to the front end of the axle of the drum records the total number of revolutions for 24 hours; an eccentric hub on the rear end of the axle opens and closes a microswitch and so registers each revolution on an operation recorder in another room. The 20 pens on each of four recorders register times of activity of 80 rats. The paper moves at a rate of 18 inches per 24 hours. A specially designed machine cuts each 24 hour length of paper into 20 strips, one for each rat. The strips for each animal are successively mounted on large sheets of cardboard between equally and constantly spaced lines by means of mounting tissue and a hot tacking iron. Each cardboard shows 24 hour records for one rat—from 12 noon to 12 noon for 93 days.

Records are also taken daily of food intake, water intake, and vaginal smears, and weekly of body weight. These records are plotted on individual charts separate from those showing activity-distribution. For these experiments 626 domesticated and 109 wild rats (trapped in Baltimore) were used—a number of which were followed with daily records for 3 years or more.

Manifestations of the Clock

Figure 2 shows activity-distribution records of three normal rats—

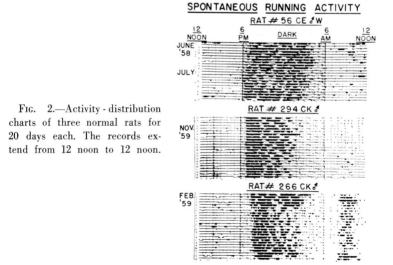

FIG. 2.—Activity - distribution charts of three normal rats for 20 days each. The records extend from 12 noon to 12 noon.

each for a period of 20 days. The records extend from 12 noon to 12 noon; the laboratory was completely dark from 6 p.m. to 6 a.m. It was illuminated with fluorescent bulbs from 6 a.m. to 6 p.m. The Norway rat is "dark"-active—most of its activity occurs during the 12 hours of darkness. Furthermore each rat has just one main activity period each 24 hours, the onsets of which are of great importance for observations on this 24 hour clock. For the first rat (56CE ♀) the onsets occurred shortly after 6 p.m.—just at the start of the dark period; for the second rat (294CK ♀) at 6:45 p.m.; for the third rat (266CK ♀) near 7:30 p.m. Noteworthy is the constancy of the times of onsets for each rat at fixed intervals after the start of the dark period at 6 p.m. Here we have the first suggestion of the presence of a timing device.

Our first step was to determine whether the times of onsets in any way are determined by periodically recurring external stimuli—sounds, odors, or light. Deafening had no effect on the times of onsets, nor did removal of the olfactory bulbs; but blinding did have a very definite effect. Blinding—by section of the optic nerves or enucleation— has very little or no effect on total amount of running activity, food or water intake. Figure 3 shows the effects of blinding produced on the activity-distribution patterns of three rats. Blinding (EE) had little or no effect on the times of onsets of activity of the first rat (160 CG ♀). Before blinding, onsets occurred near 7 p.m.; afterwards, shortly after darkening of the room at 6 p.m. The onsets of activity of the second rat (299CF ♀) occurred slightly earlier each day for 20 days following blinding (EE)—then suddenly 24 minutes earlier and with great constancy; the onsets for the third rat (301CF ♀) occurred 21 minutes later each day, also with great accuracy. With only a few exceptions, in hundreds of blinded rats, the times of onsets of activity came either definitely earlier or later each day—and by quite different amounts for each individual rat. Of 50 blinded rats in the laboratory at any one time, no two showed the same rate of onsets of activity. The wide and complete independence of times of onsets of activity would completely rule out climatic and cosmic influences and demonstrate that we are dealing here with an inherent biological clock that under normal conditions measures time in units of 24 hours—but which, after blinding of the animal, may measure time in units up to 40 minutes shorter or longer than 24 hours. In the normal rat this clock is controlled exclusively by light.

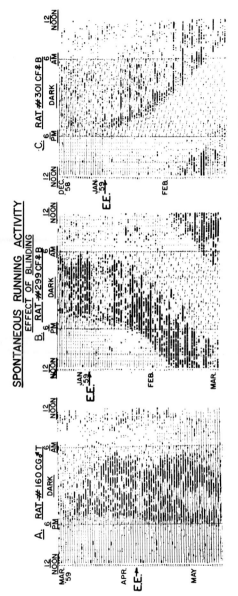

Fig. 3.—Activity-distribution charts of three rats before and after blinding (EE).

Accuracy and Constancy of the Clock

Accuracy of this clock is illustrated in Figure 4, which shows a record of a wild rat trapped in Baltimore. The times of onset of activity of this rat, which had been blinded several weeks before, came 26 minutes earlier each day with only a minute or two deviation. Noteworthy is the great accuracy of the clock—in view of the fact that this animal was a fierce, wild, suspicious rat, ever on the alert— and was subjected to the many disturbances involved in daily recordtaking, cleaning of cages, weighing of rats and food, talking of laboratory personnel and visitors, etc.

Before presenting records to illustrate constancy of the clock, methods of reading of long-term records should be explained. We saw in Figures 3 and 4 that as the onsets of activity came either earlier or later each day they ultimately reached one edge or the other of the record—that is, 12 o'clock noon. Where do the onsets go from there? The long-term record of the blinded rat (382CM ♀) in Figure 5 provides an answer to this question. At the far right 'A' shows the record of this rat from May 1 to June 3. This rat was blinded two months before the start of this record. On May 1 the onset of the main activity period occurred at approximately 10 a.m. Each day thereafter onsets occurred 38 minutes earlier; by the 15th of the month they occurred at midnight, and by June 3 at 12 noon—that is, the onsets had reached the left margin of the record. Where they go from there is seen in "B" and "C." "B" starts with the record for the following day—June 4—12 noon. It can be seen that as the onsets leave the left margin of the record in "A" they appear at the right margin of the record in "B" from which they can be followed throughout the next 32 days until they again reach the left margin on July 8. "C" shows the continuation of record to August 12. The times of onsets of activity form almost a perfectly straight line. This same record is shown in "D" in which "A," "B" and "C" are mounted one under

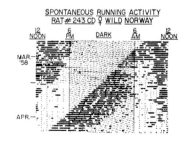

SPONTANEOUS RUNNING ACTIVITY
RAT # 243 CD ♀ WILD NORWAY

Fɪɢ. 4.—Activity-distribution chart of a blinded (several weeks before start of record) wild rat (trapped in an alley in Baltimore).

Fig. 5.—Activity-distribution chart for a blinded rat, illustrating constancy of clock over a 3½ month period.

the other, the form in which all of our records are kept for convenience and to save space. As onsets of activity leave the left margin of the chart they reappear at the right margin. Thus, these parallel lines actually represent a straight line—an uninterrupted progression in time.

Figure 6 shows a fairly typical record in which the clock manifests itself not only in times of onset of activity but in times of cessation of activity 12 hours later. This means that the clock may measure not only 24 hour but 12 hour periods as well.

Manifestation of the Clock in Blinded Rodents and Monkeys

For purposes of comparison, parallel records were taken—under the same conditions—of a few other rodents and monkeys having different biological characteristics. Some were hibernators, others non-hibernators; some "dark"—active, others "light"-active (desert rats, hamsters, chipmunks, ground squirrels, gerbils, and squirrel monkeys). Of special interest here are observations on ground squirrels. Onsets of activity of some of these animals occurred not just minutes later each day but hours later, as many as 12 to 24 hours, making a total period of 36 to 48 hours. Figure 7 shows the record of one of these animals. It was observed for over 18 months. The slopes of the times of onsets are almost too flat to measure. Strumwasser,[5] measuring brain temperature of hibernating ground squirrels, found quite regular cycles with periods of 48 hours. All this evidence indicates that under certain conditions the 24 hour clock may measure time not in units of 24 hours but in longer units of 30 to 48 hours or even longer.

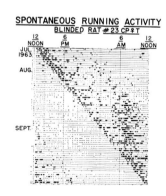

SPONTANEOUS RUNNING ACTIVITY
BLINDED RAT # 23 CP♀T

Fig. 6.—Activity-distribution chart of a blinded rat, showing onsets and terminations of daily periods of activity.

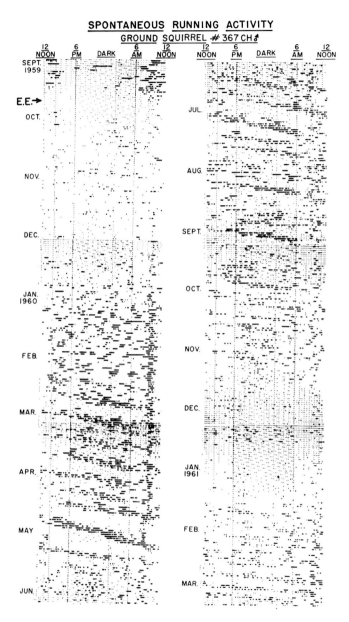

FIG. 7.—Activity-distribution chart of ground squirrel before and after blinding (EE). This animal was observed for over 18 months.

Independence of the Clock of Internal Disturbances

Next we decided to determine to what extent the clock can be influenced by internal stimuli or changes. In brief, we wanted to learn how this clock can be speeded up, slowed down, reset, or stopped. To do this, we used only blinded rats whose times of onset of activity were occurring with regularity at definite intervals either earlier or later each day, as may be seen in Figure 8. The rat (242CD ♀) "A" had been running 18 minutes earlier each day with great regularity for several weeks. A six day period of total starvation made the rat inactive for some days, but that it had no effect on the clock is shown by the fact that resumption of activity occurred at the predicted time. Likewise, a 67 hour period of water deprivation had no effect on the clock of the other rat "B" (183CN ♀).

The following three tables list forms of interference that had no effect at all on the clock. Table 1 lists general metabolic interferences that had no effect: starvation—4 to 7 days; dehydration— 67 hours;

TABLE 1.—General Metabolic

Methods	Duration of Treatment	No. of Rats
1. Starvation	4-7 days	21
2. Water Deprivation	67 hours	4
3. Dietary Restriction	14-85 days	4
4. Body Irradiation	500r total	3
5. Hypothermia	Heart stopped 0-61 min.	25

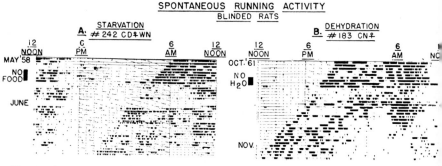

Fig. 8.—Activity-distribution chart showing (A) lack of effect of 6 days of total starvation (B) of 67 hours of dehydration on the clock.

dietary restriction to dextrose and B_1—14 to 85 days; total body irradiation and hypothermia. It indicates number of rats used for each experiment.

Table 2 lists forms of interference (as nearly lethal as possible) with the central nervous system that likewise were without effect: anoxia; convulsions produced by electroshock or caffeine injections

TABLE 2.—Neurological Interferences That Had No Effect on Clock

Method		No. of Rats
1. Anoxia		8
2. Convulsions	a. Electroshock	27
	b. Caffeine	14
3. Tranquilization	Chlorpromazine	6
4. Poisoning	LSD in food—61 days	6
5. Anesthesia	CO_2	5
	Nitrous Oxide	7
6. Alcohol intoxication		14
7. Sedation and	a. Pentobarbital	11
sleep	b. Phenobarbital	5
	c. Barbital	9
8. Acute stress	a. Forced swimming	13
	b. Restraint	5
	c. Electroshock	2

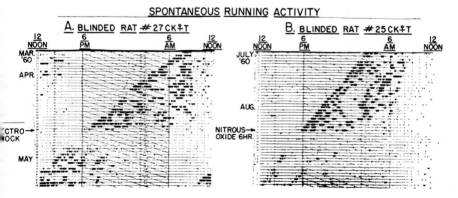

Fig. 9.—Activity-distribution chart showing lack of effect on the clock of (A) convulsions produced by electroshock and (B) of narcosis produced by inhalation of nitrous oxide.

into the fourth ventricle; tranquilization with chlorpromazine; poisoning with LSD; anesthesia produced by inhalation of carbon dioxide or nitrous oxide; alcohol intoxication—with doses large enough to produce stupor lasting for 16 to 30 hours; long-lasting sedation or deep sleep—16 to 40 hours—produced by pentobarbital, phenobarbital, or barbital; acute stress produced by forced swimming (up to 42 hours), restraint, or electric shocks. Figure 9 gives examples from two of the experiments: severe convulsions produced by electroshock—"A" and prolonged narcosis produced by inhalation of nitrous oxide—"B." Convulsions and narcosis made the rats totally inactive for six to ten days but that they had no effect on the clock is seen from the fact that resumption of activity in each instance occurred at the predicted time. Table 3 summarizes experiments on interferences with the endocrine glands. None of these procedures had any effect on the clock; gonadectomy—mating, pregnancy, and lactation; adrenalectomy; total hypophysectomy; posterior lobectomy; pinealectomy; pancreatectomy; or feeding of high amounts of thyroid powder, enough to produce severe symptoms of hyperthyroidism; or conditions of hypothyroidism produced by feeding high amounts of antithyroid drugs such as thiourea, thiouracil and propylthiouracil, or sulfamerazine; or great reduction in thyroid activity produced by chemical removal through treatment with radioiodine—I.[131]

The results of these various experiments demonstrate the complete independence of the clock of influences from the endocrine glands.

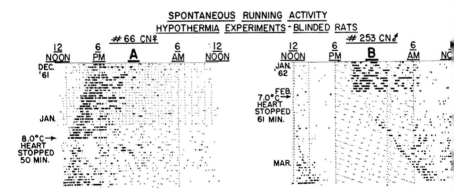

Fig. 10.—Activity-distribution chart showing effects of hypothermia on the clock of blinded rats.

Effects on Clock of Hypothermia and Prolonged Water Restriction

So far, prolonged hypothermia—stopping the heart for an hour or more—or restriction of water intake to very small amounts over long periods are the only two forms of interference that have had an effect on the clock—either slowing it down or resetting it—as may be seen in Figure 10. In the first rat—"A"—stopping the heart for 50 minutes reset the clock by about that amount; in the second rat—"B"—stopping the heart for 61 minutes resulted in a sharp change in phase. Parallel experiments on hamsters, which survive much longer periods of hypothermia, showed that the heart may be stopped for four hours or more without altering the functioning of the clock, but that stopping the heart from one to four hours in some instances did have a definite effect—stopping and resetting the clock or slowing it down as may be seen in Figure 11. In the first hamster—"A"—stopping the heart for 4 hours and 9 minutes had no effect on the clock; in the second— "B"—stopping the heart for 3 hours and 16 minutes did not have any immediate effect. Figure 12 shows that stopping the heart of a hamster—"A"—for 2 hours and 23 minutes and reducing body temperature to 0.8°C. stopped the clock for several hours and changed the phase; in another hamster—"B"—stopping the heart for 3 hours and 40 minutes stopped the clock for about that length of time and changed the phase. Results of these experiments on 84 rats and 94 hamsters will be reported in detail in my monograph on the 24 hour clock.

Thus, for all practical purposes the clock functions in complete independence of all external and internal conditions and disturbances.

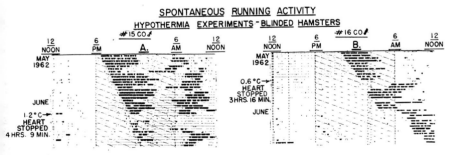

FIG. 11.—Activity-distribution charts showing failure of prolonged hypothermia to effect clock of two blinded hamsters.

"Hands" of the Clock

At this point I must call your attention to the concept of the "hand" of the clock, as illustrated in Figure 9. In the first rat electroshock treatment produced severe convulsions lasting 15 minutes and almost total inactivity lasting 6 days, but that the clock continued to run and at the same rate during the 6 days we learned from the fact that resumption of activity occurred at the predicted time. Here we see that spontaneous running activity serves as the "hand" of the clock. It tells that the clock is running and at what rate, but it can be removed without in any way affecting the functioning of the clock. Other "hands" are adrenal activity, as reflected in diurnal changes in numbers of eosinophils, since we know that the adrenals may be removed without in any way affecting the clock. Likewise, thyroid activity—as reflected in diurnal changes in metabolic rate—may serve simply as the "hand" of the clock.

Inborn Nature of the Clock

Results of our experiments have shown that the clock is innate, not in any way dependent on exposure to alternating periods of light and darkness, since both congenitally blind rats and rats blinded within a few days after birth, when the eyes are still covered with a thick layer of skin and are nonfunctional, show very regular cycles.

TABLE 3.—Endocrinological Interferences That Had No Effect on Clock

Gland	Method	No. of Rats
1. Gonads	a. Gonadectomy	15
	b. Mating	17
	c. Pregnancy and lactation	15
2. Adrenals	Total removal	25
3. Hypophysis	a. Total removal	15
	b. Posterior lobectomy	8
4. Pineal	Total removal	26
5. Pancreas	a. Partial removal	4
	b. Alloxan injection	6
6. Thyroid	a. Thyroid powder in food	12
	b. Anti-thyroid	7
	c. Injection of I^{131}	4

Location of the Clock

It will not be possible to discuss here the location of the clock beyond stating that our evidence—based on results of lesions made in all parts of the brain in over 200 animals—indicates that the clock is localized in the hypothalamus and is quite independent of influences from the

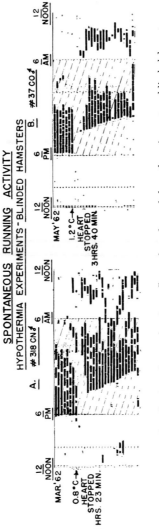

Fig. 12.—Activity-distribution charts showing effect of prolonged hypothermia on two blinded hamsters.

reticular formation. It must be located in a position from which it can exercise influence over centers governing functions of various parts of the autonomic nervous system and of mood and behavior.

Function of the Clock

This clock has two main functions in the rat: (1) to time exits from its burrow—to catch its prey, to avoid its enemies, to meet its mates and (2) to regulate and coordinate the various autonomic, endocrine, and behavioral functions of the body into their respective diurnal patterns.

Thus, in summary, we have seen that this remarkable innate 24 hour clock which plays such an important role in the life of the rat is entirely independent of all external and internal influences, particularly from the endocrine system; and it is independent of homeostasis or feedback —all of which makes it a perfect timing piece; in short, it is as independent of the rest of the organism as a wrist watch is of its wearer.

However, it must be made clear that it gives the time only twice daily; at the onset and termination of the active period. In brief it is not a chromometer that can be consulted at any hour.

MAN

Does man have a 24 hour clock? If so, what role does it play in his life?

From our observations on this clock in rats and other animals we now know what and what not to look for in man. We will not look for ability to tell time at any hour of the day without aid of clocks or watches; we will not look for ability to estimate short periods of time. We will simply look for two phases in activity and behavior separated by a sharp transition occurring at a specific time every 24 hours.

Normal Man

To my knowledge no such sharp change in activity or behavior at a specific time each 24 hours is ever experienced by normal persons. It is true that man, like various animals tested by us, has two main phases in 24 hours—one characterized by a waking state lasting about 16 hours, the other by a sleeping state lasting about 8 hours. In animals, durations of these phases in general are equal or nearly equal; and sleep may occur during active as well as inactive phases. The two unequal phases of man do not have either sharp beginnings or terminations. The few instances of sudden awakening at nearly the same

time each morning can usually be explained by sensations of hunger
from tetanic contractions of the stomach that occur with clocklike
regularity at approximately three hour intervals throughout sleep and
in some persons reach a sufficiently great intensity at a constant time
each morning to cause awakening.

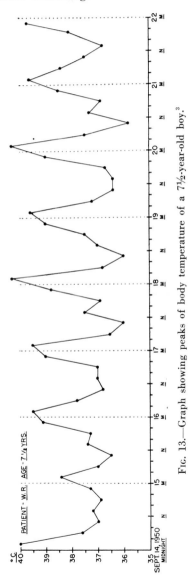

FIG. 13.—Graph showing peaks of body temperature of a 7½-year-old boy.[3]

The fact that monkeys and higher apes show these sharp changes in activity and inactivity at 24 hour intervals with great regularity with relation to light and darkness of day and night has made workers in this field conclude that man must likewise manifest this clock. However, these workers overlook one important difference between higher apes and man—that for over 350,000 years since his discovery of fire man has had light from his hearth fire throughout the night and so has no longer been exposed to alternating changes of light and total darkness.[6] His survival depended on freeing himself from this 24 hour timing device that produced such sharp changes in activity and behavior with relation to light and darkness. He had to function throughout part or all of the night hours as well. During the 350,000 years, man has almost continuously lived under conditions of constant light that required an even performance throughout most of the 24 hours.

Man does show diurnal changes in such functions as body temperature, pulse rate, etc., but these are small, slow sinusoidal changes. It is quite possible that these changes can be accounted for in large part by effects produced by rest and sleep.

Thus, in summary, normal man does not give definite evidence of possessing a 24 hour clock of the type found in higher apes and other animals.

Manifestation of the Clock in Man Under Pathological Conditions

Observations made on man under various pathological conditions have, however, demonstrated that man does still possess this 24 hour clock, but that in the process of evolution this clock has become modified in such a way to be no longer detectable by ordinary means.

Evidence that will now be presented for the existence of the clock is no longer firsthand. It comes from histories of patients in the Phipps Clinic and the Johns Hopkins Hospital and other hospitals and from the medical and psychiatric literature—most of it from the last century and early part of the present century when careful daily records were taken on patients over long periods of time uncomplicated by effects of all kinds of drugs.

Records are now at hand for many psychiatric patients who showed sudden changes in activity and behavior occurring at definite times every 24 hours with the same regularity as the onsets of activity of rats and other animals. Many of these records belong to postencephalitics. A young female Parkinsonian illustrates this type of sudden change in activity and behavior.[7] This patient reported by Leonard was under observation in the Erlangen Clinic in Germany for 9 years. Up to 9 p.m. each day she was bedridden, unable to get up or do anything for herself because of marked rigidity and severe tremors of her arms and legs. She had no appetite and would not eat or drink. Her writing was nothing more than a series of scratches, entirely undecipherable. However, she was alert, bright, intensely interested in happenings on the ward. Shortly after 9 p.m. each evening she suddenly lost her rigidity and tremors, was able to get up, to walk, to take care of herself, to eat and drink—to bring a cup of tea to her lips and to drink without spilling a drop; her handwriting became legible and neat. However, during this period she became less active and alert mentally. The period lasted for several hours. The next morning she was back in the original state.

Menninger-Lerchenthal,[8] the Viennese psychiatrist, collected many such instances of patients who suddenly, at a definite time each day, experienced sharp changes in activity and behavior. The sharp changes in mood—associated with morning-evening variations of depression are of course well known. Some epileptics also have fits at a definite time each day.[9]

Great peaks of body temperature at the same time each 24 hours may be the outstanding symptom of patients with a 24 hour cycle, as illustrated in Figure 13.[3] Peaks of body temperature—40°C. or over—were reached in this 7½ year old boy every night shortly after midnight. During the 13 years that he has been followed at the Hopkins since this record was taken, his body temperature still shows essentially the same record. No explanation of these fever peaks has been found.

I shall now ask you to consider the possibility that the 48 hour cycles seen in both medical and psychiatric patients are also manifestations of the 24 hour clock. We have records on over 100 patients that displayed this 48 hour cycle of 24 hour phase of one kind of behavior followed by 24 hour phase of a different kind—with a sharp transition between phases. I reported records of 4 patients with 48 hour cycles in 1938.[10] One of these patients, a 59-year-old woman, was admitted in 1915 to the Phipps Clinic with the diagnosis of manic-depressive reactions. She had suffered from depression most of her life. During her first five months in the Phipps Clinic she showed clear-cut alternating 24 hour phases of normal and depressed behavior. One day she was cheerful, entered readily into ward activity, shopped in town, read books and newspapers; on the following day she was sad, fearful, withdrawn, and suicidal. Hours of sleep showed the same 48 hour cycle. Pulse rate showed it much less clearly. Transitions from one phase to the other were very sharp—just as though a switch had been thrown. The case reported by Ziegler[11] in 1864 showed a close correlation between alternating days of stupor and excitement and body temperature, as may be seen in Figure 14. Arndt,[12] in Germany, and Menninger-Lerchenthal[8] collected histories of many patients.

My reasons for believing that this 48 hour cycle—and possibly also the 72 hour and 96 hour cycles—is a manifestation of the 24 hour clock are the following:

1. In many patients the length of cycles may over the course of months shift back and forth between 24, 48, 72, and 96 hour cycles.

2. Instances have been reported in which onsets of one phase of behavior come later each day just as they did in blinded rats. Thus Nacke[13] reported in 1894 that in a catatonic patient a phase of excitement lasting 25 hours was regularly followed by a phase of stupor lasting 29 hours. This meant that over several weeks onsets of each phase occurred at every hour of the day and night. Bleuler[14] in 1911 reported that in one of his patients, whom he had observed for many years, 25 hour phases of manic excitement alternated with 25 hour phases of depression. Transitions between phases were very sharp. Here again, over a period of months, onsets of the phase came at all hours of the day and night.

3. Further evidence for the 24 hour clock's ability to change from measuring 24 hour intervals to measuring 48 hour or even 72 hour units we saw in our and Strumwasser's[5] records of the ground squirrel.

Thus, it would seem likely that under pathological conditions the 24 hour clock of man may have a period of 48 hours, or even 72 or 96 hours. In all instances the phases manifest themselves in sharp changes in activity and behavior.

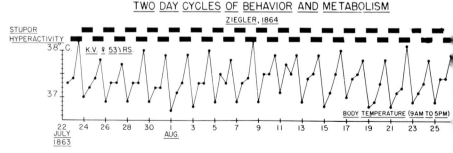

FIG. 14.—Forty-eight hour cycle of body temperature and alternating 24 hour periods of b activity and stupor.

In general these patients are normal in one phase—abnormal in the next. In the abnormal phase any one patient may be depressed or excited, or anxious, hallucinated or stuporous—in fact he may show almost any form of abnormal behavior, or he may be abnormal in both phases—depressed in one, manic in the other; or mildly depressed in one and deeply depressed in the other. Some patients are one person in one phase and an entirely different person in the other—different lives alternating every 24 hours.

The clock may manifest itself in functions of almost every organ or function of the body—sweating, salivating, etc.

Characteristics of the Clock

(1) *Sharp onsets* of two daily phases. (2) *High degree of accuracy.* In some patients shifts from one phase to another occur within minutes at the same time each day—with an accuracy comparable to that of the clock of the rat. (3) *High degree of constancy.* One of Kraeplin's[15] patients showed alternating days of so-called good and bad behavior for over 10 years. Starobinski's[16] patient showed these alternating days of depression and normal behavior for 30 years, also with great constancy. (4) *Persistence of cycles.* The fact that these cycles may persist for 30 years or more through all kinds of climatic and atmospheric conditions—external or internal disturbances that must have occurred during this long time—demonstrates also that in man this clock is not a part of a homeostatic mechanism; it is not in any way influenced by feedback.

Clinical and other evidence indicates that in man this clock is located in the hypothalamus, as it is in the rat; but this is not of immediate concern for the present purpose.

Types of Patients Showing this Clock

Almost every type of patient may manifest this clock—manic depressives, schizophrenics, catatonics, patients with brain trauma.

Etiology

The clock may manifest itself after a great variety of disturbances and conditions—fever, brain trauma, severe emotional stress, cerebral hemorrhage, apoplexy, postencephalitis, progressive paralysis, arteriosclerosis.

Relation of the Clock to the Basic Illness

Our review of the histories of many of these patients showed that the clock did not manifest itself until long after the start of the basic illness; further, that it rarely manifested itself in more than a few per cent of patients of any type; thus, only 3 to 4 per cent of manic depressives or of schizophrenics show this clock. Further, our study showed that appearance of the clock is associated with definite changes in the severity of the symptoms of the basic illness—in one phase accentuating the symptom, in the other reducing the severity or eliminating it altogether. When no mental symptoms are present the clock may show itself only in physical changes—for instances in body temperature. In short, no new symptoms are associated with appearance of the clock, only a modification of those already present.

How explain the absence of any signs of the clock in normal individuals and the clear-cut presence under pathological conditions? I shall attempt to do this on the basis of the shock-phase hypothesis formulated in my Salmon lectures in 1959.[3] It involves the following postulates:

1. The 24 hour clock is constructed of cells, each one of which has an internal programmed rhythm of 24 hours.

2. In rats and other rodents and in apes, all the cells of this clock function in phase—thus giving clear-cut onsets and terminations of each phase at 24 hour intervals.

3. That in the process of evolution, after man's discovery of fire, the cells have become progressively more and more out of phase, giving rise to an even, nonphasic performance—so that normal man gives only a slight if any indication of possessing a 24 hour clock.

4. That under pathological conditions—after a severe shock or head trauma—all of the cells of the clock may suddenly be thrown back into phase, thus giving rise to the same sharp phases seen in the rat. That the clock may regulate and control every function, from the simplest to the most highly integrated, is clearly seen in individuals who have experienced severe shock or trauma. In these individuals the clock did not suddenly start to operate; it must have been there all the time, before occurrence of the shock or trauma, exerting its control over all these functions—to keep them synchronized—regardless of all internal and external disturbances to which the individual was exposed. This is the significant implication of this study.

The clock may thus play as important a role in the functioning of the total organism as has been demonstrated for homeostatic mechanisms.

Thus, in summary, it was shown that the 24 hour clock of rats and other rodents is a strictly nonhomeostatic mechanism. It controls many different functions but is free of feedback from these functions; furthermore this nonhomeostatic clock is present in man—but not detectable under normal conditions. It appears only under pathological conditions. However, evidence indicates that it plays an important part in normal man in the regulation of many functions concerned with the control of activity of the autonomic nervous system, and with emotions and behavior.

REFERENCES

1. Bernard, C.: Leçons sur les propriétés physiologiques et les altérations pathologiques des liquides de l'organisme, Paris, Bailliers, 1859.
2. Cannon, W. B.: The Wisdom of the Body. New York, W. W. Norton & Co., 1932.
3. Richter, C. P.: Biological Clocks in Medicine and Psychiatry. Springfield, Ill. Charles C Thomas, 1965.
4. Richter, C. P.: Biological Clocks and the Endocrine Glands. Excerpta Medica International Congress Series No. 83. Proceedings of the Second International Congress of Endocrinology, London, August 1964.
5. Strumwasser, F., Smith, J. L., Gilliam, J. J., and Schlechte, F. R.: Identification of active brain regions involved in the processes of hibernation. XVI Proceedings of Inter. Cong. Zool. 2:53, 1963.
6. Coon, C. S.: The Origin of Races. New York, Alfred A. Knopf, 1962.
7. Leonard, K.: Eigenartige Tagesschwankugen des Zustandbildes bei Parkinsonismus. Z. Ges. Neurol. Psychiat. 134:76, 1931.
8. Menninger-Lerchenthal, E.: Periodizität in der Psychopathologie. Vienna, Austria, Wilhelm Maudrich, 1960.
9. Griffiths, G. M., and Fox, J. T.: Rhythm in Epilepsy. Lancet 2:409, 1938.
10. Richter, C. P.: Two-day cycles of alternating good and bad behavior in psychotic patients. Arch. Neurol. Psychiat. 39:587, 1938.
11. Ziegler, K.: Über die Eigenwärme in einem Falle von Geistesstörung mit eigentümlichen intermittierenden Erscheinungen. Allg. Z. Psychiat. 21:184, 1864.
12. Arndt, M.: Über täglichen (24 stündigen) Wechsel psychischer Krankheitszustände. Allg. Z. Psychiat. 92:128, 1930.
13. Näcke, P.: Raritäten aus der Irrenanstalt. Allg. Z Psychiat. 50:630, 1894.
14. Bleuler, R.: Handbuch der Psychiatrie (G. Aschaffenburg) Spezieller Teil. Dementia-Praecox. 1911, p. 197. Leipzig, u. Wein F. Deuticke.
15. Kraepelin, E.: Lehrbuch der Psychiatrie. 8. Aufl., 3. Bd. Leipzig, J. A. Barth, 1913.
16. Starobinski, A.: Un cas de psychose maniaque-dépressive à un jour d'alternance. Ann. Medicopsychol. (Paris) 1-2 (11th Series):344, 1921.

Part III: Behavioral Studies

11

AVERSIVE CONTROL IN RELATION TO THE DEVELOPMENT OF BEHAVIOR DISORDERS

by RICHARD L. SOLOMON, Ph.D.*

THE CONTROL OF BEHAVIOR by the use of painful, frightening, or unpleasant stimuli is called aversive control or punishment. There are many techniques for using aversive stimuli in laboratory experiments with animal Ss. In addition, there are many types of behavior to which such techniques can be applied. The behavioral outcomes produced by experimental uses of aversive stimuli are puzzling in their complexity and diversity. Aversive treatment does not unconditionally produce abnormal behavior, adaptive behavior, maladaptive behavior, good behavior, or bad behavior in a laboratory animal. Instead, we can only say that in most cases a specific behavioral outcome will be conditional upon a wide variety of variables which we can now control. We try to understand the relationships between the modes of punishment we vary and the behavioral outcomes we observe.

The criteria for the existence of abnormal or disordered behavior are vague. It is difficult to decide in the laboratory whether a given behavioral manifestation is abnormal or not. Each observer has his own way of making such a judgment. Therefore it seems best to review some of the behavioral results we observe in experiments on aversive control and then to discuss the label that seems applicable only after we have become familiar with the whole range of outcomes.

Aversive stimuli, or punishment, can be used either to establish new behavior or to eliminate already existing behavior tendencies. When it is used to establish new behavior, we refer to the process as *active* escape and avoidance learning. The animal S learns *to* do something *new* in order to terminate an aversive stimulus or to avoid it entirely. When it is used to eliminate existing behavior tendencies, we refer to

---

*Department of Psychology, University of Pennsylvania, Philadelphia, Pa.

the process as *passive* escape and avoidance learning. The animal *S* learns *not* to do what it used to do, in order to terminate an aversive stimulus or to avoid it entirely. The passive avoidance learning process fits the common sense view: learning not to do something because to do it would lead to punishment.

The most commonly used aversive stimulus in the laboratory has been electric shock applied to the skin of the *S*. When used to engender *active* avoidance learning, shock leads to reliable behavior. If the shock is very intense, it will be difficult to eliminate the newly acquired behavior by ordinary extinction procedures. Often the behavior is very stereotyped. Overt signs of emotional upset and fear, common during the early stages of active avoidance learning, disappear when the behavior becomes stereotyped. Indices of ANS involvement substantiate this conclusion. The wide varieties of avoidance training procedures based on aversive stimulation have been reviewed extensively,[26] and they need not be described here. Each method produces its own special behavioral outcome. Each animal species has its own special peculiarities of response when assaulted with aversive stimulation.

Of considerably more interest to students of abnormal behavior is *passive* avoidance learning, the cessation of responses under the impetus of punishment (usually electric shock). It is extremely difficult to bring order into the very complex empirical findings stemming from passive avoidance experiments. It seems necessary to classify the punished behavior into six categories in order to reduce the complexity and contradictions: The categories are: (I) behavior previously established by rewards; (II) consummatory behavior; (III) complex, instinctive sequences of skeletal responses; (IV) innate reflexes; (V) emotional expressive behavior; and (VI) behavior previously established by punishment.

I. First, let us look at punishment for *instrumental responses or habits previously established by reward or positive reinforcers*. The outcomes of punishment procedures applied to previously rewarded habits are strongly related to the *intensity* of the punishment. Sometimes intensity is independently defined and measured, as in the case of electric shock. Sometimes we have qualitative evaluations, as in the case of Maier's rat bumping his nose on a locked door,[19] or Masserman's spider monkey being presented with a toy snake,[21] or Skinner's rat receiving a slap on the paw from a lever.[24] As the intensity of shock applied to rats, cats, and dogs is increased from about .1

ma. to 4 ma., these differing results are obtained: (a) *detection* and *arousal*, wherein the punisher serves as a cue, discriminative stimulus, response intensifier, or even as a secondary reinforcer; (b) *temporary suppression*, wherein punishment suppresses the punished response, and later is followed by complete recovery, such that the subject later appears to be unaltered from his prepunished state; (c) *partial suppression*, wherein the subject displays lasting suppression of the punished response, without total recovery; and (d) *complete suppression*, with no observable recovery over long time periods. Any outcome can be produced by varying the intensity or duration of the noxious stimulus used[5] when we punish responses previously established by reward or positive reinforcement. No wonder different experimenters report incomparable outcomes. Azrin[4] has produced a response-rate *increase* while operants are punished. Storms, Boroczi, and Broen[27] have produced long-lasting suppression of operants in rats. The studies of Karsh,[16] Appel,[2] and Walters and Rogers[28] all support the conclusion that shock intensity is a crucial variable, and high intensities produce lasting suppression effects. There is less evidence on shock duration, but it probably acts similarly.

Other variables are as important as punishment intensity and duration. Here are just a few examples:

1. *Proximity* in time and space to the punished response controls the effectiveness of a punishment. There is a response-suppression gradient. This has been demonstrated in the runway,[7,15] in the lever box,[3] and in the shuttle box.[14] This phenomenon has been labeled the "gradient of temporal delay of punishment." Delayed punishment is ineffective.

2. The *strength* of a response, measured by its resistance to extinction after omission of positive reinforcement, is predictive of the effect of a punishment contingent upon the response. Strong responses are more resistant to the suppressive effects of punishment. Thus, for example, the overtraining of a response, which often decreases ordinary resistance to experimental extinction, also increases the effectiveness of punishment.[15,22]

3. *Adaptation* to punishment can occur. New, intense punishers are better than old, intense punishers.[22] Punishment intensity, if slowly increased, tends not to be as effective as when it is introduced at its high-intensity value.

4. In general, resistance to extinction is decreased whenever a previously reinforced response is punished. However, if the subject is habituated to receiving shock together with positive reinforcement during reward training, the relationship can be reversed, and punishment during extinction can actually increase resistance to extinction.[12] Punishment can functionally operate as a *secondary reinforcer*, or as a cue for reward, or as an arouser.

5. Punishments are extremely effective when they are tactically used as an

aid in the reinforcement of new responses that are very different from, or *incompatible* with, the punished response. When new instrumental acts are established which lead to the old goal (a new *means* to an old *end*), a punishment of very low intensity can have very long-lasting suppression effects. Whiting and Mowrer[29] demonstrated this clearly. They first rewarded rats for taking one route to food, then punished them for doing so. When the rats ceased taking the punished route, they provided a new, rewarded route. The old route was not traversed again. This reliable suppression effect is seen in connection with temporal, discriminative restraints on behavior. The punishment of urination in dogs, under the control of *indoor stimuli*, is extremely effective in housebreaking a dog, as long as urination is allowed to go unpunished under the control of *outdoor stimuli*. A *rewarded alternative*, under discriminative control, makes passive avoidance training a potent behavioral influence. It can produce a highly reliable dog.

6. Finally, I should point out that the attributes of effective punishments vary *across species* and *across stages in maturational development* within species. A toy snake can frighten monkeys, but it does not faze a rat. A loud noise terrified Watson's little Albert, yet for us it is merely a Chinese gong.

Now look at the experiments wherein punishment appears to have had only a temporary suppression effect. Most of these experiments offered the subject *no* rewarded alternative to the punished response in attaining his goal. In many such experiments, it was a case of take-a-chance-or-go-hungry. Hunger-drive strength, under such no-alternative conditions, together with punishment intensity are the crucial variables in predicting recovery from the suppression effects of punishment. Here, an interesting, yet hard-to-understand phenomenon frequently occurs, akin to Freudian "reaction formation." If a subject has been punished for touching some manipulandum which yields food, he may stay nearer to the manipulandum under low hunger drive and move farther away from it under high hunger drive, even though the probability of finally touching the manipulandum increases as hunger drive increases. This phenomenon is complex and needs to be studied in some detail. Our knowledge of it is now fragmentary. It was observed by Hunt and Schlosberg[13] when the water supply of rats was electrified, and we have seen it occur in approach-avoidance conflict experiments in our laboratory, but we do not know the precise conditions for its occurrence.

II. Now let us look at the effects of punishment on *consummatory acts*. Here the data are, to me, surprising. Consummatory acts, often being of biological significance for the survival of the individual and the species, ought to be highly resistant to suppression by punishment. The contrary may be so. Male sexual behavior may be seriously suppressed by weak punishment.[6,9] Eating in dogs and cats can be permanently suppressed by a moderate shock delivered through the feet or through the food dish itself.[18,20] Such suppression effects can lead to fatal self-starvation.[18] We have noted that puppies raised in our laboratory, if punished by the swat of a newspaper for eating horsemeat, and rewarded for eating pellets, will starve themselves to death when only given the opportunity to eat the taboo horsemeat. They eagerly eat the pellets when those are available.

The suppression of consummatory responses by punishment needs more investigation. If punishment is especially effective in breaking up this class of responses, then one can ask *why*, with some profit. Perhaps the intimate temporal connection between drive, incentive, and punishment results in drive or incentive becoming a conditioned-stimulus (CS) pattern for aversive emotional reactions (fear) when consummatory acts are punished. Perhaps some conditioned emotions interfere with vegetative activity: i.e., fear "kills the appetite" in a hungry subject. But why might the same punisher not appear to be as effective when made contingent on an *instrumental* act as contrasted with a *consummatory* act? Perhaps operants are so separated in time, and space, and response topography from consummatory behavior and positive incentive stimuli, that appetitive reactions are not effectively present during the punishment of operants. We do not know enough yet about such matters, and speculation about it is still fun.

Perhaps the most interesting variation one can study, in experiments on the effects of punishment on consummatory acts, is the *temporal order* of rewards and punishments. If we hold hunger drive constant, shock-punishment intensity constant, and food-reward amounts constant, a huge differential effect can be obtained if we reverse the time order of reward and punishment. Train a hungry cat to approach a food cup and its behavior in the experimental setting will become quite stereotyped. Then if we shock the cat's feet while it is eating, the cat will vocalize, retreat, and show fear. It will be slow to resume eating in this situation. Indeed, as Masserman[20] has shown, such a procedure is likely, if repeated a few times, to lead to self-starvation. Lichtenstein[18] showed the same phenomenon in dogs. Contrast this outcome with that found when the temporal order of food and shock is *reversed*. We now use shock as a discriminative stimulus to signalize the availability of food. When the cat is performing well, the shock may produce eating with a latency of less than 5 seconds. The subject's appetite does not seem to be disturbed. Thus, the effects of punishment are partly determined by those events that directly precede it and those that directly follow it. A punishment is not just a punishment. It is an event in a temporal and spatial flow of stimulation and behavior, and its effects will be produced by its temporal and spatial point of insertion in that flow.

III. A class of behaviors, closely related to consummatory acts but yet a little different, is the *instinctive act sequence:* complex, innately governed behavior which the ethologists study, such as nest building in birds. There has been little adequate experimentation, to my knowledge, on the effects of punishment on such behavior. There are, however, some hints of interesting things to come. For example, sometimes frightening events will produce what the ethologists call displacement reactions—the inappropriate expression of a different behavior pattern of an innate sort. We need to experiment with such phenomena in a systematic fashion.

An example of the punishment of complex innate behavior concerns the imprinting of birds on moving objects, using the locomotor-following response as an index. Moltz, Rosenblum, and Halikas,[23] in one experiment, and Kovach and Hess[17] see also Hess,[10,11] in another, have shown that the punishment of such imprinted behavior sometimes depresses its occurrence. However, if birds are punished prior to the presentation of an imprinted object, often the following response will be energized. It is hard to understand what this finding means, except that punishment can either arouse or inhibit such behavior, depending on the manner of presentation of punishment. The suggestion is that imprinting normally may be partially a function of fear or distress. The effectiveness of punishment also is found to be related to the critical period for imprinting.[17] However, the systematic study of known punishment parameters as they affect a wide variety of complex sequences of innate behaviors is yet to be carried out. Recently an article has appeared on this specific problem (see Adler and Hogan[1]). The authors showed that the gill-extension response of *Betta splendens* could be conditioned to a previously neutral stimulus by a Pavlovian technique, and it could also be suppressed by electric-shock punishment. This is an important finding, because there are very few known cases in which the same response can be both conditioned and trained. Here, the gill-extension response is typically elicited by a rival fish and is usually interpreted to be aggressive or hostile in nature. Evidently some complex instinctive acts can be suppressed by punishment.

IV. A class of behavior upon which punishment *can* be made contingent is the *simple, discrete reflex*. For example, what might happen if a conditioned or an unconditioned knee jerk were punished? We are lacking in information on this point. Can subjects be trained to inhibit reflexes under aversive motivation? Or does such motivation sensitize and enhance reflexes?

V. A class of behavior to which punishment can be applied is *emotional, expressive behavior,* such as whining and crying. There is very little experimental evidence available from which to generalize. Casual observations lead one to conclude that the punishment of emotional expression derived from pleasant stimulation can be very effective in eliminating the expressive behavior, but, in contrast, the punishment of emotional expression derived from aversive stimulation may be relatively ineffective. Here again we are faced with a dearth of experimental evidence, and so we cannot test our observational impressions.

VI. A class of behavior upon which punishment can be made contingent is that *previously established by punishment procedures:* in other words, the effect of *passive* avoidance training on existing, active avoidance responses. This use of punishment often produces an unexpected outcome. If the same noxious stimulus is used to punish a response as was used to establish it in the first place, the response may become strengthened during the initial applications of punishment. After several such events, however, the response may weaken, but not always. The similarity of the noxious stimulus used for active avoidance training to that used for punishment of the established avoidance response can be of great importance. For example, Carlsmith[8] has shown that one can increase resistance to extinction by using the same noxious stimuli for both purposes and yet decrease resistance to extinction by using equally noxious, but discriminatively different, punishments. He trained some rats to run in order to avoid shock, then punished them during extinction by blowing a loud horn. He trained other rats to run in order to avoid the loud horn, then during extinction he punished them by shocking them for running. In two control groups, the punisher stimulus and the training stimulus were the same. The groups trained and then punished by different noxious stimuli extinguished more easily during punishment than did the groups in which the active avoidance training stimulus was the same as the passive avoidance training stimulus. Thus, punishment for responses established originally by punishment may be ineffective in eliminating the avoidance response they are supposed to eliminate.

Indeed, the punishment may strengthen the responses. We need to know more about this puzzling phenomenon.

Our quick survey of the effects of punishment on six classes of responses revealed a great deal of ignorance and a wide variety of discrepant phenomena. For one to predict, in even the grossest way, the action of punishment on a response, one has to know *how* that particular response was originally inserted in the subject's response repertoire. Is the response an instrumental one which was strengthened by reward? Is it instead a consummatory response? Is it an innate, sequential response pattern? Is it a discrete reflex? Was it originally established by means of punishment? How, temporally in a behavior sequence, was the punishment used? How *intense* was it? These are but a few of the relevant, critical questions, the answers to which are necessary in order for us to make reasonable predictions about the effects of punishment. Thus, to profess or claim that punishment is typically either effective or ineffective, typically either a temporary suppressor or a permanent one, is to oversimplify complex scientific knowledge in an area where many urgent problems still remain for experimental attack.

Now, how do all of the complex empirical outcomes relate to the understanding of behavior disorders? First, we have to know the criteria for disordered behavior, and this knowledge is not easily arrived at. Sometimes, selected attributes of *instrumental* responses are used as the criteria for behavior disorder. Phenomena such as rigidity, fixation, regression, aggression, displacement, and primitivization are described. One definition of neurosis developed by Maier and by Mowrer is: self-defeating behavior, oriented toward no goal, and compulsive in quality. The behavioral phenomena that reveal neuroses are said to be fixations, regressions, aggressions, or resignations. But we are not told the necessary or sufficient experimental conditions under which these dramatic phenomena emerge, and often the phenomena themselves are vaguely defined.

When we train a rat in a T maze, using food reward for a correct response and shock to the feet for an incorrect response, there *is* a period of emotionality (squealing, struggling) during the early training, but thereafter the rat, when the percentage of correct responses is high, looks like a hungry, well-motivated, happy rat, eager to get from his cage to our hand and thence to the start box. *Evidently*, merely *going through conflict is not a sufficient condition for neurosis.* The rat is, however, unswerving in his choices. Is he therefore neurotic?

Should this be called subservient resignation? Or should it be labeled a happy adjustment to an inevitable event? Is the behavior constricted? Is it a fixation, an evidence of behavioral rigidity? "The criteria for answering such questions are vague today. Even if we should suggest some specific tests for rigidity, they lack face validity. For example, we might examine *discrimination reversal* as a test of *rigidity*. Do subjects who have received reward for the correct response, and punishment for the incorrect response, find it harder to reverse when the contingencies are reversed, as compared with subjects trained with reward alone? Or, we might try a *transfer test*, introducing our subject to a new maze, or to a new jumping stand. Would the previously punished subject generalize more readily than one not so punished? And if he did, would he then be *less discriminating* and thus neurotic? Or would the previously punished subject generalize poorly and hesitantly, thus being *too discriminating* and thus neurotic, too? What are the criteria for behavioral malfunction as a consequence of the use of punishment? When instrumental responses are used as the indicator we are, alas, left in doubt!"[25, p.250]

Sometimes the occurrence of *emotional states* is used as a criterion for behavior disorder or abnormality. The most dramatic demonstrations of emotional disturbances stemming from the use of punishment are seen in Masserman and Pechtel's work with monkeys.[21] Here the criterion for neurosis was not based on instrumental responding but rather on emotionality expressed in *consummatory acts* and *innate impulses*. The monkeys were frightened by a toy snake while they were eating. Feeding inhibition, shifts in food preferences, odd sexual behavior, tics, long periods of crying were observed. These behavioral criteria have a face validity that is hard to reject. The findings are consonant with the Freudian position which postulates the pervasive influences of traumatic experiences, permeating many phases of the affective existence of the individual and persisting for long time periods.

To reconcile all of the considerations I have set forth concerning the possible behavior peculiarities produced by punishment is a formidable task. My first guess is that emotional disturbances often arise in cases in which *consummatory* behavior or *instinctive* behavior is punished under *nondiscriminatory* control. In order for such a guess to be adequately tested, Masserman and Pechtel's interesting procedures would have to be repeated, using discriminative stimuli to signalize those times and places when it is safe or not safe for a monkey to eat. Such experiments are needed if we are to explore adequately the effects of punishment on emotionality, the appetites, and the impulses. My next guess is that the number of rewarding behavior alternatives in an otherwise punishing situation will affect the emotional aftereffects of punishments. We have seen that Whiting and Mowrer[29] gave their rats a rewarding alternative, and the resulting behavior was highly reliable. Their rats remained easy to handle and eager to enter the experimental situation. Perhaps increasing the number of behavioral alternatives leading to a consummatory response will, in a situation in which only one behavior alternative is being punished, result in reliable behavior and the absence of unusual emotional manifestations.

Let me rephrase these guesses. The punishment of instrumental acts, when there *is* an available instrumental alternative leading to reward, probably does not produce the emotional disturbances usually seen in the punishment of consummatory and instinctive behavior. In fact, there may be no emotional residue whatsoever. Perhaps an instrumental, rewarded response is better fixated than it would have been if the alternative were not punished, but even that generalization is in doubt.

Probably punishment alone is not a sufficient condition for the production of abnormal behavior. Many parametric requirements must be met before punishment does produce abnormal behavior. Of these requirements, a high-intensity, long-duration, aversive stimulus, applied to very particular types of behavior classes, as a part of a nondiscriminative procedure, and applied without a rewarded behavior alternative being available, seem to qualify as the most likely antecedents of neurotic behavior. Perhaps such guesses will prove to be wrong as new experiments on aversive control are conducted. They are arrived at with some uneasiness. "Our laboratory knowledge of the effects of punishment on instrumental and emotional behavior is still too rudimentary—much too rudimentary—to make an intelligent choice among conflicting ideas about it. The polarized doctrines are probably inadequate and in error. The popularized Skinnerian position which accepts the inadequacy of punishment in suppressing *instrumental* behavior is, if correct at all, only conditionally correct. The Freudian position, pointing to pain or trauma as an agent for the pervasive and long-lasting distortion of *affective* behavior is equally questionable, and only conditionally correct."[24, p.252] The parameters of punishment are numerous and their influences are complex and hard to trace. Though the following conclusions are certainly equivocal,

I think they fairly represent our current empirical knowledge relating abnormal behavior to the effects of punishment: (a) severe punishment may *not* lead to behavior disorders, though it *could* do so if proper conditions were met; (b) mild punishment could very well lead to a behavior disorder, though it might *not* do so if proper conditions were met. To explore thoroughly those "proper conditions" is one of the interesting tasks of experimental psychology.

REFERENCES

1. Adler, N., and Hogan, J. A.: Classical conditioning and punishment of an instinctive response in *Betta splendens. Anim. Behav.* 11:351-354, 1963.
2. Appel, J. B.: Punishment and shock intensity. Science 141:528-529, 1963.
3. Azrin, N.H.: Some effects of two intermittent schedules of immediate and non-immediate punishment. J. Psychol. 42:8-21, 1956.
4. Azrin, N. H.: Punishment and recovery during fixed-ratio performance. J. Exp. Anal. Behav. 2:301-305, 1959.
5. Azrin, N. H., and Holz, W. C.: Punishment during fixed-interval reinforcement. J. Exp. Anal. Behav. 4:343-347, 1961.
6. Beach, F. A., Conovitz, M. W., Steinberg, F., and Goldstein, A. C.: Experimental inhibition and restoration of mating behavior in male rats. J. Genet. Psychol. 89:165-181, 1956.
7. Brown, J. S.: Gradients of approach and avoidance responses and their relation to level of motivation. J. Comp. Physiol. Psychol. 41:450-465, 1948.
8. Carlsmith, J. M.: The effect of punishment on avoidance responses: The use of different stimuli for training and punishment. Paper read at Eastern Psychological Association, Philadelphia, April 1961.
9. Gantt, W. H.: Experimental Basis for Neurotic Behavior. New York, Hoeber, 1944.
10. Hess, E. H. Imprinting. Science 130:133-141, 1959.
11. Hess, E. H.: Two conditions limiting critical age for imprinting. J. Comp. Physiol. Psychol. 52:515-518, 1959.
12. Holz, W., and Azrin, N. H.: Discriminative properties of punishment. J. Exp. Anal. Behav. 4:225-232, 1961.
13. Hunt, J. McV., and Schlosberg, H.: Behavior of rats in continuous conflict. J. Comp. Physiol. Psychol. 43:351-357, 1950.
14. Kamin, L. J.: The delay-of-punishment gradient. J. Comp. Physiol. Psychol. 52:434-437, 1959.
15. Karsh, E. B.: Effects of number of rewarded trials and intensity of punishment on running speed. J. Comp. Physiol. Psychol. 55:44-51, 1962.
16. Karsh E. B.: Changes in intensity of punishment: Effect on runway behavior of rats. Science 140:1084-1085, 1963.
17. Kovach, J. K., and Hess, E. H.: Imprinting: Effects of painful stimulation upon the following response. J. Comp. Physiol. Psychol. 56:461-464, 1963.
18. Lichtenstein, P. E.: Studies of anxiety: I. The production of a feeding inhibition in dogs. J. Comp. Physiol. Psychol. 43:16-29, 1950.

19. Maier, N. R. F.: Frustration: The Study of Behavior Without a Goal. New York, McGraw-Hill, 1949.

20. Masserman, J. M.: Behavior and Neurosis. Chicago, University of Chicago Press, 1943.

21. Masserman, J. M., and Pechtel, C.: Neurosis in Monkeys: A preliminary report of experimental observations. Ann. N. Y. Acad. Sci. 56:253-265, 1953.

22. Miller, N. E.: Learning resistance to pain and fear: Effects of overlearning, exposure, and rewarded exposure in context. J. Exp. Psychol. 60:137-145, 1960.

23. Moltz, H., Rosenblum, L., and Halikas, N.: Imprinting and level of anxiety. J. Comp. Physiol. Psychol. 52:240-244, 1959.

24. Skinner, B. F.: The Behavior of Organisms. New York, Appleton-Century, 1938.

25. Solomon, R. L.: Punishment. Amer. Psychol. 19:239-253, 1964.

26. Solomon, R. L., and Brush, E. S.: Experimentally derived conceptions of anxiety and aversion. In: Nebraska Symposium on Motivation: 1956. M. R. Jones, Ed. Lincoln, University of Nebraska Press, 1956.

27. Storms, L. H., Boroczi, C., and Broen, W. E.: Punishment inhibits on instrumental responses in hooded rats. Science 135:1133-1134, 1962.

28. Walters, G. C., and Rogers, J. V.: Aversive stimulation of the rat: Long term effects on subsequent behavior. Science 142:70-71, 1963.

29. Whiting, J. W. M., and Mowrer, O. H.: Habit progression and regression—a laboratory study of some factors relevant to human socialization. J. Comp. Psychol. 36:229-253, 1943.

12

THE PRACTICAL MODIFICATION OF DEVIANT BEHAVIOR THROUGH OPERANT TECHNIQUES

by T. AYLLON, Ph.D.*

THE PRACTICAL MODIFICATION of deviant behavior has only recently been made possible by advances in the behavioral laboratory. The main influence in this development has been the work of Skinner and associates whose findings indicate that behavior is governed by its consequences. The earliest investigator to extend the basic findings to human behavior was Lindsley. In working with severely psychotic patients, Lindsley[1] was able to show that a functional analysis of psychotic behavior was possible through operant techniques. The most relevant aspects of operant methodology for the practicing clinician are that (1) it stresses the individual case; (2) it is based on arranging the behavioral consequences to fit the individual; and (3) behavioral procedures developed for single individuals are typically applicable to large groups. Anyone concerned with clinical applications cannot help but be interested in such a method.

The essential features of this methodology are (1) that the response must be objectively specifiable; (2) that the consequences or reinforcer must be effective; and (3) that the reinforcement must follow the designated response, and preferably, immediately. These characteristics were illustrated by Skinner[5] in an example in which the response consisted of the depression of a lever by a rat. The lever-pressing response could be specified objectively in terms of the force required to activate a switch, thereby fulfilling the first requirement of a response specification. The second requirement that the consequence be an effective reinforcer was met by first depriving the animal of food to ensure the effectiveness of food as the reinforcer. The third requirement was fulfilled when the rat pressed the lever which in turn activated a switch

*Anna State Hospital, Anna, Ill.

The research reported in this paper was supported in part by the Mental Health Fund and Psychiatric Training and Research Fund of the Illinois Department of Mental Health, and by Grant 4926 from the National Institute of Mental Health.

that dropped a pellet immediately. An electrical circuit provided objective recording of the response and the delivery of the reinforcement.

In adapting this method for the study of human behavior, Lindsley designed a situation to meet the above characteristics. The first requirement was met when the dimensions of the behavioral response, plunger pulling, were specified. The second requirement was met when he empirically determined the effective reinforcers for specified patients, such as candy, cigarettes, and others. The third requirement was also met by arranging for the reinforcement to occur immediately when the patient pulled the plunger which in turn activated a switch. This also provided an objective recording of the response. I will quickly review the clinical applications of this methodology and then present material based on a paper by Ayllon and Azrin published in the *Journal of the Experimental Analysis of Behavior.*

The application of operant principles to the modification of the behavior of psychotic patients requires the active participation of specially trained nurses and attendants who are in charge of the patients. In addition, to extend the methodology of operant conditioning to the behavior of psychotic patients in a free ward environment, it has been necessary to meet the characteristics of the methodology by first specifying the behavior to be studied. For example, in one application a patient entering the nurse's office was defined as the response. In so doing, the frequency of the behavior was easily observed and recorded at a given time and place. The second requirement that the consequence be an effective reinforcement was typically met by manipulating the social reaction which was frequently the reinforcer for the patients' maladaptive behavior. Third, the requirement that the reinforcer follow immediately upon the display of the response was also met by ensuring that the ward staff, composed of attendants and nurses, react to the patient in a manner such that the behavior was immediately followed by a specific social reaction. Following this procedure of giving social attention and/or withholding it for specific ward behaviors, it was possible to demonstrate the usefulness of this approach to the management of behavioral problems in mental hospitals.[2]

Subsequent efforts to condition mental patients met with considerable difficulties. Most of these difficulties centered about the effectiveness of the reinforcement. Although it is known from Lindsley's work that candy and cigarettes are very effective with specific individuals, it is clear that these individuals have to be carefully selected to be reinforced with these items. In working with chronic schizophrenic patients, we found this to be a very severe limitation. Since our interest was to use the kind of reinforcer which would have general applicability it became increasingly clear that such a reinforcer already existed in the daily life of the mental patient, namely food. The idea was to use food as the reinforcer to develop appropriate behaviors. However, intensive observations of the behavior of patients attending the dining room where the meals were served indicated that many patients refused food at different times and in some instances with a great degree of consistency. This particular observation led us to first test food as the reinforcement which would be made available to patients for minimal behaviors.

For this purpose, we organized a ward at a mental hospital in Saskatchewan, Canada in which we could regulate major events taking place in it.[1] In this environment, the patient obtained all meals in the dining room right on the ward. We set a time requirement to gain access to the dining room. The behavior was, therefore, easily measured. When patients did not arrive on time, they found the door to the dining room locked. This time requirement started with 30 minutes and was gradually decreased to 5 minutes. Very few patients failed to eat when the requirement was simply that of attending the dining room within 30 minutes from the time the meal was announced. When the requirement was changed so that access to the dining room was available only within 5 minutes from the time the meal was called, patients continued attending meals at about the same rate that they did when they had 30 minutes. It should be noted that throughout this experiment several patients were brought into the ward because of a history of refusal to eat. In this manner, approximately 25 patients were conditioned to eat without any assistance, whereas previously they had required considerable help to eat their daily meals.

Once we knew that food was a powerful reinforcer which affected the behavior of all these female schizophrenic patients, the next step involved the development of a more complex behavior using food as the reinforcer.

The next requirement consisted of dropping a penny into a box with a slot in it which admitted the patient to eat in the dining room. To obtain this penny, the patient had to go to the nurse and the nurse in turn gave her the penny. All patients learned this particular response without much difficulty. Once this complex behavior was developed, we became interested in developing a new response which would require the cooperative effort of two patients to secure the same penny. Therefore, a device was arranged so that pressing two buttons simultaneously turned on a loud buzzer and a light. Two patients were needed to operate the device. If one button was operated and not the other, the device didn't work; and if it didn't work, the patient did not get the penny. Without the penny, the patient couldn't gain access to meals. During the initial stages, verbal instructions were used to shape the patient's behavior, but soon the patients were performing appropriately.

Admittedly "man does not live by bread alone," and food is not the most widely used reinforcer for most human situations. This brings us to the second part of this report, which deals with the use of conditioned reinforcers to develop and maintain appropriate behavior in schizophrenic patients. This work is currently being carried out at the Anna State Hospital in Illinois.

For the experimental analysis of behavior, it has been useful and appropriate to select arbitrary responses for study such as lever pressing, key pushing, or knob pulling. Because we were interested in dealing with what might be intuitively considered meaningful behavior, it was necessary to consider whether behavior patterns displayed by the patients were necessary or useful for them in terms of their transaction with their own environment. In addition it was also necessary that the response be objectively defined and lead to an enduring change on the environment when it occurred. The criteria were met by observing behaviors that were being performed by the paid attendants as part of their job duties; for example, the attendants performed such jobs as serving meals, cleaning floors, sorting laundry, bathing and dressing patients, etc. These were the types of behaviors that we selected for study. A specific example of such a behavior would be washing dishes immediately following a meal. The physical change of the environment that results from this behavior is obviously the cleanliness of the dishes. Other examples that leave an enduring change in the environment are mopping of the floors, serving meals, doing clerical work such as typing, filing, etc. Each of these behaviors fulfills as well the initial requirement that a response be useful and necessary.

A problem regarding the response is that of measurement and recording. It is obviously not possible to observe every patient, every moment, of the day and night to record when and whether the patient was mopping the floor. The alternative to continuous observation was to arrange the environment in a manner such that the response selected could only be emitted at a designated time and place. Thus, in the previous example, the mop was available only at a specified time of the day and for a specific duration. The same requirement was imposed upon other behaviors. Serving meals, washing dishes, and other behaviors allowed this requirement without any special arrangement. In summary, the responses were chosen in terms of their being necessary and useful for the functioning of the patient's environment. Second, the responses were definable in that they eventuated in some enduring change in the environment that could be easily identified by the attendants and thereby recorded. Finally, the recording of the response was usually restricted to a specified time and location.

The definition of reinforcement also constituted a problem. The major problem in this area is that of the objectivity of the definition of the reinforcing stimulus. Typically, one of the types of reinforcement used in verbal conditioning with humans is that of verbal approval. One major problem in this type of reinforcement is its lack of objective specification. Although all attendants may come to be able to reinforce the patients verbally in a standardized fashion, it is still a question whether or not the attendant did indeed deliver such a reinforcement. A possible way of checking whether or not this is being done requires such an expensive apparatus that it would in turn always leave serious doubts as to the feasibility of a practical technology of behavior. Again since verbal reinforcement leaves no enduring change on the environment, it would be extremely difficult to record it even when it occurred. For this reason, only those events were selected as reinforcers that produced thoroughly enduring changes in the environment. An example of an enduring reinforcer might be the opportunity to leave the ward for a walk. The occurrence of such a reinforcer could be easily measured by the experimenter in terms of the presence or absence of the patient on the ward.

The most important consideration in selecting a reinforcer is, of course, that of effectiveness. Although some studies have used cigarettes, candy, and other similar reinforcers, these reinforcers severely limit the type of patients that could be used since obviously not all patients can be reinforced by these events. Indeed, one of the characteristics of mentally ill people seems to be the apparent absence of effective reinforcers for them. To avoid a priori definitions about what might be an effective reinforcer for patients, we relied upon observation of the behavior of the patients to discover what reinforcers might be used. In observing the patients closely, we noted that some patients hoarded various items under their mattresses; others stayed close to the exit door and requested to leave the ward; still others requested to talk to a psychologist or a social worker or physician. All these behaviors could be recorded and noted by direct observation of the patients during the day. Premack[4] has expressed a general principle that any behavior that has a high frequency of occurrence can be used as a reinforcer. Following this general principle, it was possible to arrange situations such that the behaviors that were already displayed by patients were used as reinforcers by allowing the patients to engage in those behaviors at a scheduled time.

The programming and recording constituted a problem in that delivery of the reinforcers would require numerous interruptions of the ongoing behavior, if they were to be delivered appropriately—that is, immediately upon the response. The impracticality of such a procedure led us to consider the use of a conditioned reinforcer to bridge the delay between the occurrence of a response and the availability of the reinforcing stimulus. Thus, the reinforcing stimulus itself need only be exchangeable at a later time with a conditioned reinforcer. For this purpose, we used specially made metal tokens, guaranteeing that the tokens could not be obtained outside of the ward situation. When the appropriate behavior was displayed, the token was delivered to the patient by the attendant. In this manner, the subjective aspects of reinforcing a patient were minimized, and the token exchange was made objective in that they permitted an objective check by the supervising personnel as to the appropriate occurrence of the procedure.

In keeping with operant methodology, we have employed experimental rather than statistical controls to determine the effects of specific procedures on the patient's performance. The experimental design is of the A-B-A type in which each patient serves as her own control.

Now I will describe some of the findings obtained in our research ward where the population consists of chronic schizophrenic female patients. Figure 1 shows the performance of eight patients who worked outside the ward about 6 hours a day, 5 days a week, on hospital industries. Each patient was being reinforced at the conclusion of the work upon her return to the ward. The ordinate shows that each of the eight patients worked consistently when reinforcement followed the appropriate performance on the jobs. The second segment of Figure 1 indicates that when reinforcement was not contingent upon the appropriate performance, the number of hours of work per day

was drastically reduced from 6 to 0. During this period, each patient
was given the same amount of tokens that she had obtained previously,
the only change being that they were available before she went to
work instead of at the completion of her work. The third segment
shows that when the patients were once again given the tokens only
after the completion of their job the number of hours for work returned
to six hours per day. The patients who were working six hours a day
were clearly patients who displayed organized behavior for long
periods of time. The question is whether this finding can be generalized to the behavior of the typical chronic psychotic patient who stays
on the ward because his behavior is not as organized. To answer this
question we utilized the same procedure with the rest of the patients
who stayed on the ward. This meant that we had a population of 44
patients who also were being reinforced for the types of jobs that
were capable of definition and recording. Figure 2 shows the performance of the 44 patients on the ward with respect to jobs which
led to reinforcement. On the ordinate, we see that the number of
hours of work per day for the 44 patients totaled approximately 45.
For 20 days, the procedure consisted of making the reinforcement
available upon the completion of the response or work. On the 21st
day, however, the reinforcement was available before the completion
of the job, and, during this period, we see that the number of hours

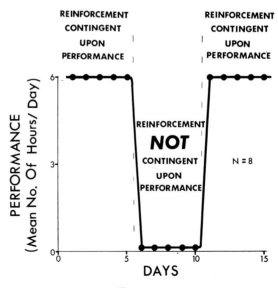

FIGURE 1

of work per day decreased rapidly and stabilized at approximately one hour of work per day. On day 41 of this experiment, the conditions of reinforcement were once again reinstated, and the results are shown on the third segment where the total number of hours of work for the 44 patients rose immediately from one hour per day to 45 hours per day. This particular finding extends those already discussed in Figure 1. It should be pointed out that the attendants' interaction with the patient, as well as the number of tokens available for work, remained constant throughout the experiment. Therefore the patients' work behavior was maintained not by the availability of tokens alone, the interaction with the attendants, or the passage of time. Rather, the findings reveal that when reinforcement is made contingent on behavior it will be maintained for as long as the contingencies are in force.

What is the practical value of this research? It must be remembered that findings from the behavior laboratory indicate that the behavior

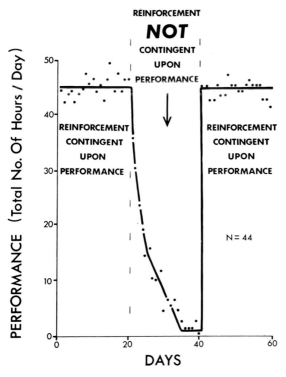

FIGURE 2

of organisms is governed by its consequences. When this information is extrapolated to the behavior of schizophrenic patients, it means that the environment in which mental patients are treated must be programmed to develop and maintain self-initiated behavior and social interaction. Indeed, the effective functioning of the patient's hospital environment must be made dependent upon the patient's own normal behavior. Specifically, the activities that are currently being accomplished by attendants, and sometimes even by the nursing staff, must be reorganized so as to allow the patient to contribute to his own rehabilitation by actively participating in the functioning of his environment. Among these activities one might include cooking and serving meals, cleaning dishes, and general housekeeping chores. It must be noted that these activities include the very behaviors that fulfill a definite and necessary function within the patient's environment. Further, they involve activities to which patients have had exposure prior to being hospitalized. So much for the behavioral requirement, but what about the reinforcement? The reinforcement can include access to social events such as dances, sports, and movies, contingent upon a modicum of normal behavior. An additional reinforcer, psychotherapy, either private or group, can be made available to every patient so long as that patient meets the behavioral requirement.

In summary, if adaptive behaviors such as independence and self-control are the *desiderata* of therapy, then the environment must be designed expressly for this purpose. Irrespective of our own personal wishes and convictions, our goal must be to enable the patient to experience human dignity by becoming useful to himself and to others. I submit to you that this goal can be defined and implemented through current behavioral techniques.

REFERENCES

1. Ayllon, T., and Haughton, E.: Control of the behavior of schizophrenic patients by food. J. Exp. Anal. Behav. 5:343-352, 1962.
2. Ayllon, T., and Michael, J.: The psychiatric nurse as a behavioral engineer. J. Exp. Anal. Behav. 2:323-334, 1959.
3. Lindsley, O. R.: Operant conditioning methods applied to research in chronic schizophrenics. Psychiat. Res. Rep. 5:118-139, 1956.
4. Premack, D. Toward empirical behavior laws: I. Positive reinforcement. Psychol. Rev. 66:219-233, 1959.
5. Skinner, B. F. The Behavior of Organisms: An Experimental Analysis. New York, Appleton-Century-Crofts, 1938.
6. Ayllon, T. and Azrin, N. The measurement and reinforcement of behavior of psychotics. J. Exp. Anal. Behav. 8:357-383, 1965.

13

DISSOCIATION OF LEARNING IN RATS AND ITS SIMILARITIES TO DISSOCIATIVE STATES IN MAN

by EUGENE SACHS, M.D.*

A NIMALS may learn to perform a conditioned response (CR)† quite rapidly under the influence of certain drugs, yet will subsequently show little evidence of the training when tested in a normal (undrugged) state. Conversely, such drugs will often attenuate or abolish CR's acquired prior to treatment. The term "dissociation of learning" has been used to describe such results.[31] The dissociation phenomenon has often been interpreted to mean that drugs induce a change in the mode of brain functioning, such that experience acquired (for example) under a given drug is unavailable in the absence of the drug. The purpose of this paper is to review relevant animal experiments illustrating behavioral and electrophysiological effects common to dissociation-producing drugs and to suggest a reinterpretation of the dissociation phenomenon. An attempt will also be made to relate the laboratory findings to dissociative phenomena in man.

Attention is a fundamental function, both in animals and in man. It is guided explicitly by external events, but the covert determinant of attention is memory. Attention is paid to what is not yet fully known, and most of what an animal already knows is implicit in what fails to attract his attention. We will try to show that it is easier to formulate an objective treatment of the data if we confront the subjective problem as it is. The strategy of "objectifying" attention and reducing the

*Brain Research Laboratories, Department of Psychiatry, New York Medical College, New York, N.Y.

This work was supported by Grant MH-08579 from The National Institute of Mental Health.

†The following abbreviations appear in this paper: CR (conditioned response); CAR (conditioned avoidance response); CDP (chlordiazepoxide or Librium); CPZ (chlorpromazine); CC (control); CER (conditioned emotional response); ECS (electroconvulsive shock); CS (conditioned stimulus); US (unconditional stimulus).

problem to one of stimulus, response, and drive simplifies a theory but not the problem. By reducing the problem of behavior to S-R bonds we may in fact complicate the solution to problems in brain function; since the fixed cost of externalizing the basis of attention, appears to be the internalization of "drives." We will suggest an alternative.

THE NATURE OF DISSOCIATION OF LEARNING

In the original work of Girden,[31-37] the drugs used to demonstrate dissociation of learning (erythroidine and crude curare) also produced paralysis by a blockade of the neuromuscular junction. As a consequence, the issue of the role of the motor response in learning came to be linked with the demonstration of dissociation of learning. It is now clear[107] that no dissociation occurs if animals learn while paralyzed by quarternary curares such as d-tubocurarine. These act peripherally but do not penetrate the blood brain barrier, and the role of the motor response appears to be a separate issue. Gardner and McCulloch[28] have recently confirmed both the original reports of dissociation of learning under erythroidine and, in the same situation, the absence of such an effect for d-tubocurarine. The crucial difference appears to be related to the central actions of erythroidine.

There have been a number of reports [44,89] wherein the performance of animals trained under a drug (chlorpromazine) is significantly worse when tested in the normal state. Otis[89] has attributed the deficit to the absence of (hypothesized) drug-produced cues which had become essential to the performance of drug trained animals. Although he has also called the phenomenon "dissociation of learning," its basis may not be quite the same as the dissociation of learning reported by Girden. It is evident in the curare work that dissociation does not occur despite the very real and massive stimulus change provided by paralysis per se. Overton[90,91] has provided a series of very stringent tests of the potency of drug-produced cues, and has shown rather conclusively that drug-produced cues do not serve to explain his findings of a very clear dissociation of learning with a variety of drugs including anticholinergics, barbiturates, and other depressant drugs.

In earlier work[99,100] we found that cats trained under altered cerebrospinal fluid concentrations of either Ca^{++} or K^+ showed a significant performance deficit when tested in the normal state. This phenomenon also could be called dissociation of learning; however, a very important difference became apparent when we contrasted this effect with the results of a concurrent drug experiment.[102] We discovered that rats trained to perform a conditioned avoidance response (CAR) with chlordiazepoxide (CDP) showed a *complete* absence of retention for the learning when tested in the normal state. In this case the dissociation was not merely a statistically significant decrement in performance, but a very dramatic total dissociation. We also found that the animals trained under CDP acquired the CAR significantly faster than controls, although the drug severely impaired performance in animals originally trained without drug. This constellation of effects was also described in the original reports of Girden, and a search of the literature revealed that it occurs coincidentally in other reports as well. This group of effects, as well as other properties of the same drugs, is sufficiently distinctive to constitute an identifiable and interesting phenomenon. It might be useful if we indicate now that the "rapid learning" produced by this group of drugs can be misleading. If we ignore the issue of "what is learned" and take the response as an index of learning because it is objective and defensible, then by such a criterion these drugs do produce rapid learning of simple consummatory or instrumental responses. We shall try to show that actually the drugged animals learn rapidly because they learn less information, which is why, when drug is withdrawn, they cannot remember information they never learned.

An Illustration

In order to provide a concrete definition of what we shall mean by

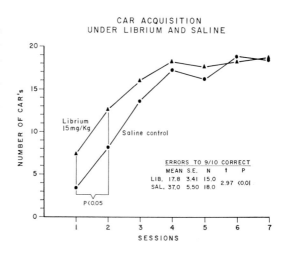

FIG. 1.—Avoidance learning curves of experimental and control groups for first seven sessions (25 days, 140 trials). Differences are significant for each of the first two days and also for an overall test of "errors to 9/10 correct response." In the figures, the trade name "Librium" is used instead of CDP or chlordiazepoxide.

CAR ACQUISITION
UNDER LIBRIUM AND SALINE

Librium 15mg/Kg

Saline control

ERRORS TO 9/10 CORRECT

	MEAN	S.E.	N	t	P
LIB.	17.8	3.41	15.0	2.97	<0.01
SAL.	37.0	5.50	18.0		

P<0.05

NUMBER OF CAR's

SESSIONS

dissociation of learning we will briefly examine some illustrative data.[102] In this experiment rats were trained in a simple hurdle-jump CAR after injections of either saline or CDP (a third group trained with chloropromazine [CPZ] failed to reach the stringent acquisition criterion of 100 per cent correct for three successive sessions of 20 trials each, and were discarded). The acquisition results are presented in Figure 1. It can be seen that the CDP-trained animals were markedly superior on the initial training sessions. The drugged animals were less active and less tense than controls and often were quite ataxic on the initial sessions, yet they learned more rapidly.

After training, the controls were divided into three groups, one of which was tested without further delay (CC group). To control for drug tolerance the remaining control groups were not tested directly, but were either given a series of CPZ injections (TC group) or CDP injections (LC group) which approximated the injection series given the experimental groups during training. The experimental animals were either given a course of saline injections (L_1 group) or tested for dissociation with no waiting period (L_2 group). Figure 2 portrays the outcome of a series of subsequent tests of retention for the CAR. The test series was constructed so that each novel test condition was bracketed by surrounding tests of retention under the same injection condition maintained during training. In the sequence of transfer tests, rats were allowed 20 seconds to respond, which was twice the latency allowed during training; and after every block of 5 test trials (in which failures were unpunished) they received 2 reminder trials in which they were shocked if they exceeded the original 10 second limit. All of the data presented in Figure 2 were based only on the 20 unpunished test trials in each test session and failures were computed as responses with a 20 second latency.

The animals trained with CDP (Librium) retained the CAR perfectly in intercurrent CDP tests; however, on tests with saline and CPZ they showed virtually no retention for the response. The L_1 group was tested in all the transfer conditions while the L_2 group was added later, only to confirm the rapid learning and dissociation. The mean rate of total failures in retention in the L_1 group was 78 per cent for the first saline test and 79 per cent for the first test with CPZ (both significant well beyond the .001 level). This rate of failure was greater than that displayed by the same animals on the very first day of training under drug (despite the doubled latency allowance). On the next two tests they improved, but not very much (50 per cent and 62.5 per cent failures). This sort of dissociation is not a statistical kind of result, and moreover it is a robust phenomenon which does not easily disappear despite reinforced reminder trials. These were no more effective in restoring the response than would be expected of ordinary learning trials.

The adverse effect of CDP on CAR performance of the controls was uniform, substantial (23 per cent failures), and significant ($p < .005$), yet it was significantly less than the effect of saline on CDP-trained animals ($p < .01$). CPZ has about the same effect as

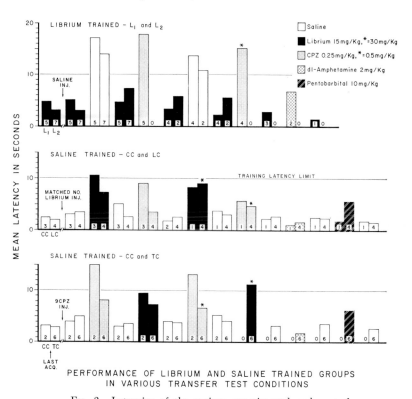

PERFORMANCE OF LIBRIUM AND SALINE TRAINED GROUPS
IN VARIOUS TRANSFER TEST CONDITIONS

Fig. 2.—Latencies of the various experimental and control groups on the last day of training (first bar) and in the various test conditions in the transfer sequence (successive bars). Failures are computed as responses with a latency of 20 seconds. Bars are split to portray separately the performance of the L_1 and L_2 group or the CC animals tested in the same sequence as LC or TC groups. The number of animals in each subgroup test is inscribed within each bar.

CDP on the CAR of controls, however its adverse effect on the CDP-trained animals is, likewise, significantly greater (p < .01). If we examine the control groups separately for evidence of tolerance attributable to drug-produced cues, no significant differences appear; however, from Figure 2 it can be seen that the direction of the differences suggests, if anything, cross tolerance.

Although CPZ and CDP both have the same quantitative effect on the CAR performance of controls, it would seem that the mechanism may be quite different and possibly of an opposite kind. It is generally found that CPZ retards CAR acquisition, and CPZ trained animals, in most reports, perform better when they are returned to the undrugged state.[1,20,21,87,94] The different or opposite nature of the effects of these two drugs is evident in a variety of "fear-motivated" test situations, including the conditioned emotional response (CER),[47,74] conflict or discriminated punishment,[29] and fixated behavior.[75] We are not presently concerned with the CPZ effect, except to note the difference. The literature on CDP, however, suggests quite unequivocally that the drug severely abrogates fear or conflict behavior in rats by almost any measure or method of testing. In the report of Lauener[74] it is evident that CDP is extremely effective in attenuating the CER in the same dose range which, we find, significantly enhances acquisition of the CAR. This seems paradoxical since it is commonly thought to be the case, at least for undrugged animals, that acquisition of the CER (fear of the CS) is a prerequisite for CAR learning. Before we approach this question let us examine additional data which suggest that abrogation of the CER, facilitation of the CAR, and dissociation of learning are commonly associated phenomena. In fact, more generally drugs, lesions, and other treatments which reduce fear also affect memory in a variety of circumstances.

Rapid learning and dissociation

In addition to CDP and the curares used by Girden, dissociation of learning is most often reported for learnings acquired under barbiturates[7,46,79,90,91] and antimuscarinic anticholinergic drugs such as atropine, benactyzine, and scopolamine.[55,90,92] It has also been reported for ethanol[17,90] and after electroconvulsive shock (ECS).[15] The type of learning which is dissociated need not necessarily be based on fear or punishment; however, it must be simple.

The barbiturates,[74,79] anticholinergics[85,86] ECS,[50,124] and ethanol[79] are, however, all well known to rather specifically attenuate the signs of fear or conflict measured by standard tests such as the CER or approach-avoidance conflict.

This same ensemble of agents is also reported to produce rapid learning of simple approach,[4,7] rapid extinction of approach-avoidance conflict,[17,79] and rapid acquisition of the CAR.[5,54,55,116] No rapid learn-

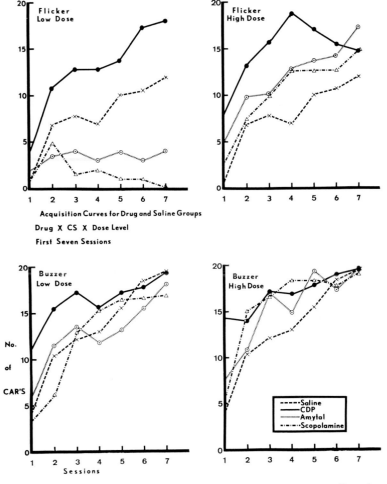

Fig. 3.—The effect of drug, dose, and CS on CAR acquisition in rats. Procedure is similar to that described for Sachs et al.[102] N = 64. Control curves based on N = 8; drug groups, N = 4. Low and high doses in mg./Kg.: CDP, 17.5 and 22.5, amobarbital, 10 and 15; scopolamine, .10 and .15. Control curve is the same in the dose comparisons.

ing of the CAR occurs in the report of Holmgren[46] although the dissociation of the CAR learned under pentobarbital is exceedingly sharp. The drug results in an initial ataxia which is severe enough to block the escape response on the early training sessions, and thus any possible early expression of the CAR might well be obscured by the motor disability.

Recently we have studied the question of the relationship of rapid CAR learning and dissociation in further detail. We used three of the drugs implicated in dissociation of learning (amobarbital, CDP, and scopolamine) at two dose levels and tested CAR acquisition using two kinds of CS, loud buzzer or a ten cps flicker. The results are seen in Figure 3. The buzzer-flicker difference was investigated because the buzzer is well known to be remarkably efficient as a CS for CAR learning, and this proved to be very much the case. Flicker-trained animals learned much more slowly, and a number of them never learned the CAR (except CDP or high-dose drug groups). After some early correct responses such rats showed a decline in performance to near zero levels.

At the higher dose level, amytal and scopolamine both improve initial CAR performance; however CDP at either dose exerts significantly greater effects than either saline or the other two drugs. There are two facets of the data worthy of particular note. The first is that in this experiment the only group of experimental animals which later uniformly showed unambiguous failures in the normal state were the animals trained in the CAR to *flicker* while under *CDP* at either dose. Some CDP-buzzer-trained animals showed a clear effect, while the amytal- and scopolamine-trained groups yielded only a suggestion that such an effect might be obtained if the training dose were higher. From the figure it can be seen that the later dissociation results do not correspond to the rapidity of acquisition per se, but rather to the degree to which the drug *improved* CAR performance over what it normally would be without drug in the saline controls. It is the spurious advantage which is later lost in subsequent tests in the normal state.

Second, if one follows the CS x dose effect for the CDP groups on the *initial* training session, it is clear that dose and CS interact, such that the mean rate of CAR's increases steadily. The rats given the high dose of CDP in the buzzer condition uniformly perform at the highest initial level of any group (Mean 71 per cent, ±15 per cent); in fact, this group appears to already possess the same knowledge of the CAR as is reached by the controls somewhere between the fourth and fifth training session. Unlike the results obtained at lower doses, the learning curve of this group no longer yields very convincing evidence of learning; rather it begins to strongly resemble "release." If it were the case that CDP at 22.5 mg./Kg. produced hyperactivity in rats, then the result might not be as puzzling. However, at this dose the rats are extremely sluggish and markedly ataxic. The sedation is quite evident after training trials, since when they are undisturbed they sleep.

The drug very clearly does not release "motor activity;" it releases the "CAR." From the associated reports, reviewed earlier, it seems reasonable that this release has something to do with the very potent abrogation of the CER by the very same dose of CDP;[74] however, the result cannot simply be explained as a competition between freezing (interpreted as motor inhibition) and an active response such as jumping. The effect appears to be on "fear," which is a much more reasonable general description of both the CER and the varied effects of CDP. Now it is somewhat unusual to suggest that the CAR occurs because fear does not; however, the usual formulation is not completely satisfactory. The CAR is said to be a learned instrumental response, however the hurdle-jump response itself is not learned; it occurs and is smoothly integrated on the first or second escape trial. Moreover, it is difficult to suppose that addition of the drug is equivalent to a sudden increment in "habit strength."

Some questions are evident. What is learned? And what is fear? These are not new questions; however, they still require answers and, in this case, answers which account for the rapid CAR "learning" under drug. In the next section we shall suggest an approach to answering these questions, and then will examine other data on the dissociation of learning to see if the approach is useful.

The Effects of Information

What is learned?

In this section we will re-examine an enduring question: What is learned? The focus of attention will shift from specific data to general questions raised by the data. The reason for this is that it is difficult to explain the previous data, and subsequent data which we shall later examine, without violating some basic tenets of an S-R analysis which have become so firmly entrenched that they seem like facts rather than theory. If we apply an S-R analysis to the collection of drug and lesion data with which we are concerned, then the symptoms fall into a bewildering array of categories. The complexity which results suggests that very many new facts must be uncovered before we can begin to comprehend the many functions performed by each region of the brain or the manifold effects of each drug (on drive. memory, emotion, response shift, habit strength, etc.). We hope to show that there is a simpler way of classifying behavior, and while much needs to be known, many unnecessary questions can arise from an attempt to fit behavior or brain function to schemes whose elementary units differ from the way the brain is organized. Let us recall that the stimulus and response are only objective indices which provide part of the necessary skeleton for a scientific study of behavior; they are not necessarily the appropriate elementary units for analysis of behavior, nor is the brain obligated to treat them as fundamental. The basic ideas we shall present are simple and many are well known, and the argument never strays far from the obvious. It is a different way of categorizing data which suggests an objective alternative to a response definition of learning.

In response to the question "What is learned?" the reply we suggest is that animals normally learn information, and that the variety of symptoms produced by the drugs which produce dissociation all proceed from the insensitivity of drugged animals to *information.* The consequences of an inability to detect the new or different reveals much about the many functions which normally depend on such an ability. Drugged animals are incurious, indistractible, uncautious, and fearless. They do not habituate, although they easily display, or may appear to rapidly learn, consummatory responses which undrugged animals will not display until they have habituated to territory. They perseverate an initial response tendency, fail to alternate or withold responses, and fail to extinguish previously learned responses. They show an immediate memory defect, a spontaneous return of previously extinguished responses, and dissociation of learning. They do learn simple instrumental and consummatory responses rapidly. In a sense they do not change in response to information but do repeat responses which are reinforced. They are S-R animals devoid of all the properties Tolman inferred.

In outline, we will first try to show that these symptoms proceed from an insensitivity to information—used in a fairly exact sense. In later sections we will return to the data which indicate that they do occur in common association, and that lesions and drugs which produce these symptoms all abolish the behavioral and EEG indices of attention.

At a later point it will be appropriate to indicate how a rigorous definition of information can be formulated. In a preliminary way let us indicate that "information" as we shall use the term is not a property of the stimulus message per se but that portion of it which is "news" or uncertain in the sense that it cannot immediately be classified among a universe of already known alternative bins or categories. This differs only in sign from the customary expression of information as a gain in certainty or as uncertainty that is reduced once the message is classified. The distinction is useful because in systems that learn, the effect of information is a change in the universe of alternatives such that the next time the message is repeated it contains less information or is more easily classifiable. "Learning" then shall refer to the change wrought in what is already known, which is brought about by receiving and classifying a message which is initially discrepant in some way from prior knowledge. If we call that part of the stimulus which is *initially* discrepant, "information" and the ensemble of pre-existing categories "knowledge," then learning is the transformation of information into knowledge. When a stimulus is known, all its information has been stored inside the brain; the stimulus remains the same but the brain does not.

Now it is evident that information is not an objective property of the physical stimulus (although, a priori or potential stimulus information is calculable). The "news" a stimulus conveys to the receiver is solely determined by its discrepancy from prior alternative categories within the receiver, and as it is repeated the discrepancy dwindles. It would seem that this is an inconvenient way to define stimulus information or the learning of it, and is less satisfactory than the customary S-R view of a pristine "stimulus." This is true and it would be a strong argument against a theory that animals learn "information," but it is not adequate to dismiss many facts suggesting that they do.

Although to formally calculate the information a stimulus conveys we need to know parameters which are buried inside the brain, there are very many objective measures which reflect the loss of stimulus information. They are in effect behaviors, EEG and autonomic measures which reflect attention, and they show a steady decline in magnitude as animals gain familiarity with an environment. The same *decline* in the signs of attention occurs in CAR learning[39,78] and is most easily studied in a simple habituation experiment.

As a neutral stimulus is repeated the signs of attention wane, and since the stimulus remains constant we can only conclude that some change has occurred inside the animal. The loss of reactivity is as acceptable as evidence of a change inside the nervous system as a positive learned response. If the decrement in "attensity" is retained only temporarily, then it qualifies as immediate or recent memory; while if it is retained permanently, as a decreased tendency to respond to a stimulus, then it qualifies as permanent memory. It might be said that animals do not pay attention to things they already know. This is not as dramatic as a CR but is much more pervasively true.

Although tedious, it is possible to find out what an animal has learned by habituation. This can be done by introducing small changes into the habituation situation to indirectly ascertain what is familiar by testing what is unfamiliar. It is commonly found that although the ostensible habituating stimulus is, for example, a tone pip, any slight change in the visual field, any new odor, sound, interruption, or irregularity will produce dehabituation and attention. The animal, in habituating, seems to have gained a fairly exact (negative) image of the entire sensory context, and if the initially distracting test stimulus is repeated often enough, the picture will expand to include it. If we begin to vary a few more parameters, such as testing for generalization of habituations (which does occur) we may come to the conclusion that by habituating to an interrelated series of such contexts, (some of whose elements are common, an animal must acquire fairly organized knowledge, whose structure must come to reflect the invariant aspects of the environment. Habituation extracts invariants selectively—since the constant features of the environment are those most prone to be repeated. Further, since the disturbance evoked by a stimulus is proportional to its unfamiliarity, the residual "knowledge" acquired by habituation is logically equivalent to an expectancy. Not that an animal actively expects stimuli, but merely that stimuli will evoke a response or compel attention commensurate with their unexpectedness (infrequent previous occurrence).

It is evident from the above that habituation or negative learning suitably fulfills the definition of "information acquisition," since as a consequence of iterations *stimulus contexts* lose their "news." The structure of knowledge must eventually come to conform to the structure of reality since detectable discrepancies compel attention until they habituate. When we subject a nervous system which can demonstrably habituate to the detectable discrepancies in a single context, to the large variety of such contexts which an animal typically encounters, the animal should inadvertently acquire the "cognitive maps" which Tolman inferred, merely if it were obliged to pay attention to information. Now the index of the knowledge gained by such a process is inattention and is not as palpable as a response; however it is quite realistic to expect that animals should ignore the well known, *unless some change occurs which makes it relevant.*

Normally we expect that animals should know the obvious perceptual facts about the structure of the environment, and we expect much of the above without close scrutiny. The process of habituation involves *responses;* however, they are not easily controllable by the experimenter since they constantly change as attention is directed in turn to each feature of the stimulus world which is still unclassified. The vicarious trial and error responses, novelty responses, orienting responses, etc. are appropriately performed by an animal for reasons we do not study but accept as natural. These responses may indeed reflect the process of classifying information, of *discarding alternatives;* and when they are finished, learning may substantially be complete or uncertainty reduced. Why else do they constantly change and finally cease? If an animal learned nothing by performing such exploratory responses, then the first one that he tried should perseverate indefinitely (which indeed occurs after drug, etc.).

Now a rat does not try to jump over a lever, nor attack it, nor will it freeze when first introduced into an otherwise familiar situation. A rat will press, bite, sniff, gnaw, lick, or rub up against a lever, and will do most of these things successively in the course of exploring, and finally will curl up and sleep and ignore the lever. Those possibilities that never occurred to the rat to even try are what the rat knew for certain about the lever the first time he saw it, and those alternatives that he exhausted in the course of exploration represent the "information" initially possessed by the lever. The gain in certainty or the reduction in the initial uncertainty of alternatives is how information is usually measured, and when the rat has learned all the things that the lever is not, he has classified the situation among his known alternatives and gained its information. Since most of this information is retained until the next day (measured by the decrease duration of attention) it is proper to say that the gain in certainty is now part of knowledge.

Now it is possible to formulate the above in terms of the response by assuming that there is an innate habit family hierarchy attached to each stimulus an animal might possibly encounter. It is a cumbersome way of expressing perception, and it does not account for its fine details nor for how an animal comes to know anything about the world. Eventually it entails the assumption that an animal is born with all the knowledge it needs in order to recognize what it sees, hears, etc. It is as if all an animal ever learned were the responses we can control by reinforcement. In effect, the stimulus is made equivalent to stimulus "information" by assuming a vast store of innate knowledge. This is not an empirical treatment.

The usual alternative to this is a curiosity drive or a stimulus hunger reduced by learning sensory information. This does not account for why animals lose their fear of intense novelty, but by and large it internalizes and makes volitional the same relationship we suggest (information compels attention). Ultimately the source of such a drive is memory, since what is new always depends on what is old. Calling "attention" a drive complicates the issue. Its sole advantage is its compatibility with S-R theory. The attention of rats or humans is compelled by distractions, incongruities, etc. independent of prior fear or curiosity.

The Response

Now, normally if an animal (in the course of exploring) presses a lever and it delivers a food pellet, acquisition of the response is not immediate. The accepted way of accounting for the resultant learning curve is to suggest that the response must be strengthened by reinforcement. The response itself is first performed by the animal prior to the reinforcing consequence. What information is learned? If the situation is made simpler and a hungry rat is merely introduced into a test box in which food is displayed in plain sight for a brief period, the rat will spend most of this limited time in exploring and will hardly eat. On successive days, although the rat is extremely hungry, the time spent eating will slowly increase, and the time spent exploring gradually decrease.[43] This also results in a learning curve. Is eating a learned response? If rats are trained in a simple drinking response, then it has been shown that when changes are made in the stimulus situation the disruption of the drinking response is proportional to the number of stimulus alterations.[26] Do these stimulus alterations evoke competing responses because of their own particular S-R connections?

There are many different labels and descriptions applied to explain data such as these. It is commonly the case that rats and many other animals will not perform consummatory responses (eating, drinking, fighting, copulation, micturition, etc.) out of territory—in a strange surrounding. The responses that compete with these consummatory activities are novelty or attention responses.[6] They include exploring, orienting, hesitant responses such as rearing or nervous grooming, and the freezing, defecation, and urination associated with the CER. As the information in the environment is increased (novel stimulus changes), rats display responses which reflect curiosity, caution, and fear, and they do not engage in consummatory activities.

If we place a rat in the center of an open field and no route of escape is apparent, it is likely that he will freeze and watch. After watching and detecting no movement, the rat unfreezes and cautiously ventures forth and finally actively explores, displaying in reverse order the novelty responses described by Bindra.[6] At every point the form of his response is appropriate to the unfamiliarity of the situation, and it is worth noting that the situation becomes increasingly familiar as a result of paying attention and learning, otherwise he would never unfreeze. As a consequence of a sequence such as this a rat established territoriality, and from latent learning experiments we know that the gain in familiarity which permits the rat to unfreeze, explore, and finally drowse in territory is equivalent to knowledge of the layout of the territory.

In the course of exploring, the rat pays attention in turn to each aspect of the environment that remains unfamiliar, and as a consequence of inspection it becomes familiar and no longer compels attention. It is not a particular response which has extinguished, but the stimulus information which has habituated. The rat will direct the same attentive response to another feature of the environment which still is uncertain.

The rat will not eat in an unfamiliar situation, and whether this relation is labeled "establishment of territoriality," "learning to eat," "extinction of a competing curiosity (or fear) drive," "distraction," "external inhibition," or "competing responses linked to the new stimuli" the essential features do not differ very much. The same unfamiliarity that inhibits eating initially, inhibits it subsequently in distraction experiments. Rats who are insensitive to information "learn" the initial approach to food more rapidly than normals, and are also indistractible subsequently. The consummatory response is not learned; it is "released" by the absence of information. Normally this occurs slowly, by virtue of a succession of attention responses which result in habituation, etc., and eating occurs when the situation retains no residual information. Drugs which make animals insensitive to information provide an instant certainty normally gained by learning.

The distinction between the certainty provided by knowledge and the certainty provided by drug becomes evident when the drug is withdrawn. The animals who experienced the situation under drug have learned virtually no information. First we will illustrate much of the preceding discussion by examining additional data on dissociation of learning in which the responses which do not occur are exploratory or cautious responses. Later we will return to re-examine the CER and CAR to see what is learned.

The Absence of Attention

The need for distinguishing between a change in response and a change in knowledge is clearest in a group of drug studies in which rapid approach "learning" and dissociation occur with barbiturates, and related effects are evident with anticholinergics. In this case the defects in attention and habituation are easily discernible and visibly related to both dissociation and perseveration of the response. We will encounter another difficulty related to the form of the response. When an animal looks at something, how are we to know that he is not really paying "attention" to it? If an animal is hyperactive, what basis is there for claiming that he is not really exploring? The question has a face validity since if an animal is not asleep his head is always pointed in some direction, yet he need not be paying attention.

Sometimes there appear to be visible differences in the nature of the response such that the animals are described in these reports as "automata," or as displaying a stereotypic or exaggerated orienting response, or as delirious, confused, or randomly directed. Thus the observable response may be different; however, this is not always dependable. There are other objective and noncircular ways of answering the question, if it needs to be answered. We hope to demonstrate that it is unrealistic and unprofitable, to avoid a consideration of what takes place inside the rat's brain.

In the report of Bloch and Silva[7] rats given pentobarbital learned to traverse an unbaited four-unit T-maze strikingly faster than controls, yet when tested in the undrugged state the pentobarbital group performed worse than they had on the first day under drug. Instead they behaved as did the saline group on the first day of training, displaying exploratory, cautious, and fearful responses typical of rats in a new situation.

The authors described the acquisition effect as pseudo learning because drugged rats performed like automata, displaying no signs of curiosity or attention. According to the authors, they did not actually learn the maze and hence could not remember. The controls who explored in the unbaited trials, at the expense of efficient maze running, displayed very clear evidence of latent learning in the later reinforced tests.

In the report of Barry et al.,[4] despite some ataxia, rats treated with amobarbital or ethanol performed a runway approach response significantly faster than controls, but only on the initial block of trials, an outcome which was observably related to the absence of initial novelty responses. The same faster running speeds of undrugged animals is also obtained in the initial extinction trials (but is explained differently, in terms of reduction of anticipatory frustration).

With pentobarbital, Rosenzweig et al.[97a] found that rats do not vary their initial preference for entering lighted alleys while controls show a curve of increasing variability and soon come to alternate choices equally. In the undrugged state the originally drugged animals first begin to show the same curve of increasingly varied choice behavior shown by the controls earlier; however, when the control group is subsequently given drug, after losing the initial preference, the original perseverative tendency is only partially restored.

Thus rats under barbiturate are not attracted or frightened by novelty, nor are they bored by repetition. The effects of the experience under drug do not appear to have registered. The drug abrogated the normal tendency of rats to prefer the maze arm other than the one they had just seen ("spontaneous alternation"). The absence of the usual spontaneous alternation might be called perseveration of response or a lack of curiosity, or might be attributed to a recent memory defect. Since the drug does not cause perseveration or response stereotypy in the already experienced controls, it would seem that the perseveration of the initial preference might well be the consequence of a recent memory or habituation defect. The failure to habituate would also explain why in the later trials, without drug, animals first began to vary their choice, as did the control initially. Although behavior was altered by drug, nothing appears to have been learned.

In a later experiment, Morosz[81] obtained the same finding (perseveration under pentobarbital) using a *trained* preference instead of an initial unconditioned tendency. Animals were first taught a maze habit and the maze was then subsequently made unsoluble. Because the maze habit was learned, the lack of variability or the perseveration produced by drug in this experiment would be called an extinction defect—a finding also obtained with amobarbital[110] in a straightforward investigation of extinction. This might suggest that the faster running speed of the drugged animals in the initial acquisition trials, as well as in the initial extinction trials,[4] are the same phenomenon. Rats run toward the goal more efficiently because they do not explore, and there is a basis for inferring that they do not explore because there is no reason to explore—nothing has changed. Thus they are not distracted by the initial novelty of the test situation nor by the abrupt change to extinction conditions later on, a change which ordinarily detracts from the exclusive interest animals show in the goal box, and which normally results in their looking elsewhere for food.

Rushton et al.[98] tested the activity of rats given an amobarbital-amphetamine mixture and briefly exposed to an unfamiliar Y-maze. They found that the drugged rats were twice as active as controls. In a subsequent retest half of each original group was drugged and half undrugged. On the retest they found that the drug did *not* increase the activity of those rats who initially experienced the maze in the normal state, but retained its ability to enhance activity in the group who had also received the drug initially; thus previous experience determined the nature of the drug effect. The report is similar in import to that of Moroz;[81] however, the addition of amphetamine heightens the activity levels of rats in an unfamiliar situation. For this reason it might seem that the greater activity of drugged rats is equivalent to exploration. If we interpret the contribution of amobarbital in the light of previous barbiturate results, we might conclude that rats given the drug mixture are twice as active in an unfamiliar situation, and the situation continues to be unfamiliar as a consequence of its being experienced under drug.

The distinction between activity and exploration is more clearly seen with the anticholinergic drugs. These are often reported to result in hyperactivity of a randomly directed, confused, or "delirious" nature (e.g., White et al.[119]) On tests of spontaneous alternation[84] rats given scopolamine alternate significantly *below* chance levels while normal rats in this and many other reports alternate far above chance levels (in many reports at 90 per cent or better). The heightened activity is therefore not exploratory in the sense of investigating the new and different. Rats do not appear to be able to selectively detect the new and different, and hence the new and different never becomes old and boring.

Carlton[14] has reviewed much of the literature on the behavioral effects of anticholinergics. The same defect shows up in learned alternation tests and, like the barbiturate effect, results in a failure in extinction. At higher doses of barbiturate, animals fall asleep and cannot be tested; while with the anticholinergic drugs it appears that as the dose increases, the effects of previous experiences are progressively *reversed;* thus previously extinguished appetitive responses reappear, previous habituated preferences disappear,[14] and previously extinguished CAR's reappear.[30,55] Also, the confused hyperactivity is reported to increase as the dose *increases*.[86,119]

The loss of knowledge: Surprise vs. Attention

The anticholinergic drugs abolish the neocortical and hippocampal rhythms associated with attention, arousal, or wakefulness;[93,119] a phenomenon which Wikler[122] called the "dissociation of EEG and behavior" because animals whose EEG's are indicative of sleep are behaviorally active or even excited. The barbiturates produced similar EEG changes, but at slightly higher doses, behavioral sleep occurs as well. It is clear that these drugs can to varying degrees affect "attention" without impairing activity levels. The behavioral effects of the anticholinergic drugs (and barbiturate-amphetamine mixtures) may tell us something about the state of attention which normally obtains in the sleeping state.

As the dose level of anticholinergic drugs is increased, animals not only fail to habituate or extinguish responses, but show a progressive dehabituation and a reversal of prior extinctions. In the previous section we suggested that information is acquired and stored as habituation, and here it is evident that as the dose is increased animals first display an insensitivity to information, and subsequently a loss of prior knowledge. The delirious or confused symptoms also suggest such an amnesia or agnosia, and may provide some measure of just how much knowledge is implicit in what animals normally ignore. The role of knowledge in determining what can be information (or the role played by memory in focusing attention) is, perforce, covert. All we can ever observe is what animals *do* pay attention to. Why do the drugged animals become increasingly agitated as the dose is increased?

The delirium caused by the anticholinergics is clearly not explorative in the sense of orienting to the new, and it might be more interpretable if we made a distinction between attention and surprise or startle. The *completely* unfamiliar contains no "information" the first time it occurs —no alternatives pre-exist. (No dehabituation can occur until one habituation trial has occurred.) Surprise or startle have the property that they occur on the first one or two presentations and disappear as soon as the stimulus can be expected. In effect they are inhibited by learning or attention. One interesting distinction is that startle elicits hippocampal desynchronization in the cat, and that the theta rhythm and orienting movements rapidly supplant this response, after a very few trials.[39] On this basis Grastyan has proposed a distinction between learned and unlearned orienting responses and has suggested that the theta rhythm and orienting are rapidly learned. Also, the symptoms of septal and hippocampal lesions (which abolish the hippocampal theta rhythm[13]) include an explosive startle response which is very slow to accommodate or an incessant "exploration" which is accompanied by a spontaneous alternation defect. Since, as we will later see, the lesions result in nearly all of the symptoms previously seen with the drugs, there is a substantial basis for contrasting surprise and attention. For example, in rabbits at very low barbiturate doses pain elicits only hippocampal desynchronization instead of the normal theta rhythm,[40] providing some objective basis for assuming that stimuli register differently inside the brain as a function of either knowledge or drug.

The formal argument is clear. Unfamiliarity is not identical to information; it can only become uncertain after some initial information has been acquired, when alternative *possibilities* have been established but their *probabilities* have not.

The persistence of the initial unconditioned attraction of rats under pentobarbital to the lighted alleys[81] illustrates the same "surprise" which differs from attention in that it is neither directed at information nor reduced by knowledge. The increasingly excited delirium of animals given anticholinergic drugs might be said to reflect a progressive gain in surprise which occurs because knowledge acquired by prior habituations is progressively lost. There is one very interesting indication that such symptoms do provide a clue to what happens to attention during sleep.

Jung[60] reports an experiment with humans wherein the EEG and autonomic response to a startle stimulus (gun shot) was studied both in the waking and sleeping states. In the waking state the startle response was fully habituated on repetition such that the signs of autonomic and EEG arousal (beta rhythm) disappeared. During sleep, however, subjects dishabituated completely and failed to rehabituate. The full autonomic response was restored and the stimulus continued to elicit a clear (but different) EEG response (alpha activation) without abatement. If, instead of alpha activation, the gunshot elicited the initial beta rhythm, the subject awakened.

Thus in normal human sleep, in the absence of attention or vigilance, the startle response reappears in a slightly altered form and fails to accommodate thereafter. The septal lesion produces this condition, at least temporarily in rats, and it may be attenuated more rapidly if rats receive supplemental sensory experience.[45] The nonaccommodating startle response remains a permanent property of neodecorticate animals.[59] In the case of startle (and also laughter) in humans, the conditions for its occurrence and nonoccurrence are not a mystery. It is a response to the totally unexpected which is inhibited in one or at most a few trials by the information gained by the previous exposures —when attention or expectation becomes possible. In young children, startle and laughter are clearly responses to surprise; however, as knowledge is gained it appears that the two become more differentiable according to stimulus intensity (and laughter also acquires a social function). It remains true that a joke works best the first time, and that the humor of the joke is not an objective property of the joke.

Incessant laughter is reported to occur (in humans) as an effect of a high dose of benactyzine. The cause of the laughter could not be communicated in the drug state and could not be recalled in the normal state.[72] The symptom recurs in related reports of agents that produce dissociation in humans, as does amnesia and delirium. Does a drug make a joke funny or does it stimulate a laughing drive or does it make a person silly, as it were, by depriving him of his wits?

The relation between incessant laughter in humans and incessant random activity in rats is purely formal at best. The same drug, benactyzine, does produce both effects and its mode of action is quite general—inhibition of cholinergic transmission. Further it is plain that in humans prior *knowledge* inhibits surprise, which is also why humans *stop* looking at an object. There is no reason to suppose that the rat brain obeys fundamentally different laws. When a rat perseverates it does not follow that this is *caused by* an inability to shift response and when rats become increasingly hyperactive it need not be motor activity, *as such*, that has been released. It is true that perseveration and hyperactivity are all that we can observe, but it may be misleading to incorporate the observations directly into explanations. It may obscure features which are common to rodent and human behavior, and hence enpoverish the animal research of its applicability.

A condition which enhances arousal, such as food deprivation, increases the exploratory activity levels of rats; however, it does not increase activity in a constant stimulus environment but specifically makes them more reactive to novel stimuli. Associated with the increased "interest" of stimuli is an increase in the rate of spontaneous alternation, and on subsequent tests of latent learning the result is apparent— they learn more about the environment. By contrast the drugs that abolish EEG arousal (without producing sedation) result in hyperactivity which appears different to observers—randomly directed, confused, or delirious rather than exploratory. In a situation in which the stimulus possibilities are reduced it is found that the hyperactivity which had occurred in a new or complex environment is replaced by perseveration. Spontaneous alternation falls below random levels, and learned alternation deteriorates as well. Each glance brings in no information—even if reinforcement is contingent on recall. Thus learned delay and alternation become impossible. The failure in habituation which prevents stimuli from losing their information prevents the animal from gaining it; thus we find perseveration in the drug state and dissociation in the undrugged state.

Initially the environment is the source of the "activity drive" in this case as well. In the evidence reviewed on the effects of barbiturates and the barbiturate-amphetamine combination, rats retain habituations acquired in the normal state[81,98] but fail to habituate to new environments while in the drug state. The anticholinergic drugs produce a reversal of prior habituations and extinctions, and the effect of increasing doses (with environment constant) is increasingly excitatory. Unlike the gain in stimulus "information" produced by excitants, we suggest that the increased activity in this case is caused by a loss of knowledge, such that the environment becomes increasingly unfamiliar. The distinction between excitation vs. disinhibition of motor activity is then equivalent to attention vs. surprise. Attention wanes when the stimulus habituates, while the surprise endures uninhibited by information and results in no retention.

Conflict and Fear

In response to an increase in the number of stimulus changes in the environment normal animals display responses reflecting curiosity, caution, and fear. Although the information in each stimulus change cannot be quantified, clearly these qualify as responses to increasing uncertainty—to possibilities which can be detected but not classified. Fear naturally occurs in response to the uncertain but not to the unknown. Ignorance (of possibilities) is bliss. Fear is an emotion insofar as it involves many visceral and autonomic components; however, it is occasioned by uncertainty and it is normally reduced by knowledge.

The pseudo-CER (freezing, etc.) is elicited by stimulus change alone, and the CER produced by pairing CS and shock may also be most easily understood in the same terms. In a similar situation in which an animal can identify the source of danger (and the region of safety) it does not occur in response to pairing shock and tone.[49] Instead the animal, quite unemotionally, passively avoids the region of danger for the duration of the CS. The CER, like the pseudo-CER, may be understood as an attention response—not that an animal is curious but that he must look if he cannot discern a safe route of escape. He does not understand the territory. Although it is produced by conditioning procedures it grows progressively weaker as CS-shock pairings are repeated, and finally it disappears spontaneously.[48] In the course of CER training, Coppock[19] has shown that a large increase in orienting to the CS ensues. The reason the CS grows weaker rather than stronger with pairings seems to be that information is gained by paying attention, and as a consequence habituation occurs to the CS.

While it is true that an animal will approach the mildly new or withdraw from the highly uncertain, the problem of casting the behavioral responses to information in a reinforcement framework is that information declines as knowledge is gained. Consummatory approach or avoidance responses are stable; they are protected from extinction and are disrupted by stimulus change. The drugs that attenuate the animal's response to information exert comparatively little effect on consummatory responses. Moreover, it is the fear response that occurs in the poorly understood situation that is selectively vulnerable to ECS[16] rather than the discriminated passive avoidance. The crucial effect of ECS is not best understood in terms of positive or negative reinforcement, but rather appears to affect the response to uncertainty—whether it attracts curiosity or induces withdrawal. When the animal can clearly identify the region of danger and the region of safety, he already knows the situation rather well and is not apt to freeze. It takes many more ECS shocks to interfere with such established knowledge than it takes to eliminate his response to the less well known. An animal may passively avoid because he is freezing, not because he understands where the region of danger is; and if the measure of passive avoidance is failure to approach, the two responses may appear identical. The assumptions that fear is a "negative drive", that a stimulus is stimulus information, and that a response is a measure of learning generate immense complexity. This is most evident in the case of the CAR.

First let us examine some data on the dissociation of "conflict extinction training." There are two experiments[17,79] in which the transfer to the undrugged state of conflict extinction training is explicitly tested, and both cases (alcohol and amytal) result in rapid extinction under drug which does not transfer to the normal state. Miller[79] contrasted amytal and CPZ, using the conflict extinction as a model of therapy, and concluded that while amytal facilitates the extinction, the benefits do not transfer (while CPZ training is carried over). Miller[79] also demonstrates that alcohol and amytal attenuate fear in a variety of other situations and that whether the dissociation of amytal training is regarded as a test of conflict extinction or conflict retention is purely a matter of nomenclature. From the curves presented, it appears that full attenuation occurs on the first day.

The same attenuation of conflict is reported for benactyzine, other barbiturates, CDP, and ECS in data cited previously, in which no transfer is measured. In these studies the drugs simply are said to attenuate conflict or approach-withdrawal, etc. The drugs make the animals insensitive to uncertainty or danger, and whether the effect is considered to be therapeutic or maladaptive, it seems to be purely symptomatic. The same information that animals do not detect, they do not learn or remember. The boldness animals gain by drug is normally gained by learning; by paying attention to the source of conflict and, as its information is reduced, by approaching it more closely, etc.

The CAR—what is learned?

The CAR is generally taken as a valid example of a learned *response*. Its learning is usually said to involve two factors, acquisition of fear as a consequence of CS-shock pairings and the learning of an instrumental response which is reinforced by reduction of the learned fear drive. A more recent version of the two factor theory[83] suggests that the CAR is maintained by positive reinforcement—that is, animals jump to obtain safety or security rather than to avoid fear.

While we agree that the CAR is a consummatory activity, conserved because it leads to safety, we will try to demonstrate that it is essentially a cognitive problem whose solution involves identifying the region of danger and the region of safety, and that past the point at which the first escape response is learned or performed, the problem does not involve the response at all. Fear is an attention response to great uncertainty and persists so long as the region of safety remains unknown and then disappears, and the CAR is preserved from change only when the region of safety is discovered; at this point the autonomic signs of fear and the EEG signs of attention diminish and soon disappear.

The difficulty is created by the fact that animals learn *stimulus contexts* not a CS per se. The fact that they do learn stimulus contexts was indicated in the discussion of habituation, and the fact that they do not normally learn to isolate the CS from context (unless this is specifically made a problem) is shown by the inability of a CS to elicit a CR out of the original experimental context (Pavlovian external inhibition). There is reason to believe that this is a specific problem in the case of the two-way CAR. The one-way hurdle-jump CAR is learned twice as rapidly as the two-way CAR, yet it can involve the same apparatus, CS, US, and response.[77] The obvious difference and the usual explanation is that in the two-way task conflict is produced by requiring an animal to return to the place where he had just been shocked. For conflict to exist it must logically be the case that the animal fails to recognize that the region of danger is not a place, nor a compound of place plus CS (as is usual in his experience and as is true of the one-way task) but an abstract CS. In order for the animal to learn to abstract the CS from its stimulus context and react to it specifically, he must at least accumulate sufficient experience to learn what is *not* dangerous; he may need to learn that it is not the box that is appearing and disappearing but the light source that is flickering. The light is the danger signal, not the bars which actually hurt him, and it is not a specific place that is safe but CS offset.

While the two-way CAR transfers almost immediately to the one-way, the reverse is not the case. In fact there is virtually no savings, despite the similarity of CR, CS, US, and test box.[77] What needs to be learned? Suppose we take the problem as formulated—conflict. How is the conflict reduced? By experiencing each of the nonessential features of the situation without the painful consequence—i.e., by habituation of irrelevant alternatives. Equivalently, the CS is abstracted from its context.

The CER or freezing response, as previously suggested, occurs when an animal cannot identify a region of safety; thus he must look. The uncertainty of the context is largely created by the US, whose information does not habituate by repetition but is terminated only by a response. Animals not only freeze to CS or US but concurrently attempt to classify the situation by a number of strategies involving attempts at aggression or escape, which initially are equally attention responses. The same escape response will eventually be a consummatory response when it is performed not as a question but as an answer. When the animal performs it initially he cannot know that it will be successful, and in this sense it is a question: It occurs in response to uncertainty. The escape response solves the question of the US and it is maintained. This occurs quite rapidly.

When the escape response occurs to the CS it qualifies as a CAR, yet it may still be a question rather than an answer. There are two good reasons for believing this is true. First of all the CAR will increase markedly in the initial sessions, although it is not reinforced by either CS offset or US offset.[62,63] Such CAR's occur despite nonreinforcement or punishment, and thus they cannot be performed to obtain relief. Further, the unreinforced groups show a gradual late decline at about the same time the normally reinforced group shows the usual abrupt rise in CAR performance. The same sort of discontinuous change in the slope of learning curves is often taken as evidence of "insightful solution" in less emotional learning situations, and since the problem was soluble in this group and not in the others, there is good reason to believe that they "caught on" to the answer.

Also, in a number of recent reports;[18,96] it is found that a fair proportion of rats show an early rise in CAR performance and a subsequent paradoxical gradual decline and spontaneous extinction, although CAR's *are reinforced* as usual by CS offset and by the withholding of the US. Since the same phenomenon occurs in the insoluble nonreinforced CAR, perhaps it is that these rats have been asking a question and never caught on to the fact that they had received an answer. Reynierse et al. report that these rats show an increasing tendency to freeze. It may be that they had not caught on to the answer but continued to ask the same question because of the success of the escape response, and that they finally froze because they could not discover a region of safety.

The definition of danger and safety is easily discernible for the US, and the escape response meets the problem exactly. However, if, as it appears from the report of Lubar and Perachio,[77] cats cannot easily extract the CS from its context, which is the crucial exteroceptive discrimination, then the problem cannot be trivial for rats. Until they begin to know what is dangerous (the CS) and what is safe (its offset), how can they appreciate the answer when they receive it.

Now it is both questionable and tedious to attempt to reconstruct what the rat can know and what he cannot. Let us shift the burden. (a) Why are there no savings from the one-way to the two-way CAR? (b) Why do rats perform the CAR although they are not reinforced? (c) Why do they spontaneously extinguish although they are reinforced? Is this a strengthening of S-R connections by reinforcement? What is the reinforcer?

Whatever is the exact nature of the difficulty faced by normal animals in acquisition of the CAR, the ease of acquisition of the drugged animals is less inexplicable. They have much less of a problem to learn, since they cannot discern the complexities which frighten the normal animal. The problem of achieving safety is more easily met, since the requirements are minimal. Less information is detected, less is learned, and less is recalled. Normally the response is the answer to the problem of the CAR; however, drugged animals appear to already know the answer. Their performance in the normal state suggests that they have yet to learn the problem.

It is possible to be more specific in the case of the rapid acquisition displayed by septal rats. These animals learn a two-way CAR much more rapidly than normals but show no advantage on the one-way problem. This suggests that they learn more rapidly because they are actually learning an easier task. This is supported by related reports (reviewed later) which suggest an immediate memory defect. The conflict which is said to make the two-way problem difficult in normals presupposes that they detect the discrepancy between the outcome of the previous trial and the requirements of the present trial. Normals hesitate to jump into a region whose dangerous possibilities have just previously been established and so they freeze. Septal rats do not freeze because they do not detect this discrepancy, hence literally the problem involves less information, less "emotionality," etc. The same analysis should hold for drugged animals.

In the following section we will try to show that the hippocampal theta rhythm provides an excellent objective index of "attention" as defined by exacting behavioral tests, and that the lesions which abolish the rhythm produce the same kinds of symptoms as the drugs, with one exception: dissociation of learning.

An objective measure of attention

The hippocampal theta rhythm occurs in response to novel exteroceptive stimuli and declines with repetition and may thus be said to follow information or be a sign of attention. It also is elicited by unconditioned stimuli such as pain,[40] which may be considered homeostatic information about which certainty is gained by relief rather than repetition. It accompanies the orienting response (but not startle) and occurs early in simple approach or avoidance conditioning, ceasing as the consummatory response (CAR or appetitive instrumental CR) appears. It disappears in the well-trained animal except for distractions and procedural variations at the onset of extinction or differentiation, when it recurs accompanied by orienting.[38] In the report of Torii and Sugi[114] it is evident that it accompanies the same spectrum of novelty responses described by Bindra.[6]

The hippocampal theta rhythm does not disappear but abruptly increases in frequency and regularity in the case of an approach discrimination in which a decision between alternatives is required on every trial;[2] it breaks up, however, during the consummatory response. In Sidman avoidance its sudden increase in frequency and regularity initiates the response, such that an animal leaves the neutral corner and approaches the lever.[11] It accompanies deliberate movements[117] or attention to external events;[38] it, however, does not occur when the animal makes automatic adjustments or when his glance shifts about in the course of his ordinary activities.

One very clear reason for identifying the rhythm as reflecting attention is its very good covariation with the orienting response. The turning of the receptor surface toward the novel stimulus source is the essential aspect of both orientation and attention, and one could hardly find a better objective measure of attention than the orienting response.

However, an even subtler measure is demonstrable in the work of Elul and Marchiafava.[24] These workers have measured the accommodative changes to near and distant test objects that take place in the eyes of both pretrigeminal and normal cats and also the concomitant electrical activity in various brain regions including the hippocampus. They find that accommodative changes to the distance of test objects depend very much on the nature of the test object, particularly on its familiarity. The accommodative response wanes on repeated presentations and gradually foreshortens, returning to baseline before the offset of the exposure. Finally, when the test object has become sufficiently familiar, the eye no longer responds to it by adjustments in focal length, which brings it into clearest focus. In effect it becomes part of the background as a consequence of habituation; a fact which reminds us that the only reason why it could serve as a test object in the first place was its initial unfamiliarity.

During barbiturate or ether anesthesia or in light sleep, the fixated *open* eye remains tonically accommodated for far and displays no phasic response to test objects. In the waking state any sudden change elicits a shift toward accommodation for near. A number of variables, including hippocampal and neocortical arousal, pupillary dilation, and, in mobile controls, orienting movements, covary with this nonspecific reaction; however, only the hippocampal theta rhythm was found to follow the sustained accommodation changes associated with specific and prolonged inspection of the test object. In general the hippocampal theta rhythm exhibited a remarkably detailed covariation with the fine characteristics of the accommodative reaction. Some of these details are worth noting for they indicate that accommodation is far from being only a reflex response to movement. First of all, changes in focal length occur in response to auditory, tactile, and olfactory stimuli as well as visual, and these habituate in about 5 presentations in contrast to the 10 or 20 required for visual objects. The habituated response is restored by slight changes in procedure or is briefly reactivated after interruption of a test series. Also the habituability of a test stimulus depends on factors other then stimulus parameters; thus animate objects such as cats, kittens, rats, etc. elicit the response longer than most inanimate objects, but certain of these such as feather dusters prove equally durable test objects.

Whether these relationships are interesting or not depends on one's point of view; the kinds of variables which are operative here are typical of habituation phenomenon. It has often been suggested that dehabituation and attention are not different processes (e.g., Fernandez-Guardiola et al.[25] but only different measures of the same process. The accommodation data reflect the same relation, but in a way that permits us to relate these in a very realistic way to the gradient or focus of attention. In the visual field at least, the relative clarity of focus produced by accommodative changes is the most exacting objective measure of the field of visual attention; the object of attention is brought into clearest focus.

Absence of the hippocampal theta rhythm: lesion data

The hippocampal theta rhythm (4 to 7 cps) originates in the vicinity of the hippocampal pyramids, although the frequency of the rhythm appears to be determined by septal pacemaker units (reviewed by Stumpf et al.[111]). The rhythm is thus dependent upon the integrity of hippocampus; however, it is most effectively and permanently abolished by lesions of the septal nuclei.[13,40] Such lesions do not impair the neocortical arousal response.

The rhythm is disrupted by electrical stimulation of septal region (above 12 cps) or by drugs such as barbiturates and anticholinergics, which also block neocortical arousal (reviewed by Petsche et al.[93] While we know of no data for ECS, there is one report that the theta rhythm is blocked by ethanol .[12] The effect of CDP on the frequency of the theta rhythm and the speed of a discriminated approach response (as in Adey et al.[2]) is portrayed in Figure 4 (in preparation.[103]). Similar effects are obtained with scopolamine and amytal. Both the decline in frequency and the correlation coefficient, however, are greatest with CDP (amytal exerts the same frequency effect, but animals sleep). It can be seen that CDP disrupts a behavior normally accompanied by hippocampal theta, and that the correlation between the drug effect on theta frequency and reciprocal latency is very substantial (mean $r = .85$, $N = 10$).

The similarities between the lesion effects and drug effects previously examined might now be considered. First of all, septal lesions result in a very exaggerated startle response, which accommodates very slowly;[70] however paradoxically, these animals who can repeatedly be surprised by loud sounds cannot be distracted by white noise while they are lever pressing for food,[115] nor do they respond to sudden stimulus change with the pseudo-CER,[42] nor do they freeze in response to air blasts if they are stimulated or lesioned in septal region.[64] Lesions or self-stimulation of septal region attenuates the CER,[8-10,42] and septal lesions significantly facilitate the two-way but not the one-way active CAR.[27,65,68,70,113] Septal rats and cats display a passive avoidance defect[61,105] such that neither a natural nor a learned consummatory response tendency is discouraged by punishment, and while they show fast acquisition of an appetitive lever pressing response and respond at very high rates, they have great difficulty learning to inhibit non-reinforced incorrect responses.[23]

In short, consummatory responses are easily stamped in by reinforcement, but not stamped out by habituation, extinction, (nonreinforcement), or punishment (see also Schwartzbaum et al.[104,124] The response defect might be said to be "an inability to change response" or perseveration. Their indistractability and fearlessness (manifested in lack of conflict, withdrawal, and CER), however, are very good indications that they are insensitive to information. Hence the startle response (surprise) persists uninhibited by attention, and consum-

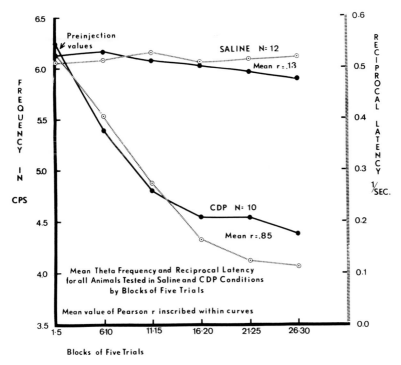

FIG. 4.—Covariation of frequency of hippocampal theta rhythm and speed (reciprocal latency) of discriminative approach performance in cats: effects of saline and CDP 20 mg./Kg. Procedure same as Adey et al.[2] Each session, 30 trials, injection administered after first block of five trials. Control curve and Pearson r based on mean of 12 animals; CDP value based on N = 10.

matory responses are performed uninhibited by information (novelty or danger). The very striking aggression which is typical of these animals is quite exactly—fearlessness. It is information, based on knowledge of possibilities, which normally constitutes the fear which prevents rats from attacking humans.

Instead of the whole array of novelty responses displayed by normal animals in the open field test, hippocampal rats are reported to display a peculiar stereotyped running pattern, and it is the unabating persistence of the same initial response which interferes with the ability of hippocampal rats to solve subsequent Hebb-Williams maze problems.[66] Here it is apparent that when rats do not display the succession of attention responses, directed at those features of the environment which still contain information, and these alternatives are not remembered and discarded by habituation, then the initial question does indeed perseverate. In a strange situation hippocampal rats may be more persistently active then normals;[22,66,97,112] however, this is not quite equivalent to curiosity or exploration because in tests of spontaneous alternation (as in the drug data) they alternate at random levels or below.[22,97] The same defect occurs in learned alternation[73] in which it may also be called perseveration or an immediate memory defect. In the report of Karmos and Grastyan[63a] hippocampal cats display an exaggerated and peculiar variant of the orienting response which never ceases. If the source of the auditory cueing stimulus is changed, the cats appear disoriented or confused and have trouble localizing the new location of the cue; suggesting that this persistent orienting is surprise, an attention defect. Aside from the latency variations caused by this persistent orienting, the cats have no trouble learning an appetitive stimulus discrimination habit, although they cannot learn a successive discrimination, suggesting an impairment of immediate or recent memory.

In two reports[53,121] hippocampal rats do very well on the acquisition of a simple straight alley approach habit, and much better than normals on early training trials. In one report[121] the lesioned rats prove significantly more resistant to distractions introduced after the habit had been well learned. Their insensitivity to novelty or lack of exploration might thus explain both their initial superiority and their subsequent indistractability. The attention defect that interferes with localization of a useful cue in the cats is reflected as a lack of distractability to extraneous stimuli in the rats.

In the other report[53] instead of a subsequent distraction test, rats were shocked for entering the goal box, in which case the hippocampal rats displayed a striking passive avoidance defect (or a lack of the normal approach-avoidance conflict, or perseveration or inability to recall the aversive experience, or inability to inhibit a response tendency). Hippocampal lesions produce a passive avoidance defect in a number of other reports,[66,67,112] as well as attenuation of the CER.[9] There is one report of CAR facilitation in hippocampal rats[52] and other reports of a deficit in CAR acquisition.[80] Lesions are also reported to produce a loss of retention in the newly learned but not the overtrained CAR.[51]

There are a number of extinction deficits reported for both hippocampal and septal animals.[52,104,118] One very interesting finding[56] is reported for the extinction of a simple runway approach habit in hippocampal rats. If extinction trials are massed (every ten seconds) then extinction proceeds quite normally in hippocampal rats. However, extinction is impossible if trials are spaced (every ten minutes). Thus it appears that the extinction defect and the recent memory defect are related. In a subsequent experiment[57] lesioned rats already extinguished by massed trials were shifted to spaced trials, and massed trials were commenced in the group failing to extinguish with spaced trials. The massing of trials allowed the formerly spaced group to extinguish normally. However, the already extinguished group given spaced trials displayed a *rapid reacquisition curve as extinction trials continued.* The recent memory defect and the extinction defect appear inseparable. The same reversal of extinction was cited for the drug and ECS data (see review by Carlton).[14]

Inattention—The Absence of Change

The group of treatments examined yield symptoms which become more distinctly familiar each time a new method of relieving fear or disrupting memory is investigated. The list of similarities is extensive. First, novelty or orienting responses are impaired. These include spontaneous alternation, manipulative and exploratory behaviors, distraction, external inhibition, hesitation, vigilance, approach-withdrawal behaviors, rearing, crouching, pseudo-CER, etc. These are all unconditioned responses elicited by "neutral stimuli" that are different from those with which the animal is already familiar. When the neutral CS is paired with pain, airblast, or other unconditioned stimuli, the same responses are conditioned, and the neutral stimuli elicit a "fear drive", or approach-avoidance conflict, passive avoidance, or the CER. The conditioned "drive" and the "conditioned" responses are also impaired by the treatments; however, the extent depends heavily on training variables. These all appear to be orienting responses elicited by and directed at stimulus uncertainty. Their form seems to depend entirely upon the animal's discrimination of the danger. They normally habituate or extinguish with stimulus experience, or are conserved from change if they lead to food, safety, etc.

The responses which replace the absent novelty responses are perseveration, enduring exaggerated surprise reactions, startle and random hyperactivity, delerium, etc., or non-extinguishing instrumental responses. These persist, and whether they appear to be oriented to the new or disoriented, they are not affected by outcomes. In this sense they are not questions but exclamations. Consummatory systems are generally promoted by the absence of novelty, although except for the potentiation of sleep the effect is often particular. Simple approach, the two-way CAR and in one case unreinforced maze learning are significantly enhanced (and dissociated in the normal state when learned under the drug).

Finally, recent memory is impaired, habituation and extinction are blocked, and, with some of the treatments, the effects of previous habituation and extinction are reversed. Instrumental approach or avoidance habits are spared if overlearned, while newer habits are affected variously. Since retention of the instrumental response is taken as the appropriate test of memory loss, the absence of any clear effect has been taken to indicate that the amnestic effects that result from these treatments in humans are not confirmed by clear evidence of a similar impairment in other species.

The fact that the treatment effects can be placed in such close correspondence with symptoms predictable from the absence of the hippocampal theta rhythm suggests that attention has something very important to do with how the forebrain functions. In humans it is doubtful whether important instances of learning occur in the absence of attention or awareness, although attention is certainly not related in any necessary or obligatory way to behavior; it is normally the case that intricate, automatized motor and verbal skills are executed unattended, and indeed occur also in states of somnambulism, fugue and psychomotor seizure. The dictionary defines learning as "the acquisition of knowledge or skill by experience or study." The salient requirement is only that something new becomes known.

From the defects that appear when the rhythms of attention disappear, there is an excellent basis for concluding that learning, as it is defined in the dictionary, does not occur without attention in animals either. The treatments impair rhythms reflecting attention and behaviors which occur to novelty, symptoms which imply that the news has not registered. When the drugged animals are later tested without the drug it appears that indeed the news has not left an impression. Animals who, without incentive, had rapidly "acquired" a four unit T maze[7] now crouch and explore intensively as the controls had once done. If we take the dictionary seriously, these animals are amnestic.

Now since so very much of the basic experimental data underlying S-R theory has been obtained in the single T maze, there is no question but that the behaviorist would classify the drug effect as rapid learning, not automatic behavior, and it would be the loss of the maze habit which would be called amnesia, not the animal's seeming unfamiliarity with the surroundings. The question is, did the drug promote learning, or did it uncover a routine sensory-motor competence which the rats have already acquired, but do not display because they normally must pay attention to what is new? By routine sensori-motor competence we refer to the unconditioned responses displayed by a cat or mouse when they escape from cages and evade pursuit.

The question arises again in scopolamine data, where at .5 mg/Kg an equivalent dissociation of experience with a distracting stimulus occurs in rats so that in the normal state the stimulus appears not to have habituated under the drug.[14a] In other work spontaneous and learned alternation is blocked.[14,84] At the same dose rats will emit instrumental lever pressing responses for thousands of unreinforced extinction trials and will "remember" and emit formerly extinguished habits as well.[14] Thus, "negative" learning is blocked, reversed etc., but "positive learning" is facilitated, protected and restored. Is the function of the forebrain to inhibit learning?

At 300 mg/Kg of scopolamine rats will acquire a T maze escape habit,[90] yet a total dose of but 5 mg will cause a maximal delerium in humans such that higher doses produce no further effect. A one pound rat can therefore "learn" when injected with a quantity of drug which would cause delerium in 4,500 pounds of human. What is habituated and what is learned? Is cholinergic transmission necessary for learning?

Attention vs. Reinforcement

The contradiction is not accidental but recurrent, if we examine the acquisition of the CAR or the appetitive instrumental response.[38] It seems that there is a reciprocity between EEG measures of attention and behavioral measures of performance. When the theta rhythm begins to wane and the signs of fear diminish one might say the problem was over; or one might say learning had begun, since as attention wanes the learning curve rises sharply. From this viewpoint it appears that reinforcement inhibits attention. The question has been answered, and further questions cease. The treatments of course split this down the middle, abolishing the CER, facilitating CAR.

Attention is a response to stimulus information, an inquiry raised by changing circumstances; and its result is a change in the significance of stimuli. Reinforcement is an unlearned answer which conserves successful adaptations from change. Both adaptation to change and conservation of successful adaptations are clearly essential for survival. If learning is defined by a behavioral measure, as the behavior theorist insists, then there is little to show except the product. The questions which are raised by stimuli and answered by knowledge of what the world is like, habituate. The only questions which perseverate as answers are those protected from change by reinforcement. The only objective behavioral evidence of negative learning available to show the operationist is the decline in novelty responses, and it can be shown that this occurs with storage of information, not the passage of time, nor the loss of drive. It is perfectly plain that suspension of questions (induced by drugs, lesions etc.) results in perpetual surprise and perseveration. This is evidence that novelty responses do not have to occur or diminish, fear does not "wear off", looking responses are not reinforced by "seeing" but only as questions are answered; and if they are not asked during a hiatus in the drug state, they are resumed.

The definitive state of inattention is sleep, and the conservation of knowledge from change is its outstanding property. Consummatory reinforcement shares this property, as well as many EEG similarities, and both are promoted by the treatments. Curiously yet another view of the same treatment syndrome is obtained from reported effects of continuous stimulation of positively reinforcing areas. Thus: attenuation of CER,[8] facilitation of CAR during stimulation (which reverts to nonperformance when current is discontinued), blockade of extinction, discrimination defects,[108] confusion, immediate memory defects, inability to eliminate errors,[88] and of course perseveration of the reinforced response.

The Amnestic Syndrome—Loss of Familiarity and Differences

The treatment effects in rats result in impairment in habituation and a loss in prior habituations, which together might be described as a loss of familiarity, and equally, there is an insensitivity to novelty, an absence of fear, etc. In humans the analogous effects are antero- and retrograde amnesia and a loss of fear and spontaneity. There are obvious parallels in other features of the amnestic syndrome[69] in humans: confusion, disorientation, and related defects in attention and immediate memory; also perseveration, automatic behavior, and a dissolution of inhibitions. The amnestic syndrome symptoms are reproduced by drugs,[95,120,123] and as we shall see are commonly followed by amnesia for experience in the drug (or twilight) state. Moreover, humans with amnestic disorders do not lose reinforced instrumental responses, nor even routine motor skills which unquestionably qualify as learned responses (writing, speaking, walking, etc.). They follow directions well, but lose memory, that is, knowledge of past events.

There is solid evidence that the treatments which impair memory in humans impair habituation in the rat, and the implication that the underlying function is the same is worth a close reexamination. We would like to begin by pointing out a latent excitatory effect of habituation which suggests a strong resemblance between the learning of a "fact" and habituation to a stimulus, and indicates why the loss of memory implies the loss of fear.

First, although "negative learning" entails extinction of the orienting response to the CS, it is one kind of learning in which the change in behavior is entirely secondary to the learning of the stimulus. There is no impairment or change in the orienting response *per se* and it is clear that the loss of behavior is precisely circumscribed to a fairly exact replica of the stimulus context. Further, as habituation trials proceed, increasingly finer stimulus changes will dehabituate the evoked potential and elicit orientation.[106] This is an interesting effect of simple experience with a CS. It implies that identical repetitions result in overt loss of attention to an increasingly precise representation of the stimulus context; but more important is its covert property. It produces a latent sensitization to increasingly refined differences so that the improved knowledge of a "fact" consists of an increase in the clarity of its resolution from background differences. Behaviorally this implies that the animal becomes more vulnerable to distractions (if they occur) as he becomes less attentive to the CS. When the orienting response extinguishes, it sows the seeds for the conditions of its future evocation. The next time something similar, yet not the same, occurs, it will become "news" without having previously been seen, not because it is similar to a CS which has become ineffective but because it is different. This is a strict but a very much subtler determinism than the strengthened S-R bond and its generalization gradient of stimulus similarity. Habituation produces a weakening of the stimulus-orienting response bond and a gradient of generalization to stimulus differences. The orienting response is predicted and controlled in advance of experience by the sensitizing effect of previous experience.

This dual property is seen more clearly in a number of instances where the effect of sensitization to differences initially overrides the desensitization to identities and results in an initial net excitatory effect. It is often reported[25] that early in habituation the evoked potential grows initially with repetition and later it declines as habituation trials continue. This inverted U-shaped function is reasonably explained as the outcome of a unitary process if the sampling population is treated in the manner customary for contiguity theories. In initially habituating and losing sensitivity to a unique sample of a much wider sampling distribution, the future sensitization to potential difference far outweighs the loss of reactivity to similarities. The effect of initial habituation yields a generalization gradient of sensitization to differences (which amounts to a failure in discrimination). However, as the animal successively attends to each of the differences that have been sensitized, they habituate in turn, *if they are present* in the object world, until the animal finally acquires an insensitivity which matches the shape of the object and its envelope of common variations, and when this occurs the animal ceases orienting. The animal has been forced to learn whatever differences he could detect, until none remained. When the animal has learned what the CS is, then the orienting response wanes and behavior can be reliably controlled by reinforcement.

The same inverted U-shaped function is seen at the extremes of inexperience and experience, in the fearlessness of infant rats on one hand and the boldness of feral rats (or rats given enriched experience) on the other. The effect of experience on groups of young rats is a steady parallel increase in independent measures of fearfulness and exploration,[31a] which rises from minimal levels at weaning, to peak at sexual maturity. The function levels off in adult laboratory-reared rats whose opportunity for further experience is limited.

In effect the infants are agnostic, they lack experience, and if there are no habituations to be perturbed the stimulus has little information. As the brain acquires habituations by experience, stimulus differences become increasingly discernible and effective. The initial effect of knowledge is to sensitize the naive animal. Facts initially raise more questions than they answer; they expand the horizons of possible worries and the sphere of interest. The absence of fear in the feral rats is confidence based on knowledge. They are not easily perturbed since they have already habituated to the range of stimuli they are likely to encounter. Messages have less information, and experienced animals "learn" faster and are less emotional for this very same reason.

The continuum of responses which occur to successive increases in stimulus change varies from approach to hesitation and finally to withdrawal or freezing. They also occur in the reverse order in the open field test, as rats unfreeze, cautiously advance, and actively explore. The stimulus controlling distance of approach in both cases appears to be difference from the familiar. Both infant rats, with a minimum of prior experience, and feral or specially reared rats who are most experienced, are extreme groups with respect to the absence of fear in the open field test. Feral rats are least likely to encounter differences, and young rats have acquired no familiarity. The relation is fulfilled once again by treated animals whose loss of prior habituations is established independently. Since the effect of increasing experience is a susceptibility to novelty in the young rat (and the young of many species), the loss of familiarity may reasonably deprive stimuli of their "news". The basic defect is amnesia, a loss of knowledge, and its result is agnosia, an absence of information.

It is memory or knowledge gained that is controlling the approach withdrawal gradient, in advance of experience, since the difference from the familiar is not a property of the stimulus. Totally unfamiliar stimuli (words, guns) are not effective; recognizably unfamiliar (partially familiar) stimuli are news. A rat approaches a new situation only as closely as his knowledge of it warrants, a relation which keeps him alive in advance of the kinds of aversive training procedures that would otherwise be necessary (narrow escapes from eagles, owls, snakes, cats, dogs). It is further learning which enables him to approach more closely, so that ultimately he might find food or establish territory in the same open field. It is knowledge stored as desensitization to redundancy which sensitizes him to differences, and the effects of partial knowledge are excitatory when most of the differences he has been sensitized to are yet to be encountered; and fear, caution and curiosity subside with further knowledge.

The Source of Fear

So very often humans do not know why they are afraid, and one can see why from the rat's problem in the unfamiliar situation. He does not know why he is frightened; there are many objectively unfamiliar things around, but he does not even notice these. Everything he sees as new is something a little different than he is used to, and as he looks at each thing he becomes used to it and his worries evaporate one by one, and he sees that his fears which were nameless were also groundless. As he looks still further at the situation he becomes curious and begins to see possibilities. He investigates each until finally he becomes bored, and concludes that open fields are really boring, and are biologically meaningless stimuli. In effect, he confuses verbal labels with epistemology and cannot see why he ever was afraid or even curious about the "open field test"; he sees that it was a snap test now that he knows exactly what it is.

When the frontal patient or the inebriate remembers the names of things but loses inhibitions or fears and acts irresponsibly like a child (who also knows the names of things), he also has lost memory for the significance of events. What he fails to recollect are the myriad of nameless social pressures, *worries*, which normally arise and deter normals, which abnormally deter neurotics, and which need never deter the very rich or the very poor, or whoever does not care about such things because they are really neutral stimuli. The feeling of fear may feel like a drive, not a cognitive question, but the source of the fear drive is the forebrain, not the hypothalamus.

This becomes much clearer in the transition between the drunken and the sober state or when the amytal interview is over. The drug provides relief from the overriding feeling of fear and dissolves inhibitions providing "release" and less dramatically, the worries are also forgotten. With his confidence now unimpaired by any uncertainty, the drunkard does all the things that the neurotic does not dare. The approach component of the approach-avoidance conflict has unlimited opportunity to gain habit strength in the drug state, but further reinforcement does not produce learning. The conflict returns at full strength the next morning. This is described in various ways; in the psychoanalytic view the unconscious is resistant to change and must be made conscious in order for change to occur, or in the

Pavlovian framework, the orienting reflex must be extinguished before learning can begin, or as we suggest, information which does not register cannot habituate, and problems never faced are never solved. The neocortical EEG rhythms of attention, orientation and consciousness are indistinguishable, and will support any of these interpretations of dissociation of "learning" in animals and humans. The phenomena are very similar.

Dissociative States in Humans

The treatments which produce dissociative states in humans are summarized by Kubie,[71] who includes sleep and related states of altered awareness, from reverie to hypnogogic trance and somnambulism. He regards these as essentially similar to states induced by barbiturates, scopolamine, alcohol, and the twilight states following insulin and shock treatment. These treatments commonly produce relief from anxiety, and have been used in conjunction with techniques of abreaction, narcoanalysis, narcosynthesis and psychoexploration. The dramatic changes in behavior which occur do not transfer well to the normal state.[41a,103a]

Amnestic symptoms are reported to occur during these states, and in reports of amytal effects reviewed by Wikler,[123] human subjects exhibit impaired attention, recent memory defects, slower reaction and recognition time, and a freer flow of associations. Yet performance on arithmetic problems is less susceptible to distraction. In a variety of reports the achievement of a favorable amytal interview correlated well with subsequent response to shock and coma treatments.

In a report by Quigley[95] on the effects of atropine-insulin combinations on medical student volunteers, again the symptoms mentioned are confusional symptoms and automatic behavior. Most striking was a very extensive amnesia evident in the response to everyday questions. Subjects reply unhesitatingly with confabulations which are totally imaginary and incorrect, with full belief in the validity of their answers. They remember how to talk, but they have lost knowledge; questions remind them of less. When cells do not fire, habituations are difficult to dehabituate.

The treatments which produce the amnestic syndrome and/or dissociation of learning in humans and animals are the same. In humans it is clear that the drug state produced by synaptic inhibition entails the unavailability of prior knowledge. When facts are lost there are no differences to attract attention, worry, interest, thinking or any of a number of ways that information "feels." The information in the stimulus, or its attensity, is a function of the knowledge it disturbs. When knowledge is lost, stimuli lose information. Attention which is focused by stimulus information blurs, resulting in the symptoms of confusion, disorientation and delerium. The dull impact leaves a dim impression, and perseveration and a loss of immediate, recent and remote memory, which reflect the absence of information in the amnestic state, are not improved in the normal state. No information has registered.

Control of the Orienting Reflex by Knowledge

The information in a stimulus is the knowledge it brings to attention, what it reminds you of by virtue of its differences from prior knowledge. That is what compels the orienting response. If you have not been sensitized by prior knowledge, you will not focus on the stimulus, it will not come to attention, and you will have no recall of it. There is no information in a message in an utterly strange language. No "act of will" nor "code for information" nor reinforcement will improve your virtual lack of an immediate or remote memory for Bengali or Finnish; by comparison English nonsense syllables are meaningful words. If no prior habituations exist for a message to dehabituate, humans will not and *cannot* pay attention nor remember the stimulus, independent of volition, RNA, interest or reinforcement. A "fact" becomes a fact only when the brain is sensitized to it by related knowledge. Its "meaningfulness" is determined by prior knowledge, and until the brain is sensitized by previous experience, both reinforcement and a "code" are useless. Once a fact attracts attention, they are both irrelevant; when it is attended to, learning is over.

Of the thousands of well-known stimuli which are present in the stimulus field at every single glance, the eye is almost invariably focussed precisely at the *least* familiar, the largest question (the weakest S-R connection). Each one of the thousands of stimuli in the periphery of attention was once in clearest focus when it was news, which is why each is now ignored and will not be recalled tomorrow, although each is seen. What you paid attention to today is what is learned and will be recalled tomorrow and ignored thereafter. It will sensitize you to stimuli different from it, which previously would have gone by unnoticed; you will appreciate new "facts" but you will not perseverate on known ones.

A known fact may be converted into a behavior by a question which dehabituates it and makes it information once again. The use of language by the behaviorist to interrogate knowledge converts the knowledge gained by, for example, paying attention to a lecture (CS) into a strengthened response (one of an immense number of possible responses, depending on how the question is phrased). In lower animals we cannot manipulate attention by the use of language, to dehabituate knowledge, but when the identical CS is repeated the orienting response extinguishes. If one wishes to test what response humans learn by orienting to a lecture, why use a new CS to test a response never emitted, why not repeat the CS?

Operational definitions are far more essential in studying the orienting reflex of humans by use of the human orienting reflex, because attention is always directed at the new, never at the well known. It is not controlled by an act of will, but is a function of the brain. It is designed to detect the news, and that is its chief limitation as an instrument of knowledge.

The Economics of Information Storage

If one is prepared to regard consciousness in a perfectly naturalistic way, as what the orienting reflex feels like in a very large brain, then one need not seek any "code for information" other than the nerve impulse. If one does not expect to find a "knower" at the end of the line but only a diencephalon to focus attention by lateral (reciprocal) inhibition, a decision among coordinate alternatives as to the most pressing question, then there is no point in transmitting facts, there is no one there who "knows." In order to direct the orienting reflex and control the distance of approach one must transmit questions, not facts. One need not fight the connectivity of the nervous system as entrophy but can use it as information storage capacity.

Instead of a code for information, one needs only sensory maps and a set of increasingly abstract blank maps which transmit information, but become insensitive to redundancy. At the synapse 10^4 endboutons converge to jointly determine one spike output, a relation which forces coarsening or abstraction (one stands for many). If *only* the nerve impulse conveys information, then the synaptic membrane must store it, else the detail coarsened by convergence is permanently lost. Divergence of axon collaterals at each synapse scatters the coarsened message locally to an audience of thousands. If the initial sensory maps are transmitted inward in this fashion, then the structural infidelity of synaptic transmission which coarsens and disperses detail, guarantees that each cell specializes and receives a different alternative view of the possible abstract interrelations of detail on the sensory surface—somewhat coarser than its precursors, somewhat finer than its audience, and similar to, but different than, its neighbors. Instead of using the cells in a synaptic network in redundant fashion to duplicate the incomparable fidelity of one axon, this allows each cell to receive, from its 10^4 inputs, a slightly different and extremely rich impression of the world.

With lateral inhibition among coordinate (and adjacent) alternatives at every level, as on the retina, one leaves decisions such as inhibition in local hands. The image is always sharpened by the most intensely stimulated cell, which is the one most competent to inhibit neighboring cells whose view is most nearly similar but different. Thus a message may precisely select the most relevant difference and selectively inhibit marginally similar alternatives without an extra-local director. As attention is focused on the most relevant question and information is stored by habituation, the surround inhibition exerted on nearby cells relaxes; and the future sensitivity to marginal differences is determined in advance as each fact is deposited.

Information is stored on the cognitive map, as on the retinal, by a complementary loss of sensitivity to information. The dendritic receptor is not free to adapt as a whole like the retinal cell, since it is itself a mosaic of 10^4 input channels and, to maintain its sensitivity, must habituate selectively to an intense source. If initially the membrane is equally responsive to each input, its information storage capacity of 10^4 equiprobable or equally potent alternative connections approximates the face of a television tube. If the structure of the membrane underlying each endbouton is degraded cumulatively as an aftereffect of an improbably high rate of discharge (on-burst) then each input will be depositing information, or each patch of membrane will be storing it, as a local gain in entropy, which is the exact complement of the information (nonrandom signal) impinging on it. Information will be stored by an exact definition without violation of the second Law of Thermodynamics, and information will cause a physical change proportional to energy. The information conveyed by an input will be accumulated by the only competent local "judge," and its functional consequence is the only safe decision a patch of membrane can be trusted to make—to respond *less*.

Thus some lawful regularity in the external world gives rise to nonrandomly intense or redundant spike discharge in the nervous system. The improbable signal in each input channel forms its own register and deposits information on the synaptic surface as a complementary loss of sensitivity. The *tabula rasa* has been engraved by experience and in losing its initial sensitivity has stored the information in every impinging channel. The membrane surface, in the analogy of the television screen, darkens with knowledge and fires only when a majority of its residually sensitive (ignorant) inputs agree. Thus it stores as knowledge whatever non-random signal it is in a position to detect, and transmits as information what it can reliably detect but not classify. It transmits information, the residual question, always to a cell which is better located to detect the similarities underlying more detailed differences. The net always concentrates and focuses the question on more abstract surfaces, and if the question reaches the diencephalon before it is "understood" it may direct the orienting response. Thus knowledge functions to screen and trap answers and to focus the orienting response on residual questions. Memory focuses attention.

The concrete analogy to the retinal map, which adapts to illumination level, and fires "on" or "off" bursts in response to change in illumination, is fulfilled by the common attention-habituation unit,[106] where the stimulus is "change from the familiar" and the decrement is often permanent. The "memory image," like the retinal after-image, should be negative in sign. Like the negative figural aftereffects of central origin, it should be an enduring complementary negative image with strong edge properties at the margin, caused by prolonged attention to stimulus instead of response.

The purpose of sketching in this outline of a mechanism is to show first that habituation is an attractive possibility which requires the most easily met conditions. It also serves as a vehicle for exposing the formal skeleton of the problem. This provides a much more forceful argument. Information storage capacity and entropy are the same quantity. There are many possible attractive information storage devices; however, if you ignore the disorder that actually exists, it does not disappear, it becomes entropy, in an amount equal to capacity. If codes are transmitted through the synaptic net, or circuits reverberate across the grain of the cognitive map, information has to be actively supplied to counter every real connection not drawn in on the blueprint. An ignorant crowd of 10^4 also vote on every message sent, and if you override them with a preemptory command to fire, a divergent network scatters the command endlessly. In order to avoid the coarsening effect of convergence by a multiplex transmission code, or the divergent scatter by branching instructions or identification signals, the information—which must be actively supplied to combat the entropy of connections—cascades as a power function for each synapse crossed.

The question is, why transmit coded intelligence through chaos—who will understand? Corticothalamic efferents exit periodically via fiber bundles which converge on the thalamus and convey to this one locus a wide sampling of cortical activity. At this locus, where coordinate sensory alternatives are represented, lateral or reciprocal inhibition may select and sharpen as it does elsewhere. The orienting reflex can be directed at the largest question, without a "knower".

By allowing the chaotic connectivity to go its way, the location of each of 10^{10} cells in the cortex becomes an individuated view of the relative probability of 10^4 possible regularities in the way the world could be. The location of a cell on a map is its unique significance. It can only be affected by a certain class of possible relations, and if you send it a message in your code, it will mistake it for a "fact". The code and map are antithetical.

The brain provides a matrix of maps of all the possible ways the world could be, which is only affected by non-random indications of the way the world is, and with each indication it loses its unpredictable connectivity and becomes more orderly. The degradation of membrane structure pays the entropy bill for information storage. The brain does not create a new structure, it copies the world and pays for the copy just as the degradation of silver halide pays the bill for the photograph.

As brain size and connectivity increase in phylogeny, the simple effect of adding equiprobable connections and creating new possible detail is seen in the prolonged incompetence in the *infants* in the series. Information storage *capacity* increases as the number of the *blank* maps increase. The infant becomes the adult by storing information, and to do so, he must use up the capacity by reducing equiprobable connectivity. The number of cells in a network whose input is a segment of the sensory map, determines the number of different alternative possibilities that are available for spanning that segment—the information it can yield. A converging network forces swift certainty by radically disregarding possibilities and wasting detail. The precocious development the rat gains by rapid classification is a permanent limitation. The intervening detail that is not represented does not have to be learned and cannot be learned.

The interposition of additional stages into the reducing network expands the volume of the pyramid of detailed possible interrelations whose relative probability now can and must be learned before the same certainty is attained. Cells which habituate also discard alternatives, but do so on the basis of experience, so that the alternatives discarded are not wasted by a structural decision but are retained as stored knowledge of invariants. The same abstract function (e.g., perceptual constancy) may be obtained rapidly or slowly, but the conclusion, more slowly reached, stands for more information and can be affected by more possibilities. It is based on more experience and contains more knowledge. It is plain that a fine initial set of sensory maps would be wasted on the rat—he would shortly coarsen them. And the strategy for brains that can afford the cells and the time to use fine maps, is to prevent coarsening by slowly percolating fine detail through the net and forcing it to enter into every possible relation. By habituating to each invariant represented, every possible fact is extracted. Habituation is neither simple nor complex—that depends upon the information represented on the map. It is merely information storage.

The problem of a "code for information" implies that either the brain already has a code for everything it can or will learn or that it can solve the paradox of learning a (translation) code from experience to encode what it will learn from experience. The problem of "how shall a thing be called" is one that arises when one already has a language for things. Once one knows what a thing is, then any name will do. Two adult logical positivists who already speak a language may agree to define CS as "Anything that strikes them as sense data, by intersubjective verification." However, to provide for the coincidences in this subjective view, the brain must depend on the existence of a lawful objective reality outside the observer. The problem it faces is "what is a fact?," a problem in epistemology, not in semantics, syntactics or verbal behavior.

If you do not know the "true name of a fact," a code for information as it arrives, or a new connection or any way to actively *construct* experience, you need a map for redundancy and you have to wait. A fact will validate itself gradually by objective verification on only one observer, and will become clearer as you look at it. A lawful universe does not broadcast laws, but it cannot broadcast lies, and a map vulnerable only to redundancy (reflected as nonrandom signal) will collect only "facts"; the more disorderly the initial local connectivity of the map, the more complex are the interrelationships that can become "facts". The increasingly abstract maps generated by synaptic convergence must, in time, trap the subtler, more abstract regularities that underlie the first-order retinal distribution. When the head moves the cognitive map sees a stabilized image of the world, although the retinal map transmits a blur of motion. Because the world is invariant under every spatial and temporal transformation, it will eventually deposit its laws as knowledge on a map that traps invariants by habituation. A capricious universe is by far the best source of information. A lawful one repeats, which detracts from the variety of messages it sends, but makes it an excellent source of knowledge. It can become familiar, and on a map, a fact and its surround are simultaneously defined, the familiar and the marginally different.

The Gain and Loss of Information

Objective measures of the simple effect of experience with a CS suggest one way of defining a fact. The habituation of the evoked potential implies that the nervous system becomes less sensitive as a function of redundancy, and since the stimulus does not change, the nervous system must. Since information is transmitted as the nerve impulse, this complementary loss of sensitivity to the entire context, which occurs as a function of redundancy, qualifies as information storage. And if the effects of small changes in the stimulus context are tested, then the specific sensitivity acquired to variations implies that knowledge creates information at its margins.

The computation of information as the uncertainty in classifying a message among a universe of known alternatives is automatic. The information in messages is contained in its effect on the sensitized fringe surrounding each fact. In effect, what you can learn from a message is whatever about it is marginally different from what you already know. The more you already know, the more you are sensitized to, and the more you remember later. Dehabituation implies that messages excite the nervous system directly in regions which have been sensitized by previous knowledge to potential differences, and the nature of the problem directs the orienting response. The aftereffect of information is stored as knowledge (further desensitization), the object is better known, and the sensitized margins (of future information) widened. This strategy forces the structuring of knowledge along lines of relevance and guarantees its unceasing expansion.

Vision is not an intrinsically neutral stimulus modality. In the frog, who sees with his tectum, information is computed as change in location, and the size of the moving edge controls approach and withdrawal in advance of experience; and as with pain and olfaction, this hardly changes with experience. The frog is drawn instantly by a moving worm, and though he is poised to strike, if it does not move again, he does not appear to *recognize* it. If nothing moves the frog will sit motionless and stare at the same view for many hours. If something moves it is not neutral, and if it does not, it is not familiar.

Familiarity is recognition, it is not a property intrinsic to seeing. Both attributes are synonyms for knowledge, and they are acquired as information is learned. The forebrain definition of information as "change from the familiar" is an enormous advance over the midbrain definition. However, it requires the accumulation of familiarity. The price of controlling the orienting response and the approach-withdrawal gradient by news rather than movement, is an eternal vigilance which keeps the rat incessantly busy. The more familiarity he acquires the more differences he notices, and in CS modalities this results in the accumulation of much useless information. Most very novel environments are not dangerous and most mildly novel ones do not yield food, yet the rat cannot know in advance which will turn out to be biologically meaningless stimuli, and so must scrutinize each until he knows precisely what it is. He does not acquire as much familiarity as humans do by paying attention, nor does he lose as much by cholinergic blockade.

REFERENCES

1. Ader, R., and Clink, D. W.: Effects of chlorpromazine on the acquisition and extinction of an avoidance response in the rat. J. Pharmacol. Exp. Ther. 121:144-148, 1957.
2. Adey, W. R., Dunlop, C. W., and Hendrix, C. E.: Hippocampal slow waves; distribution and phase relations in the course of approach learning. Arch. Neurol. 3:74-90, 1960.
3. Ashby, W. R.: Design for a brain (revised). New York, John Wiley & Sons, 1960.
4. Barry, H., III, Wagner, A. R., and Miller, N. E.: Effects of alcohol and amobarbital on performance inhibited by experimental extinction. J. Comp. Psychol. 55:464-468, 1962.
5. Bignami, G.: Effects of benactyzine and adiphene on instrumental conditioning in a shuttlebox. Psychopharmacologia 5:264-279, 1964.
6. Bindra, D.: Stimulus change, reactions to novelty, and response decrement. Psychol. Rev. 66:96-103, 1959.
7. Bloch, S., and Silva, A.: Factors involved in the acquisition of a maze habit,

analyzed by means of tranquilizing and sedative drugs. J. Comp. Physiol. Psychol. 52:550-554, 1959.

8. Brady, J. V.: Motivational-emotional factors and intracranial self-stimulation. *In:* Electrical Stimulation of the Brain. D. E. Sheer, Ed. Austin, University of Texas, 1961, pp. 413-430, 1961.

9. Brady, J. V., and Nauta, W. J. H.: Subcortical mechanisms in emotional behavior: affective changes following septal forebrain lesions in the albino rat. J. Comp. Physiol. Psychol. 46:339-346, 1953.

10. Brady, J. V., and Nauta, W. J. H.: Subcortical mechanisms in emotional behavior: the duration of affective changes following septal and habenular lesions in the albino rat. J. Comp. Physiol. Psychol. 48:412-420, 1955.

11. Bremner, F. J.: Hippocampal activity during avoidance behavior in the rat. J. Comp. Physiol. Psychol. 58:16-22, 1964.

12. Brown, B. B., and Shryne, J. E.: Cat personality characteristics and neurophysiological correlates as an animal model for psychiatric research. Effect of alcohol: Fed. Proc. (Abstr.) 24:2 (Part I): 328, 1099, 1965.

13. Brugge, J. F.: An electrographic study of the hippocampus and neocortex in unrestrained rats following septal lesions. Electroenceph. Clin. Neurophysiol. 18:36-43, 1965.

13a. Candland, D. K. and Campbell, B. A.: Development of fear in the rat as measured by behavior in the open field. J. Comp. Physiol. Psychol. 55: 593-596, 1962.

14. Carlton, P. L.: Cholinergic mechanisms in the control of behavior by the brain. Psychol. Rev. 70:19-39, 1963.

14a. Carlton, P. L. and Vogel, J. R.: Studies of the amnesic properties of scopolamine. Psychonom. Sci. 3:261-262, 1965.

15. Carson, R. C.: The effect of electroconvulsive shock on a learned avoidance response. J. Comp. Physiol. Psychol. 50:125-129, 1957.

16. Chorover, S. L. and Schiller, P. H.: Reexamination of prolonged retrograde amnesia in one-trial learning. J. Comp. Physiol. Psychol. 61:34-41, 1966.

17. Conger, J. J.: The effects of alcohol on conflict behavior in the albino rat. Quart. J. Stud. Alcohol 12:1-29, 1951.

18. Coons, E. E., Anderson, N. H., and Myers, A. K.: Disappearance of avoidance responding during continued training. J. Comp. Physiol. Psychol. 53:290-292, 1960.

19. Coppock, H. W.: Stimuli preceding electric shock can acquire positive reinforcing properties. J. Comp. Physiol. Psychol. 47:109-113, 1954.

20. Denenberg, V. H., Ross, S., and Ellsworth, J.: Effects of chlorpromazine on acquisition and extinction of a conditioned response in mice. Psychopharmacologia 1:59-64, 1959.

21. Doty, L. A., and Doty, B. A.: Chlorpromazine-produced response decrements as a function of problem difficulty level. J. Comp. Physiol. Psychol. 56: 740-745, 1963.

22. Douglas, R. J., and Isaacson, R. L.: Hippocampal lesions and activity. Psychonom. Sci. 1:187-188, 1964.

23. Ellen, P., and Powell, E. W.: Effects of septal lesions on behavior generated by positive reinforcement. Exp. Neurol. 6: 1-11, 1962.

24. Elul, R., and Marchiafava, P. L.: Accommodation of the eye as related to behavior in the cat. Arch. Ital. Biol. 102:616-644, 1964.
25. Fernandez-Guardiola, A., Toro, A., Aquino-cias, J., and Guma, E.: Evolution of chiasmatic, thalamic and cortical electrical responses during photic habituation. Bol. Inst. Etud. Med. Biol. (Mex.), 22:39-69, 1964.
26. Fink, J. B., and Patton, R. M.: Decrement of a learned drinking response accompanying changes in several stimulus characteristics. J. Comp. Physiol. Psychol. 46:23-27, 1953.
27. Fox, S. S., Kimble, D. D., and Lickey, M. E.: Comparison of caudate nucleus and septal-area lesions of two types of avoidance behavior. J. Comp. Physiol. Psychol. 58:380-386, 1964.
28. Gardner, L., and McCullough, C.: A reinvestigation of the dissociative effect of curareform drugs. Amer. Psychol. 17: 398, 1962.
29. Geller, I., Kulak, J. T., and Seifter, J.: The effects of chlordiazepoxide and chlorpromazine on a punishment discrimination. Psychopharmacologia 3:374-385, 1962.
30. Gellhorn, E.: Physiological Foundations of Neurology and Psychiatry. Minneapolis, University of Minnesota Press, 1953.
31. Girden, E.: Cerebral mechanisms in conditioning under curare. Amer. J. Psychol. 53:397-406, 1940.
32. Girden, E.: Generalized conditioned responses under curare and erythroidine. J. Exp. Psychol. 31:105-119, 1942.
33. Girden, E.: The dissociation of blood pressure conditioned responses under erythroidine. J. Exp. Psychol. 31:219-231, 1942.
34. Girden, E.: The dissociation of pupillary conditioned reflexes under erythroidine and curare. J. Exp. Psychol. 31:322-332, 1942.
35. Girden, E.: Role of the response mechanism in learning and in "excited emotion." Amer. J. Psychol. 56:1-20, 1943.
36. Girden, E.: Conditioned responses in curarized monkeys. Amer. J. Psychol. 60:571-587, 1947.
37. Girden, E., and Culler, E.: Conditioned responses in curarized striate muscle in dogs. J. Comp. Psychol. 23:261-274, 1937.
38. Grastyan, E., Lissak, K., Madarasc, I., and Donhoffer, N.: Hippocampal activity during the development of conditioned reflexes. Electroenceph. Clin. Neurophysiol. 11:409-430, 1959.
39. Grastyan, E.: The significance of the earliest manifestations of conditioning in the mechanisms of learning. In: Brain Mechanisms and Learning. J. F. Delafresnaye, Ed. CIOM Symposium. Oxford, Blackwell, 1961, pp. 243-251.
40. Green, J. D., and Arduini, A.: Hippocampal electrical activity in arousal. J. Neurophysiol. 17:533-551, 1954.
41. Green, J. D., Clemente, C. D., and de Groot, J.: Rhinencephalic lesions and behavior in cats; an analysis of the Kluver-Bucy syndrome with particular reference to normal and abnormal behavior. J. Comp. Neurol. 180:505-545, 1957.
41a. Grinker, R. R. and Spiegel, J. P.: War neuroses in North Africa: The Tunisian campaign Jan.-May, 1943. New York, Josiah Macy Jr., Foundation, 1943.

42. Harvey, J. A., Jacobson, L. E., and Hunt, H. F.: Long-term effects of lesions in the septal forebrain on acquisition and retention of conditioned fear. Amer. Psychol. 16:449, 1961.

43. Hebb, D. O.: The Organization of Behavior: A Neurophysiological Theory. New York, John Wiley & Sons, 1949.

44. Heistad, G. T.: A bio-psychological approach to somatic treatments in psychiatry. Amer. J. Psychiat. 114:540-545, 1957.

45. Heller, A., Harvey, J. A., and Moore, R. Y.: A demonstration of a fall in brain serotonin following central nervous system lesions in the rat. Biochem. Pharmacol. 11:859-866, 1962.

46. Holmgren, B.: Conditioned avoidance reflex under pentobarbital. Bol. Inst. Estud. Med. Biol. (Mex.) 22:21-37, 1964.

47. Hunt, H. F.: Some effects of drugs on classical (types) conditioning. Ann. N. Y. Acad. Sci. 65:258-267, 1956.

48. Hunt, H. F.: Implications of psychiatry for some research in psychology. Med. Psychol. III: 209-213, 1963.

49. Hunt, H. F.: Problems in the interpretation of "experimental neurosis." Psychol. Rep. 15:27-35, 1964.

50. Hunt., H. F., and Brady, J. V.: Some effects of electro-convulsive shock on a conditioned emotional response (anxiety). J. Comp. Physiol. Psychol. 44:88, 1951.

51. Hunt, H. F., and Diamond, I. T.: Some effects of hippocampal lesions on conditioned avoidance behavior in the cat. Acta Psychol. 15:203-204, 1959.

52. Isaacson, R. L., Douglas, H. S., and Moore, R. Y.: The effect of radical hippocampal ablation on acquisition of avoidance response. J. Comp. Physiol. Psychol. 54:625-628, 1961.

53. Isaacson, R. L., and Wickelgren, W. O.: Hippocampal ablation and passive avoidance. Science 138:1104-1106, 1962.

54. Jacobsen, E., and Sonne, E.: The effect of benzilic acid diethylamino-ethylester, HCl, (benactyzine) on stress-induced behaviour in the rat. Acta Pharmacol. Toxicol. 11:135, 1955.

55. Jacobsen, E., and Sonne, E.: The effect of benactyzine on the conditioned responses in the rat. Acta Pharmacol. Toxicol. 12:310, 1956.

56. Jarrard, L. E., Isaacson, R. L., and Wickelgren, W. O.: Effects of hippo-campal ablation and intertrial interval on runway acquisition and extinction. J. Comp. Physiol. Psychol. 57:442-444, 1964.

57. Jarrard, L. B., and Isaacson, R. L.: Hippocampal ablation in rats: research on effects of intertrial interval. Prepublication copy, 1965.

58. John, E. R.: Higher nervous function: brain functions and learning. Ann. Rev. Physiol. 23:451-484, 1961.

59. Jouvet, M.: Recherches sur lese mecanismes neurophysiologiques du sommeil et de l'apprentissage negatif. In: Brain Mechanisms and Learning. J. F. Delafresnaye, Ed. CIOM Symposium. Oxford, Blackwell, 1961, pp. 445-475.

60. Jung, R.: Correlation of bioelectric and autonomic phenomena with altera-tions in consciousness and arousal in man. In: Brain Mechanisms and Consciousness. J. F. Delafresnaye, Ed. CIOM Symposium, Oxford, Black-well, 1954, pp. 310-338.

61. Kaada, B. R., Rasmussen, E. W., and Kreim, O.: Impaired acquisition of passive avoidance behavior by subcallosal, septal, hypothalamic, and insular lesions in rats. J. Comp. Physiol. Psychol. 55:661-670, 1962.

62. Kamin, L. J.: The effects of termination of the CS and avoidance of the US on avoidance learning. J. Comp. Physiol. Psychol. 49:420-424, 1956.

63. Kamin, L. J.: The effects of termination of the CS and avoidance of the US on avoidance learning: an extension. Canad. J. Psychol. 11:48-56, 1957.

63a. Karmos, G. and Grastyan, E.: Influence of hippocampal lesions on simple and delayed conditional reflexes. Acta Physiologica. 21:217-224, 1962.

64. Kasper, P., and Usher, D.: The role of the septal area in behavioral and endocrine responses to neurogenic stress. Paper read at sixth annual scientific meeting, The Psychonomic Society, 1965.

65. Kenyon, J.: The effect of septal lesions upon motivated behavior in the rat. Unpublished doctoral dissertation, McGill University, 1962.

66. Kimble, D. P.: The effects of bilateral hippocampal lesions in rats. J. Comp. Physiol. Psychol. 56:273-283, 1963.

67. Kimura, D.: Effects of selective hippocampal damage on avoidance behavior in the rat. Canad. J. Psychol. 12:213-218, 1958.

68. King, F. A.: Effects of septal and amygdaloid lesions on emotional behavior and avoidance responses in the rat. J. Nerv. Ment. Dis. 126:57-63, 1958.

69. Kral, V. A., and Durost, H. B.: A comparative study of the amnestic syndrome in various organic conditions. Amer. J. Psychiat. 110:41-47, 1953.

70. Krieckhaus, E. E., Simmons, H. J. Thomas, G. J., and Kenyon, J.: Septal lesions enhance shock avoidance behavior in the rat. Exp. Neurol. 9: 107-113, 1964.

71. Kubie, L. S.: The valve of induced dissociated states in the therapeutic process. Proc. Roy. Soc. Med. 38:681-683, 1945.

72. Larsen, V.: The general pharmacology of benzilic acid diethylaminoethylester hydrochloride (benactyzine NFN, suavitii r, parasan r.). Acta Pharmacol. Toxicol. 11:405, 1955.

73. Lash, L.: Response discriminability and the hippocampus. J. Comp. Physiol. Psychol. 57:251-256, 1964.

74. Lauener, H.: Conditioned suppression in rats and the effects of pharmacological agents thereon. Psychopharmacologia 4:311-325, 1963.

75. Liberson, W. T., Kafka, A., and Schwartz, E.: Effects of chlordiazepoxide (librium) and other psychopharmacological agents on "fixated" behavior in rats. Biochem. Pharmacol. (Abstr.) 8:47, 1961.

76. Lubar, J. F.: Effect of medial cortical lesions on the avoidance behavior of the cat. J. Comp. Physiol. Psychol. 58:38-46, 1964.

77. Lubar, J. F., and Perachio, A. A.: One-way and two-way learning and transfer of an active avoidance response in normal and cingulectomized cats. J. Comp. Physiol. Psychol. 60:46-52, 1965.

78. Majkowsky, J., and Jasper, H. H.: Cited in E. N. Sokolov: Higher nervous functions: the orienting reflex. Ann. Rev. Physiol. 25:545-580, 1963.

79. Miller, N. E.: Some recent studies of conflict behavior and drugs. Amer. Psychol. 16:12-24, 1961.

80. Moore, R. Y.: Effects of some rhinencephalic lesions on retention of con-

ditioned avoidance behavior in cats. J. Comp. Physiol. Psychol. 57:65-71, 1964.

81. Moroz, M.: Effects of pentobarbital sodium on the behavior of rats in the Krech hypothesis apparatus. J. Comp. Physiol. Psychol. 52:172-174, 1959.

82. Morrell, F.: Electrophysiological contribution to the neural basis of learning. Physiol. Rev. 41:443-494, 1961.

83. Mowrer, O. H.: Learning Theory and Behavior. New York, John Wiley & Sons, 1960.

84. Meyers, B., and Domino, E. F.: The effect of cholinergic blocking drugs on spontaneous alternation in rats. Arch. Int. Pharmacodyn. 150:525-529, 1964.

85. Naess, K., and Rasmussen, E. W.: Approach-withdrawal responses and other specific behavior reactions as screening test for tranquilizers. Acta Pharmacol. Toxicol. 15:99-114, 1958.

86. Navarro, M. G.: Conditioned emotional responses and psychotropic drugs. Acta Physiol. Lat. Amer. 10:122-128, 1960.

87. Niki, H.: Differential effects of two kinds of tranquilizers upon avoidance learning and fear-motivated discrimination learning. Jap. Psychol. Res. 9:1-13, 1960.

88. Olds, J., and Olds, M. E.: Interference and learning in palaeocortical systems. *In:* Brain Mechanisms and Learning. J. F. Delafresnaye, Ed. CIOM Symposium. Oxford, Blackwell, 1961, pp. 153-183.

89. Otis, L. S.: Dissociation and recovery of a response learned under the influence of chlorpromazine or saline. Science 143:1347-1348, 1964.

90. Overton, D. A.: Control of learned responses by drug states. Unpublished doctoral dissertation, McGill University, 1962.

91. Overton, D. A.: State-dependent or "dissociated" learning produced with pentobarbital. J. Comp. Physiol. Psychol. 57:3-12, 1964.

92. Paskal, V. and Vanderwolf, C. H.: Some effects of atropine sulfate on learning in the rat. Paper read at Canad. Psychol. Assoc. Hamilton, Ontario, June, 1962.

93. Petsche, H., Stumpf, C., and Gogolak, G.: The significance of the rabbit's septum as a relay station between the midbrain and the hippocampus. I. The control of hippocampus arousal activity by the septum cells. Electroenceph. Clin. Neurophysiol. 14:202-211, 1962.

94. Posluns, D.: An analysis of chlorpromazine-induced suppression of the avoidance response. Psychopharmacologia 3:361-373, 1962.

95. Quigley, J. P.: Mental disturbances from atropine or novatropine given to subjects under the influence of insulin. J. Amer. Med. Ass. 109:1363-1364, 1937.

96. Reynierse, J. H., Denny, M. R., and Zerbolio, D. J.: Avoidance decrement: replication and further analysis. Psychonom. Sci. 1:401-402, 1964.

97. Roberts, W. W., Dember, W. N., and Brodwick, M.: Attention and exploration in rats with hippocampal lesions. J. Comp. Physiol. Psychol. 55: 695-700, 1962.

97a. Rosenzweig, M. R., Krech, D. and Bennett, E. L.: Effects of pentobarbital sodium on adaptive behavior patterns in the rat. Science, 123:371-372, 1956.

98. Rushton, R., Steinberg, H., and Tinson, C.: Effects of a single experience on subsequent reactions to drugs. Brit. J. Pharmacol. 20:99-105, 1963.

99. Sachs, E.: The role of brain electrolytes in learning and retention. Fed. Proc. 20:339, 1961.

100. Sachs, E.: The role of brain electrolytes in learning and retention. Unpublished doctoral dissertation. University of Rochester, 1962.

101. Sachs, E.: Rapid avoidance learning under drugs. In preparation.

102. Sachs, E., Weingarten, M., and Klein, N. W. Jr.: Effects of chlordiazepoxide ("Librium") on the acquisition of avoidance learning and its transfer to the normal state and other drug conditions. Psychopharmacologia. 9:17-30, 1966.

103. Sachs, E., Schoenbrun, R., Schapino, S., Simpson, W., and Spong, P.: Correlation between the frequency of the hippocampal theta rhythm and the speed of discriminative approach performance in cat: effects of drug. In preparation.

103a. Sargant, W. and Slater, E.: Physical methods of treatment in Psychiatry. Baltimore, Williams and Wilkins, 1954.

104. Schwartzbaum, J. S., Kellicutt, M. H., Spieth, T. M., and Thompson, J. B.: Effects of septal lesions in rats on response inhibition associated with food-reinforced behavior. J. Comp. Physiol. Psychol. 58:217-224, 1964.

105. Schwartzbaum, J. S., and Spieth, T. M.: Analysis of the response-inhibition concept of septal functions in "passive-avoidance behavior. Psychonom. Sci. 1:145-146, 1964.

106. Sokolov, E. N.: Higher nervous functions: the orienting reflex. Ann. Rev. Physiol. 25:545-580, 1963.

107. Solomon, R. L., and Turner, L. H.: Discriminative classical conditioning in dogs paralyzed by curare can later control discriminative avoidance responses in the normal state. Psychol. Rev. 66:202-219, 1962.

108. Stein, L.: Reciprocal action of reward and punishment mechanisms. In: The Role of Pleasure in Behavior. R. G. Heath, Ed. New York, Harper and Row, 1964, pp. 113-139.

109. Stein, L.: Facilitation of avoidance behavior by positive brain stimulation. J. Comp. Physiol. Psychol. 60:9-19, 1965.

110. Stretch, R., Houston, M., and Jenkins, A.: Effects of amobarbital on extinction at an instrumental response in rats. Nature (London) 201:472-474, 1964.

111. Stumpf, C. N., Petsche, H., and Gogolak, G.: The significance of the rabbit's septum as a relay station between the midbrain and the hippocampus. II. The differential influence of drugs upon both the septal coil firing pattern and the hippocampus theta activity. Electroenceph. Clin. Neurophysiol. 14:212-219, 1962.

112. Teitelbaum, H., and Milner, P.: Activity changes following partial hippocampal lesion in rats. J. Comp. Physiol. Psychol. 56:284-289, 1963.

113. Tonini, G., Riccioni, M. L., Babbini, M., and Missere, G.: Evaluation of central pharmacological actions in rats with septal lesions. In: Psychopharmacological Methods, Voltava, Z., Ed. New York, Pergamon Press, 1963.

114. Torii, S., and Sugi, S.: Electrical activity of hippocampus in unrestrained rabbits. Folia Psychiat. Neurol. Jap. 14:95-104, 1960.
115. Tracy, W. H.: Changes in noise-maintained behavior following septal forebrain lesions in the albino rat. Abstract of doctoral dissertation, Boston University, 1956.
116. Vanderwolf, C. H.: Improved shuttle-box performance following electroconvulsive shock. J. Comp. Physiol. Psychol. 56:983-986, 1963.
117. Vanderwolf, C. H., and Heron, W.: Electroencephalographic waves with voluntary movement: study in the rat. Arch. Neurol. II:379-384, 1964.
118. Webster, D. B., and Voneida, T. J. Learning deficits following hippocampal lesions in split-brain cats. Exp. Neurol. 10:170-182, 1964.
119. White, R. P., Nash, C. B., Westerbeke, E. J., and Possanza, G. J.: Phylogenetic comparison of central actions produced by different doses of atropine and hyoscine. Arch. Int. Pharmacodyn. 132:349-363, 1961.
120. White, R. P., and Carlton, R. A.: Evidence indicating central atropine-like actions of psychotogenic piperidyl benzilates. Psychopharmacologia 4: 459-471, 1963.
121. Wickelgren, W. O., and Isaacson, R. L.: Effect of the introduction of an irrelevant stimulus on runway performance of the hippocampectomized rat. Nature (London) 200:48-50, 1963.
122. Wikler, A.: Pharmacologic dissociation of behavior and EEG "sleep patterns" in dogs: morphine, n-allylnormorphine, and atropine. Proc. Soc. Exp. Biol. Med. 79:261-265, 1952.
123. Wikler, A.: The relation of Psychiatry to Pharmacology. Baltimore, Williams and Wilkins, 1957.
124. Williamson, G. J.: The effect of electroconvulsive shock on an instrumental conditioned emotional response ("conflict"). J. Comp. Physiol. Psychol. 54:633-637, 1961.
125. Zucker, I., and McCleary, R. A.: Perseveration in septal cats. Psychonom. Sci. 1:387-388, 1964.

14

PARALLELS BETWEEN ANIMAL AND HUMAN NEUROSES

by JOSEPH WOLPE, M.D.*

EXPERIMENTAL NEUROSES have been a widely recognized phenomenon since they were first produced in Pavlov's laboratories more than half a century ago. These are states of chronic behavioral disturbance produced experimentally by behavioral means (as opposed to direct assaults on the nervous system by chemical or physical agents). The bizzareness of some of the neurotic behavior early encouraged the belief that experimental neuroses were the result of some kind of lesion in the central nervous system—a view that is still widely held, despite published evidence[15] showing beyond reasonable doubt that they are a special class of learned emotional reactions. In this paper I propose to present this evidence concisely and then to show that in all respects in which comparisons have been made human clinical neuroses have the same attributes as those experimentally induced.

There are two basic methods for producing experimental neuroses. The first is typified by Pavlov's celebrated circle-and-ellipse experiment. At the beginning of the experiment, a luminous circle was projected before a dog confined by the usual harness on the laboratory table and each time was followed by a piece of food within easy reach of the animal, to condition an alimentary (food-approach) response to the circle. After this, an ellipse was conditioned as an inhibitory stimulus through being consistently not followed by food; and then, subsequently, the shape of the ellipse was made rounder in stages. At each rounder stage the inhibitory effect of the ellipse was clearly established by interspersing its nonreinforcements with reinforced presentations of the circle. But a point arrived at which discrimination between the two shapes was no longer possible. The animal then became increasingly agitated, and finally a state of severe disturbance developed. Disturbance was henceforth always manifest when the animal was brought back

*Temple University Medical School, Philadelphia, Pa.

to the experimental chamber. (It is now known that the autonomic disturbance produced by strong simultaneous incompatible action tendencies is indistinguishable from that produced by noxious stimulation.[2])

The other basic method for producing experimental neuroses consists of applying to the spatially confined animal either a large number of weak noxious stimuli (usually in the form of electric shocks) or a small number of stronger noxious stimuli. About a quarter of a century ago, numerous experiments employing noxious stimulation were carried out, particularly by Liddell and his associates (e.g., Liddell;[6] Anderson and Parmentor[1]) at Cornell and by Masserman[7] in Chicago. Misled by certain features of their own experimental arrangements, these workers were at one in believing that these neuroses were also due to conflict. Masserman,[7] for example, ascribed the neuroses he induced in cats to a conflict between food-approach motivation and avoidance-of-shock motivation, because the high-voltage low-amperage shock was inflicted on the animals at the very moment when they were approaching food in response to a conditioned stimulus. However, I subsequently demonstrated,[14,16] in a similar experimental setting, that such neuroses could be produced by shocks administered to animals that had never been fed in the experimental cage. Recently, Smart[13] found, in a comparative study of variations on this experimental model, that there was very little difference on 16 measures of neurotic behavior between a "shock only" group of cats and two groups who were shocked either while approaching food or while eating in the experimental cage.

EXPERIMENTAL NEUROSES AS LEARNED BEHAVIOR

The fact that at least some experimental neuroses can be induced without conflict in itself removes the grounds for the supposition that they result from neural damage or "strain" and provides a presumption that learning is their basis. In that case the typical positive characteristics of learned behavior should be evident. If experimental neuroses are learned, they must have the following features in common with all other learned behavior.

1. The neurotic behavior must be closely similar to that evoked in the precipitating situation.

2. The neurotic responses must be under the control of stimuli that were present in the precipitating situation—that is, the responses must occur upon the impingement on the organism of the same or similar stimuli.

3. The neurotic responses must be at greatest intensity when the organism is

exposed to stimuli most like those to which the behavior was originally conditioned and diminish in intensity as a function of diminishing resemblance, in accordance with the principle of primary stimulus generalization.

All three of these features were clearly demonstrable in the neuroses I produced in cats by administering high-voltage, low-amperage shocks in a small cage.[14,16] The shocks evoked a variety of motor and autonomic responses (e.g., pupillary dilation, erection of hairs, rapid respiration). After an animal had received between three and about a dozen shocks it would be found to be continuously disturbed in the experimental cage; and then no more shocks would be given. The disturbance in each case consisted of just such responses as had been evoked by the shocks. Muscle tension, pupillary dilation, and other reactions of the sympathetic division of the autonomic nervous system were found in all animals, and vocalizing and clawing at the netting in most. But some displayed special reactions which, invariably, had been observed previously in response to the shocks. For example, one cat who had urinated while being shocked always urinated subsequently within a few seconds of being put into the experimental cage. Another developed a symptom that it seems permissible to call hysterical. He jerked his shoulders strongly every few seconds in the experimental cage. This jerking suggested an abortive jumping movement and seemed clearly relatable to the fact that on the first occasion on which he was shocked he had jumped through a hatch in the roof of the cage that had been left open. This similarity between evoked behavior and acquired behavior satisfied the first of the stated criteria of learned behavior.

The control of the neurotic reactions by stimuli involved in the causal situation was evident in several ways. First, the reactions were always at their strongest in the experimental cage, and the animals strongly resisted being put into it. Then, the sounding of a buzzer that had preceded the shocks could invariably intensify whatever reactions were going on. Finally, in the case of animals to whom the experimenter had been visible at the time of shocking, his entry into the living cage could at once evoke these reactions in the animal previously at ease.

Primary stimulus generalization was evident on several continua. Each animal displayed neurotic reactions in the experimental room (Room A) *outside the experimental cage,* though at an intensity clearly less than within the cage. Since stimuli from this room were acting upon the animal at a distance at the time of shocking, direct conditioning to them of neurotic reactions must have occurred. Now, if the animals were placed in one of three rooms* called B, C, and D in order of their physical resemblance to Room A, neurotic reactions would be aroused in each of them, but always least strongly in Room D and most strongly in Room B, though never as strong there as in Room A. Another instance of primary stimulus generalization was on an auditory intensity continuum. Presentation at close range of the buzzer that had preceded the shocks would always disturb an animal greatly, and the farther away he was when it sounded the weaker would his reactions be.

Thus, these experimental neuroses had all three of the qualifying characteristics of learned behavior. As will be shown below, human neuroses, too, possess these characteristics and also resemble those experimentally produced in other telling respects.

HUMAN NEUROSES AS LEARNED BEHAVIOR

The commonest human neurotic response constellation is anxiety —a sympathetic-dominated pattern of autonomic responses. In those neurotic patients—a large majority—in whom a history of the onset of unadaptive anxiety reactions can be obtained, one finds their origin almost always related to an occasion or recurrent occasions of high anxiety, or to a chronic anxiety-evoking state of affairs. Symonds,[19] reviewing the onset of anxiety states in 2000 flying crew members of the Royal Air Force, found a history of anxiety evocation at the onset of 99 per cent of cases. As might have been expected, the nature and degree of stress needed to evoke significantly high degrees of anxiety varied according to pre-existent factors in the individual— as is also true of experimental animals.

Just as in the experimental neuroses, stimulus aspects of the causal situation making impact on the person at the time of causation become conditioned to human neurotic anxiety responses. For example, a lawyer's fear of public speaking was traced to an occasion in law school when he was humiliated by a lecturer when speaking before a class; and a woman's phobia for sharp objects began when she was in the

---

*Rooms A and B were both situated about 30 feet above ground level, overlooking a fairly busy street, but Room A was the brighter, also having windows on its sunny side. Both rooms contained very dark laboratory furniture, the greater quantity being in Room A. Room C, about half the size of A or B, contained laboratory furniture lighter in color and less in quantity than that in B, and was out of earshot of the busy street. Room D, situated on the next floor up, was extremely bright with white-washed walls and with large windows on two sides. It contained only a light-colored kitchen sink, a concrete trough, and some large cartons.

hospital after an unwanted pregnancy, when, while cutting fruit with a sharp knife, she was assailed with terror at the thought that she might harm the baby with the knife. Of course, it is not to be inferred from this that *only* stimuli present at the precipitating events are triggers to neurotic reactions, for second order conditioning often occurs (see below).

Both primary stimulus generalization and secondary generalization are found in human neuroses. In almost all phobias of the classical kind there is primary stimulus generalization. For example, fears of heights increase monotonically with increasing height, and claustrophobia varies in inverse relation to available space and in direct relation to span of confinement. Secondary generalization also occurs, in which the stimulus situations are not physically similar but produce a common mediating response (in Osgood's sense) to which anxiety is a consequent. For example, in a particular patient a tight dress and irremovable nail polish, though physically disparate, were placed in the same continuum of secondary generalization because both produced a closed-in feeling.

Other Points of Correspondence Between Animal and Human Neuroses

Second Order Conditioning

Once neurotic anxiety responses—i.e., high intensity responses to stimuli that *objectively* spell no danger—have been conditioned, second order conditioning becomes possible in both animals and humans. The following experiment was done on each of two cats.

The animal's neurotic anxiety responses to all the visual stimuli had been deconditioned (by a technique briefly described below), but were still elicited by the buzzer. A piece of meat was dropped in a corner of the laboratory, and as the animal eagerly ran towards it, the buzzer was sounded. It recoiled, hair erect, pupils dilated, body rigid; and hesitated before again advancing, upon which the buzzer was again sounded. Repeating the procedure several times resulted in the establishment of anxiety and avoidance reactions to that corner of the room and also to the sight of food dropped on *any* floor. The spread of human neurotic reactions to new stimuli in a precisely parallel way is extremely common. For example, a patient who had developed a fear of social groups, one day sat calmly in a half-empty movie house. During the interval the place became crowded and she was surrounded by people on all sides. A high level of anxiety was aroused; and this, by contiguity, became conditioned to movie houses, even if empty.

Similarity of Precipitating Factors

I have referred to the fact that experimental neuroses are produced either by ambivalent stimulation, which evokes simultaneous high intensity incompatible responses, or by noxious stimulation. At the source of human neuroses, either conflict or the presence of a stimulation that directly evokes intense anxiety is similarly found. The crucial point appears to be that both of these kinds of stimulation produce high levels of autonomic disturbance, which Fonberg[2] has demonstrated to be for all practical purposes physiologically identical.

Resistance to Extinction

An outstanding feature of human neuroses is their resistance to extinction—i.e., the neurotic response does not decrease in strength no matter how often the patient is exposed to the stimulus situations that evoke them. It is the same with the neurotic cat, who shows the same high level of anxiety when placed in the experimental cage again and again, even if for hours.

The core of this resistance is the autonomic complex of reactions that comprises anxiety. Motor response components of experimental neuroses are far less resistant to extinction. Two factors appear to account for the resistance of anxiety to extinction. First, a relatively low level of muscle action is apparently involved in autonomic responses, so that there is presumably little of the fatigue-associated process responsible for reactive inhibition (RI) upon which extinction apparently depends.[3] Second, each time an organism is removed from an anxiety-evoking situation, there is a sharp reduction of the neural state of excitation that is conveniently termed anxiety drive. The reinforcing effect that this drive-reduction has upon the anxiety response habit counteracts any tendency toward extinction.[14]

At this point, taking together the similarities noted, it is plain that both the animal and human neuroses are subsumed by the following definition (cf. Wolpe[14]) :

A neurosis is a persistent unadaptive habit acquired in one or a succession of anxiety-generating situations. Autonomic responses of an anxiety pattern are usually their preeminent constituent.

But there are further resemblances.

Simultaneous Approach and Avoidance Gradients

It is a fairly common clinical experience to find a patient who is repeatedly drawn into situations that evoke great anxiety. From afar the situation is attractive—"the brave music of a *distant* drum"—but within there is nothing but distress. A parallel phenomenon was observed in those neurotic cats who had received food-approach conditioning in the experimental cage before the neurosis was induced by noxious stimulation. These had learned, during the period of their food-approach training, to jump spontaneously into an open "carrier" cage (in which they were to be carried to the laboratory) when it was placed upon the floor of the living cage. After they had been made neurotic they continued their spontaneous jumping into this "carrier" cage, and only began to manifest anxiety on the way downstairs to the laboratory. This observation, of course, exemplifies the rule that the spatial gradient of avoidance is steeper than that of approach.[8]

Elimination of Neurotic Habits by Counterconditioning
(Reciprocal Inhibition Mechanism)

Even after 2 or 3 days' starvation, neurotic cats were inhibited from eating in the experimental cage, or in the experimental room, and usually in one or more of the rooms, B, C, and D (described above) that in varying degrees resembled the experimental room. But always there was a room in which generalization was low enough to evoke a measure of anxiety so weak that eating was not inhibited. The eating was at first delayed and constrained, but subsequent portions of food were accepted with progressively increasing alacrity, while manifestations of anxiety reciprocally diminished, eventually to zero. The animal would thereafter eat in a room more similar to the experimental room, where successive feedings likewise eliminated all signs of anxiety. The same treatment was successfully applied right up the generalization continuum to the experimental cage. Apparently each act of feeding to some extent inhibited anxiety and diminished its habit strength in the stimulus situation concerned.

Eating was long ago employed clinically in similar fashion by Jones[4] to overcome children's phobias. In the human adult, parallel effects have been achieved with more than a dozen other responses that are also inhibitory of anxiety.[18] The most widely applied have been assertive, sexual, and relaxation responses.[16] The use of relaxation in a technique called systematic desensitization corresponds particularly closely with the therapeutic animal experiments described above. The patient is trained in deep muscle relaxation, and, subsequently, when he is deeply relaxed, stimulus situations that evoke neurotic anxiety responses are presented to his imagination. At first, the weakest member of a continuum of disturbing situations is presented—for example, in an acrophobic continuum it might be looking out of a second floor window. The visualizing is terminated after a few seconds, and then, a few seconds later, repeated. With repetitions the amount of anxiety evoked by the scene diminishes; and when it has fallen to zero a "stronger" scene—e.g., looking out of a 3rd floor window is introduced and similarly treated—and so on, until the greatest relevant (asymptotic) height has been dealt with. There is almost invariably complete transfer between what can be imagined without anxiety and what can be experienced in reality without anxiety.[12,16]

These therapeutic changes in animal and human neuroses accord with a common rule—that *if a response inhibitory to anxiety can be made to occur in the presence of anxiety-evoking stimuli, it will weaken the conditioned connection between these stimuli and the anxiety responses.* Conditioned inhibition of anxiety evidently develops on the basis of reciprocal inhibition.[15]

Permanence of Therapeutic Effects

When anxiety response habits are thoroughly deconditioned in the animals, relapse and symptom substitution are never observed. The same is the case with human subjects who are treated by conditioning methods. It is important, however, to realize that *thorough* treatment always implies removing from the stimuli concerned *all* power to evoke anxiety. *The stimuli must be disconnected from the responses:* This is fundamental therapy, in contrast to attempts to modify responses as such—for example, by direct suggestion—without reference to their stimulus sources. There is strong evidence that once anxiety response habits are eliminated, they do not relapse. There is *no* evidence of an "unconscious" reservoir of forces that may at any time erupt in symptomatic discharges. In a study of follow-up studies of 249 cases who had apparently recovered after nonpsychoanalytic types of therapy of various kinds, it was found that only 4 relapses had occurred after periods ranging from 2 to 15 years.[17]

CONCLUSION

The practical implication of the general parallelism between animal and human neuroses is that if the latter, like the former, can be considered to be purely a matter of habits (predominantly of the autonomic nervous system) their treatment will be most effective when designed according to laws of learning. Methods so designed have already been yielding almost 90 per cent recoveries or marked improvements in neurotic cases in an average of about 30 sessions per patient.[5,16] Recently, in a striking and beautifully controlled study at the University of Illinois, Paul[11] showed that "dynamically" oriented psychotherapists, in treating students with severe anxieties in public speaking situations, obtained significantly better results with a conditioning technique—systematic desensitization—than they did with their own brand of insight therapy.

REFERENCES

1. Anderson, O. D., and Parmenter, R. A.: Long term study of the experimental neurosis in the sheep and dog. Psychosom. Med. Monogr. 2 (No. 3 and 4) : 1941.
2. Fonberg, E.: On the manifestation of conditioned defensive reactions in stress. Bull. Soc. Sci. Lettr. Lodz. Class III. Sci. Math. Natur., 1956, 7, 1.
3. Hull, C. L.: Principles of Behavior. New York, Appleton-Century-Crofts, 1943.
4. Jones, M. C.: A laboratory study of fear. The case of Peter. J. Genet. Psychol. 31:308, 1924.
5. Lazarus, A. A.: The results of behavior therapy in 126 cases of severe neuroses. Behav. Res. Ther. 1:69, 1963.
6. Liddell, H. S.: Conditioned reflex method and experimental neurosis. In: Personality and the Behavior Disorders. J. McV. Hunt, Ed. New York, Ronald Press Co., 1944.
7. Masserman, J. H.: Behavior and Neurosis. Chicago, University of Chicago Press, 1943.
8. Miller, N. E.: Experimental studies of conflict. In: Personality and the Behavior Disorders. Hunt, J. M., Ed. New York, Ronald Press Co., 1944.
9. Napalkov, A. V., and Karas, A. Y.: Elimination of pathological conditioned reflex connections in the experimental hypertensive state. Zh. Vyssh. Nerv. Deiatel. Pavlov 7:402, 1957.
10. Osgood, G. E.: Studies on the generality of affective meaning systems. Amer. Psychol. 17:10, 1962.
11. Paul, G. L.: Insight Versus Desensitization. Stanford, Stanford University Press, 1966.
12. Rachman, S.: Studies in desensitization III. Speed of generalization. Behav. Res. Ther. 4:7, 1966.
13. Smart, R. G.: Conflict and conditioned aversive stimuli in the development of experimental responses. Canad. J. Psychol. 19:208, 1965.
14. Wolpe, J.: Experimental neuroses as learned behavior. Brit. J. Psychol. 43: 243, 1952.
15. Wolpe, J.: The formation of negative habits: a neurophysiological view. Psychol. Rev. 59:290, 1952.
16. Wolpe, J.: Psychotherapy by Reciprocal Inhibition. Stanford, Calif., Stanford University Press, 1958.
17. Wolpe, J.: The prognosis in unpsychoanalyzed recovery from neurosis. Amer. J. Psychiat. 116:35, 1961.
18. Wolpe, J., and Lazarus, A. A.: Behavior Therapy Techniques. London, Pergamon Press, 1966.
19. Symonds, C. P.: The human response to flying stress. Brit. Med. J. 2: 703, 1943.

DISCUSSION

HOWARD F. HUNT, Ph.D.*

We are indebted to Dr. Solomon for a most articulate and thoughtful review of one of the very prickly topics in modern psychology—aversive control. Painful stimuli have powerful effects on behavior, as our easy recourse to punishment in everyday life testifies, but these effects cannot be well understood within the framework of any simplistic analysis. They are often temporary, sometimes exact a high cost in emotional disturbance, and often produce unwanted side-effects more serious and refractory than the behavior that we were trying to control. When he discusses why "a punishment is not always a punishment," Dr. Solomon emphasizes the absolute necessity of behavioral analysis—analysis of the responses, consideration of the characteristics of the species, the details of the situation in which the behaviors occur and their sources of strength, the exact contingencies that prevail between response and reinforcement—as a precondition for effective tactical use of aversive stimulation in the control of behavior. This emphasis could not be more timely. Punishment, as a monolithic category, has been dissolved by the acid of experimental data, and further progress demands careful study of the constituents so revealed.

Indeed, not only "punishment" but even "passive" avoidance is suspect as a category. It is a crude topographical class that includes members which are diverse dynamically. Some instances of "passive" avoidance are really "active" and thus should be analyzed as escape-avoidance behavior. Here, unwanted instrumental behavior has been stopped by painful consequences simply because the arrangements led the organism to acquire an incompatible instrumental escape-avoidance behavior reinforced by termination of the stimuli that warned of the coming painful event.

Further, though we tend to lump most punishment of instrumental behavior under the heading of "passive" avoidance, Dr. Solomon has pointed out that the instrumental chain ending at the consummatory response is far from homogeneous with respect to the effects of punishment. Shock disrupts consummatory behavior much more easily than

*New York State Psychiatric Institute and Columbia University, New York, N.Y.

it disrupts instrumental responses coming earlier in the chain, yet the consummatory response is more closely associated with the primary reinforcement that maintains the chain and usually contains both unlearned and overlearned components essential to the organism's survival (e.g., chewing, swallowing, ways of eating). According to our usual understanding of the laws of learning, such responses should be more rather than less resistant to disruption.

This paradox is of our own creation, of course, because paradoxes do not exist in nature but arise out of our interpretations of events. Perhaps the difference between the consummatory and other members of an instrumental chain is only one of degree. The parameters of this difference should be explored and specified. My guess is that the reactions evoked both by rewarding stimuli (in consummatory behavior) and by the shocks, and how they are conditioned and controlled, will turn out to be important.

If so, the term "passive" may be a bad one altogether insofar as it directs our attention toward superficial, topographic aspects of the situation and away from the behavior that is occurring and the contingencies that control it. The organism whose unwanted behavior has been stopped by punishment in a "passive" avoidance situation is doing something, of course. If not actively avoiding or escaping as described above, he is likely to be showing a conditioned emotional response of the "fear" or "anxiety" type which effectively competes with and thus suppresses the unwanted behavior. As unpublished experiments in my own laboratory have indicated, this reflexive reaction cannot be eliminated by punishment with shock whenever it appears. Such a procedure actually makes it stronger. The behavior is not under the control of its consequences, as is instrumental (operant) behavior, but rather is an instance of Pavlovian (respondent) conditioning. Shock originally evoked a complex of reflex responses that included it, was the reinforcing stimulus that conditioned it to the stimuli in the present situation that evoke it, and further punishment simply reinforces the conditioning. To try to eliminate such conditioned emotional behavior by punishing it is like trying to get rid of conditioned Pavlovian salivation by placing more food on the tongue. Thus, it appears that the organism is not only doing something in "passive" avoidance, but also that that behavior often may be a kind of behavior not under the control of punishing consequences.

In thinking about punishment, it is also important to remember that punishing stimuli may not always punish and rewarding stimuli not always reward. The reasons for this need not be mysterious. In his comments on the Holz and Azrin experiments, Dr. Solomon brought out how a shock that would ordinarily punish may become a discriminative stimulus that signals the availability of food, as a function of differential reinforcement with food. Similarly, the easy disruption of consummatory behavior can be understood if we realize that the appetitive stimuli which evoke consummatory behavior, such as eating, are paired with shock in consummatory punishment and may become conditioned stimuli evoking fear reactions incompatible with eating. In effect, the stimuli associated with getting and eating food acquire conditioned aversive properties and the power to evoke an emotional disturbance through Pavlovian conditioning. The organism is rewarded for backing away from these stimuli (or quickly loses interest in eating if he does not). This sort of thing should and probably does suppress consummatory behavior promptly.

The problem really is not why consummatory behavior is so responsive to punishment but rather why punishment of earlier members of an instrumental chain is less effective. The statements above, by themselves, would suggest no good reason why the chain could not be blocked anywhere with equal ease. The definitive experiment on this problem, using multimember chains with the members spread out temporally and topographically to permit close observation of punishment effects at each point, has yet to be done, to my knowledge. Dr. Solomon has hinted at a solution, however, in saying, ". . . the nature of operants is such that they are separated in time and space and response topography from consummatory behavior and positive incentive stimuli, so that appetitive reactions are not clearly present during the punishment for operants." I would go even farther to suggest that the earlier members of a chain are, to some substantial degree, under the control of discriminative stimuli. Only those discriminative stimuli controlling the punished member are closely associated with shock. Unless the shock is severe, the other members retain much of their power and still provide the occasion for the occurrence of earlier members of the chain, repeatedly leading the individual right back up to the punished member. This increases the probability that that member will occasionally occur and be punished. After such punishment if the organism is not removed from the situation and if no subsequent members are punished, he is free to romp merrily through the remainder of the chain to his reward. If this sort of thing happens very often, the punishment shocks may actually become a signal for "safety," just as they became the signal for availability of food in the Holz and Azrin experiment. This explanation is as speculative as the others, but careful experimental analysis of behavior should be helpful here.

In his attempt to explain dissociation in learning and memory, as produced by drugs and other agents, Dr. Sachs has undertaken an important and formidable task. Further, he has had the courage to follow out many of the consequences of his formulation as they would apply to other phenomena in learning, the problem of drive and attention, and the electrophysiology of habituation and adaptation. His discussion brings together a tremendous diversity of material. The scope of his inquiry is such, however, that a fair critical treatment is impossible here. One or two comments can be made, nevertheless.

In brief, Dr. Sachs proposes a cognitive psychological model employing an information theory rhetoric as an alternative to the S-R connectionism so popular with behavioral researchers. Among many other things, he suggests that drugs which produce dissociation in learning do so by "reducing stimulus inputs" so that whatever learning or habituation is going on during learning under the drug is defining the behavioral situation with respect to only a limited sample of the contingencies and stimuli. When the organism is later tested without the drug, he is in an at least partially new situation, significant parts of which he is ignorant of, so he acts as if the prior learning experience had not occurred. The reduction of input here is not to be understood as necessarily implying analgesia or anesthesia. Rather, the reduction is in substantial part a function of the organism's drug-produced alterations in behavior, altered sensory sensitivities, altered attention and scanning, and the like, so that habituation and information input are restricted. The poor performance on the nondrug test reflects naïveté and ignorance attributable to restricted contact with the situation under the drug.

Dr. Sachs attempts to rule out generalization decrement as an explanation of dissociation. Here, responses learned under drug conditions are said to be weakened under nondrug conditions because drug-produced stimuli, present at learning, are incorporated into the stimulus complex controlling the behavior. In the tests in the nondrug state, these stimuli are absent; the stimulus situation for the organism is now different, and his learned responses are weaker because they are being tested under circumstances different from the learning situation—the learning shows a decrement in accordance with the laws of generalization.

I entertain only a modest enthusiasm for generalization decrement as an explanation. It is a problem to be solved, rather than an explanatory principle. Dr. Sachs' formulations do not rule it out clearly, however. In fact, "reduction of input" as a function of the drugs would seem to imply that the nondrug tests *must* take place in a stimulus context different from that which prevailed at the time of training. His argument really is that absence of drug-produced stimuli does not contribute significantly to the change.

Actually, Dr. Sachs wishes to deal with the problem under the headings of cognition, habituation, attention, and the effects of knowledge and information input. He extends his formulations to confront and be tested by diverse experimental data. He erects a number of imaginative hypotheses to produce a systematized formulation of fear, avoidance, drive, habituation and attention in his attempt to answer the crucial questions, "What is learned?" and "What is fear?" These analyses represent the major thrust of his presentation.

Unavoidably, the argument contains a lot of speculation and its fabric is stretched very thinly in spots as it attempts to cover an immense and heterogeneous domain. While Dr. Sachs' formulation has much heuristic merit, not unexpectedly it seems to me to be marred by a number of possible inconsistencies that need to be faced and reduced. For example (and here I may be revealing only my own limitations), early in the paper he seemed to imply that fear (the "pseudo-CER" and the CER) reflected ignorance of a situation, and later that an organism became increasingly capable of fear only as knowledge of the situation increased. Elsewhere, there is a suggestion that both mechanisms may operate. As another example, the formulation appears to imply that a fully informed organism—one with full knowledge—would be pretty inert and nonreactive. However, in earlier parts of the discourse it is argued that knowledge and habituation are preconditions for brisk, smooth performance of avoidance behavior, undistracted by fear, curiosity, exploratory tendencies, and the like.

Despite these difficulties, however, I must say I was intrigued by this approach to explaining the action of dissociating drugs by considering the drugged subject as an ". . . S-R animal devoid of all the properties Tolman inferred."

The papers by Dr. Ayllon and Dr. Wolpe bring behavior control and learning techniques out of the laboratory and into the hospital and consulting room. This application, usually called "behavior therapy," is one of the fastest growing buds on the mental health tree. In passing, it should be noted that the behavior therapists did not discover learning. There is, after all, a good deal of informal learning theory even in Freud. What is new is the *systematic* and *self-conscious* application of behavior control and learning procedures to the alleviation of pathological behavior, and this is a most promising development.

For a number of years, Dr. Ayllon has been carrying out demonstration experiments showing clearly that the behavior of regressed psychotics can be modified and controlled by its consequences. As his present paper shows, this is easier to say than to do. Care in specifying desired behavior, ingenuity on selecting rewards, and close administrative concern for consistency are essential prerequisites for even modest success.

In his earlier work, he capitalized imaginatively on the fact that patients can be rewarded by selective attention from ward personnel and used this as a reinforcer. For procedural reasons (partly because the behavior of ward personnel is a problem in behavior control, too), the current research employs a clever combination of token reward and access to some preferred activity as conditioned and primary reinforcers, respectively. The system works, as the data indicate, and the half-facetious thought occurs to me that we may be well on our way to rediscovering finance capitalism.

I hope that Dr. Ayllon can surmount procedural difficulties and develop new and better ways to use attention and response from other people as reinforcers. These are potent factors in the control of the behavior of all of us in everyday life. Thus, such social reinforcement should be a powerful aid in getting the new, desirable behavior of the patients to generalize to situations outside the immediate training environment.

This is a serious problem in the practical application of operant control, and dependable solutions have yet to be developed. Here, in these experiments, the data indicated that the desired behavior was under the specific and secure control of the experimental reinforcers; leave them out and the desired behavior disappeared. This is precisely what is likely to happen when the patients leave the ward for the outside world, unless control has been transferred to other reinforcers and discriminative stimuli, possibly social, that are available and normally used to maintain behavior there.

This paper also implies an admonition by raising the possibility that pathological behavior can also be maintained by inadvertent reinforcement hidden in the arrangements for managing patients. Actually, I am borrowing from an earlier Ayllon paper here, a paper which pointed out instances in which ward personnel inadvertently reinforced "sick" behavior by paying attention or otherwise responding to it. I feel justified in dragging the point in, though, to call attention to an important but little-recognized possibility that is often overlooked in treatment, that a cryptic behavior control effect may accidentally work at cross-purposes with other therapeutic efforts being deliberately employed.

We are truly indebted to Dr. Wolpe for his succinct summary of his work and thinking. His comments on his animal research should remind us of his substantial contribution to our current view that animal experimental neuroses are learned and not the result of abnormal behavioral or nervous system processes. Further, the paper shows clearly how his therapeutic formulations grew out of his animal research, and what can be accomplished by systematic extension of learning principles derived from animal behavior to the human case. Both gain, I think, from being joined in context.

Contemporary behavior therapists have profited immensely from Dr. Wolpe's enthusiastic advocacy and from his explicit statement of his views. These throw down a clear intellectual challenge to advocates of more traditional views. Unfortunately, the controversies that have developed have generated more heat than light. The data presented on both sides have tended to be illustrative rather than analytic, and the argument has been largely reiterative.

With respect to the problem of symptom substitution and relapse, for example, Dr. Wolpe presents data arguing that it does not occur; and the opposition stubbornly asserts, on doctrinal grounds, that it must. If we are to make a serious judgment on this matter, we need follow-up data collected and presented in greater detail than are presently available in the literature. Also, somebody should start with the hypothesis that maybe Dr. Wolpe is correct and carry out behavioral analysis and experimentation to show why and how symptom substitution is avoided in systematic desensitization therapy. Perhaps counterphobic behavior develops because it receives social reinforcement by the therapist (and other associates of the patient). This may simply replace the phobia, and the symptomatic fear may not be extinguished at all. Such alternatives need to be explored.

Happily, such analytic experimentation is on the increase, though usually with college students as subjects. By and large, the outcome of the studies reported has favored Dr. Wolpe's position. The confirmation must be regarded as somewhat tentative, however, because the phobias and anxieties involved are generally minor symptomatic expressions rather than the ruling passions seen in clinically phobic patients.

Finally, I do not find the reported comparisons between the effectiveness of desensitization and "dynamic" therapies entirely convincing as to the relative merits of the two approaches. I believe the data, of course, and consider the experiments carefully done. However, should we lump together all therapists who do not use desensitization and who try to help their patients develop insight by verbal, dyadic interaction? "Dynamic" or "insight" therapists differ a great deal in what they *actually do*, and this is probably what is important. A speech therapist or student counselor at the University of Illinois and a senior training psychoanalyst at the New York Institute of Psychoanalysis are probably far apart on dimensions much more relevant than geography.

In Memoriam, Franz J. Kallmann

Franz Kallmann was a unique figure in the development of both psychiatry and human genetics, and his death, on May 12, 1965, at the age of 67, leaves a void that cannot be filled. There are other geneticists, though few, who will continue to carry on twin studies, and there are other psychiatrists and psychologists who will study mental disease and senescence in fruitful ways; but there is no one on the horizon who can speak the language of all these disciplines and provide a bridge of intercommunication between them so effectively as Franz Kallmann did.

Kallmann's early training was in medicine and psychiatry. Born in Silesia on July 24, 1897, the son of a surgeon and general practitioner, he received his medical training at the University of Breslau, which awarded him the degree of Doctor of Medicine in 1919. Among his professors were Alzheimer, Foerster, and Minkowski. The atmosphere was brilliant and stimulating. Kallmann decided upon psychiatry as his specialty, but criminology and forensic psychiatry occupied a special place in his training. While an intern at All Saints' Hospital in Breslau he often accompanied the police on their rounds, and thus chose for his doctoral thesis the subject, "Accidental Stab Wounds as a Cause of Death."

After four years in psychiatric hospitals and clinics in the Breslau region, Kallmann was invited to join the staff of the Psychiatric Institute of the University of Berlin, where he worked under the renowned mentor Karl Bonhoeffer. Kallmann's range of interest and knowledge now broadened in new directions. On the one hand, he studied psychoanalytic method at the Berlin Psychoanalytic Institute, under Alexander, Fenichel, and Rado. On the other hand, he began work in neuropathology as an assistant to Creutzfeldt. In 1928 Kallmann was made director of the neuropathology laboratories in two mental hospitals in Berlin, and accepted an invitation to become a fellow at the new psychiatric research institute founded in Munich by Kraepelin, and which has now become the Max Planck Institute of Psychiatry. Here Kallmann began his psychiatric family studies, under Rüdin, Luxenburger, Lange, and Schulz. And here he commenced, with the assistance of his wife Helly Kallmann and some assistants, the vast study of the incidence of schizophrenia among the sibs and descendants of schizophrenic subjects, a project that was to be the subject of his first book and would occupy him in one way or another throughout his life.

In 1933 the policies of the Nazi regime in respect to enforced sterilization of psychotic patients and other "racial" views of human genetics forced Kallmann into opposition. By 1936 he was no longer permitted to speak at scientific meetings in Germany and chose exile in the United States. With him came the completed manuscript of his first definitive study *The Genetics of Schizophrenia*, which was published in English translation shortly afterwards (1938). Through the support of such American leaders in psychiatry as Nolan D. C. Lewis and David M. Levy, Kallmann was invited to join the staff of the New York State Psychiatric Institute at Columbia University, where he remained until his death. During the ensuing almost thirty years, he organized and developed the department of medical genetics there, and as Professor of Psychiatry at the College of Physicians and Surgeons of Columbia University trained many promising young psychiatrists and human geneticists in a multidisciplinary approach to the problems of mental disorder. It was a type of training such as could not be found in any other medical school in the United States.

Kallmann's influence upon generations of medical students, psychiatric residents, and psychoanalytic candidates was profound, since he insisted upon the breadth of view consistent with the inclusion of genetic factors in the analysis of the etiology of all disease and especially of mental disorders. His twin studies, starting with the analysis of the genetic factors in schizophrenia, were extended to include manic depressive psychosis, mongolism, senescence and senility, homosexuality, mental deficiency of various kinds, and abnormalities of behavior associated with deafness. But his use of the twin method of investigation was not limited to mental disorders. My own first awareness of his exciting and significant investigations came in 1943, upon the publication, with his colleague D. Reisner, of Kallmann's classic studies of the significance of genetic factors in tuberculosis. How fortunate it was for the advancement of medical and genetic knowledge that these studies were undertaken when they were, and by as careful and well-informed a team of workers! A decade later, after the introduction of streptomycin and isoniazid treatment, the study would not have been possible.

Kallmann was well aware of the deficiencies of the twin method of studying the role of genetic factors in any disease or phenomenon of growth, yet he made the most of the method by including as many parameters of relationship as possible. Comparisons of monozygous twins, separated or living together; comparisons of monozygous twins with dizygous twins of the same sex; comparisons of twin differences with those between sibs; comparison of twin differences with those between parents and offspring, husband and wife, and controls selected from the general population and paired randomly—all these batteries of comparative degrees of similiarity and difference added to the force and clarity of the conclusions drawn. To be sure, at best the twin method only indicates the presence and the strength of the hereditary etiological factors in the entire background of social, nutritive, and other environmental etiological differences. It never tells one the precise nature of the transmission of the genetic predisposition or even how many gene differences are commonly involved. Whether the important differences of the genotype are unifactorial or multifactorial, dominant or recessive or intermediate, are questions that must be answered by other means, such as pedigree analysis, chromosome studies, and other classic or novel genetic methods. Kallmann was thus on difficult ground when he attempted to discern the exact mode of genetic determination of schizophrenia or manic depressive disease, and when he suggested that the former is attributable to a single recessive (homozygous) gene and the latter to a single dominant gene. The problem is complicated by the inability to secure sharp, universally accepted diagnoses of such mental disorders as these. Nevertheless, Kallmann's ideas of the relatively simple predisposition to schizophrenia and manic depressive psychosis have not been disproved; and more recent studies by others tend to confirm most of his conclusions, in particular that the two disorders are genetically distinct. We must await newer and better methods of psychiatric diagnosis and genetic investigation before we shall know fully about the genetic bases. Considering the difficulty and uncertainty of diagnosing twin pairs as monozygous or dizygous at the time when Kallmann's significant work was done, it is indeed remarkable to see how much he accomplished in this difficult area, which he summarized effectively in his book *Heredity in Health and Mental Disorder* (1953). From his day on, no one will be able to ignore the importance of the genetic element in human illness, especially in mental disorders.

Among numerous honors bestowed upon him were the Samuel W. Hamilton Medal and Lectureship of the American Psychopathological Association in 1960, the Gold Medal of the City of Salerno in 1961, and the Gold Medal of the Eastern Psychiatric Association in 1961. He served the last-named organization as its president in 1963-64. He was president of the American Psychopathological Association at the time of his death, which prevented the preparation and delivery of the customary presidential address.

It is appropriate also to mention the able group of younger workers who began their studies of human genetics under Franz Kallmann, or who worked with him as colleagues, and whose contributions are evident from the many joint papers they wrote with him. In addition to Reisner, already cited, the roll includes John D. Rainer, who worked with Kallmann on the genetics and demography of behavior patterns in deafness; Gordon Allen, who assisted in a study of mongolism in twins; Gerhardt Sander (deceased), who was a co-worker in the studies of longevity and senescence in twins; Lissy F. Jarvik, who has contributed both to the studies of senescence and of tuberculosis; Arthur Falek, on longevity and senescence; and numerous others.

Franz Kallmann's influence in promoting interdisciplinary contacts between psychiatrists and geneticists was manifested in yet another significant way. He was probably more persistent and more influential in bringing about the establishment of the American Society of Human Genetics in 1948 than any other single person. On every appropriate occasion he urged the need for a society that would bring together medical men and human geneticists to discuss their interests in common problems. He insisted that the Society, when established, should found a journal for this purpose. It was a fitting recognition of his efforts to establish the Society that he was elected its fourth president. His presidential address, given on September 9, 1952, and published later in that year in the newly established *American Journal Of Human Genetics*, was on the subject "Human Genetics as a Science, as a Profession, and as a Social-Minded Trend of Orientation." The very title of this thoughtful and far-seeing paper indicates the breadth and vision of a man whom friends remember as kind, warm, and modest.

Bentley Glass, Ph.D.
Academic Vice President, State University of New York at Stony Brook

In Memoriam, Paul H. Hoch

Paul Hoch's broad range of psychiatric interests and knowledge were best characterized by his choice of topics for the meetings of the American Psychopathological Association and were documented in the yearly volumes, such as this one, of the proceedings of this organization, which were edited by him and Joseph Zubin. In almost all of them Hoch's discussions, papers, and lectures showed his grasp of the most diversified subjects and his ability to pinpoint the essentials of any problem under debate.

His professional life history provided him with an intimate acquaintance with many subjects, and his superior intellect qualified him as one of the most sought after speakers at any psychiatric meeting.

Paul Hoch was born on October 31, 1902, in Budapest, where he went to school. He received most of his medical and psychiatric training in Germany, where he attended Medical School in Munich and Göttingen. In 1926 he graduated from the University of Göttingen where, after his graduation, he did research at the University Institute for Anatomy. In 1927 he began his psychiatric career at the Psychiatric-Neurological University Hospital in Göttingen under Schultze, but interrupted this for a year to work at the famous psychiatric hospital, Burghölzli in Zürich. In 1932 he became "Privatdozent" in Göttingen, but a few months later had to leave Germany for political reasons.

The first part of his career already reflected his broad interests in the field of psychiatry and neurology and the wide scope of his approach to every problem he encountered. A first neurological paper on amyotrophic lateral sclerosis envisaged the importance of social and legal aspects of the disease. His second paper dealt with a subject which later became his main field of interest, the treatment of schizophrenia. When it was written in 1930, actual treatment of schizophrenia was limited to rather fruitless attempts with fever and sleep therapy and treatment with atropine in schizophreniform psychoses related to post-encephalitis. This paper is a remarkable essay on the methodology of evaluation of treatment results and contains remarks on the theory of schizophrenia which are still valid today. In other research he extended his interest to the possible neuropathology of the disease and wrote on "The pathology of the chorioid plexus in schizophrenia." From then on he concentrated on clinical subjects, a development which

326

probably was strengthened by the time he spent in Zürich, where his essentially Kraepelinian psychiatry was enriched by the concepts of Bleuler, which later had such great influence on Hoch's formulation of "pseudoneurotic schizophrenia." A report to his teacher in Göttingen about his work in Zürich contained recommendations and organizational plans which could have predicted his later administrative activity in the United States.

After arriving in this country in 1933, he spent the first ten years at the Manhattan State Hospital in New York as a ward psychiatrist. Undoubtedly these years contributed greatly to the achievements of his later career. It was during this time that insulin coma treatment was introduced, and Paul Hoch established one of the best treatment units, to which later metrazol and electric convulsive therapies were added. It is interesting that a first comparative study between insulin and convulsive therapy which he had prepared was never published, probably because his conclusions were not in accordance with what was then the official opinion regarding the value of these treatments. It was also during these years that his great knowledge and his brilliant means of applying this knowledge to any problem under discussion were discovered by those who were responsible for Paul Hoch's rise in the profession.

In 1943 Nolan D. C. Lewis asked him to join the staff of the New York State Psychiatric Institute and the Department of Psychiatry of the College of Physicians and Surgeons of Columbia University. Prior to this, he had served as a consultant to the Hospital of War Neuroses at Gladstone, N. J., under the U. S. Public Health Service. It was at the Psychiatric Institute that he met representatives of various disciplines connected with psychiatry and became a prominent member of a group of scientists who remained his personal and professional friends until his death. In 1948 he became Chief of a newly created Department of Experimental Psychiatry at the Psychiatric Institute.

These were the most fruitful years of Paul Hoch's clinical work. His knowledge of psychopathology, on the one hand, and research design, on the other, equipped him for those investigations which, over the years, made him an outstanding figure in the field of psychopharmacology. The psychomimetic drugs, such as the old mescaline and the new LSD-25, were applied to various types of psychiatric disorders. There was a fortunate combination of these studies with simultaneous work in psychosurgery. In these clinical areas he and his co-workers were the first to shift the emphasis and indications for

psychosurgery from the deteriorated schizophrenic to the most promising groups of nondeteriorating psychiatric illnesses. His work on
pseudoneurotic schizophrenia was tested on the material thus treated
and followed in his department. An increasing number of associates felt
for the first time the influence of Paul Hoch as a teacher. It was
generally hoped that this period would lead to the logical step of a
professorship in psychiatry, but at this juncture his career took him to
even more influential tasks. In 1955 he was appointed Commissioner
of Mental Hygiene of the State of New York. It was a break with
tradition that a nationally and internationally known clinician rather
than a hospital administrator was chosen for such a position. Later
on, many other states followed the example given by New York. Paul
Hoch, the Commissioner, was so successful that he was reappointed by
the next administration. He immediately embarked on application of
his knowledge of recent developments in hospital management in other
countries and sent a group of hospital directors to England, where
they observed and later introduced in New York the "open door
hospital" and similar organizational changes. At the same time the
new psychotropic drugs had become available, and the combination
of different hospital policies and easily applicable drug treatment
reduced the number of mental hospital patients to a considerable
degree for the first time. Paul Hoch's importance in the field of
psychopharmacology made him a leading figure in the evaluation of
the new psychotropic drugs. He was instrumental in the creation of
the Collegium Internationale Neuro-Psychopharmacologicum, of which
he later became President. While the emphasis of his work changed
from a clinical standpoint to a public health approach, he continued
in his private practice with the clear purpose of maintaining contact
with the individual patient.

His position in the forefront of American psychiatry led automatically to a great number of committee appointments and to the presidency
of such organizations as the Society of Biological Psychiatry, the
Schilder Society, the Rudolf Virchow Medical Society, the American-
Hungarian Medical Society, and the American College of Neuro-Psy-
chopharmacology. His continued work in the Program Committee of
the American Psychopathological Association led to his election as
president of this organization.

His position as Commissioner of Mental Hygiene enabled Paul Hoch
to enlarge the services of this department in many directions. He
created research positions in several state hospitals, established pro-

grams for narcotic addicts, and broadened the services for children and adolescents. A special Division for Mental Retardation was a step to improve the long-neglected care of the mentally retarded. His last achievement was a radical change in commitment laws, abolishing court commitments and replacing them with hospital admission by physicians only, similar to the admission of other sick persons. This accomplishment was one of many illustrations of the great influence he had on lawmakers and others outside of the psychiatric profession.

Paul Hoch's untimely death on December 15, 1964, at the age of 62 and at the height of his career was felt as a tremendous loss by psychiatrists all over the world.

Lothar B. Kalinowsky, M.D.

APPENDIX

MEMBERSHIP OF AMERICAN PSYCHOPATHOLOGICAL ASSOCIATION*

OFFICERS

Franz J. Kallmann, M.D., Pres.†
722 West 168th Street
New York 32, New York

Seymour S. Kety, M.D., Pres.-Elect
National Institute of Mental Health
Bethesda 14, Maryland

Bernard C. Glueck, Jr., M.D.,
    Vice-Pres.
Box 2070
Hartford, Connecticut

Fritz A. Freyhan, M.D., Secretary
St. Vincent's Hospital
New York, N.Y. 10011

Howard F. Hunt, Ph.D., Treasurer
722 West 168th Street
New York 32, New York

Jerome D. Frank, M.D., Councillor
Department of Psychiatry
The Johns Hopkins University
Baltimore, Maryland

Lauretta Bender, M.D., Councillor
44 Malone Avenue
Long Beach, New York

COMMITTEE ON PROGRAM:

Paul H. Hoch, M.D., Chairman†
722 West 168th Street
New York 32, New York

Joseph Zubin, Ph.D.
722 West 168th Street
New York 32, New York

MEMBERS:

Theodora M. Abel, Ph.D.
Palisades
Rockland County, New York

David Abrahamsen, M.D.
1035 Fifth Avenue
New York, New York

Nathan Ackerman, M.D.
43 East 78th Street
New York, New York

Alexandra Adler, M.D.
30 Park Avenue
New York, New York

Leo Alexander, M.D. (L)
433 Marlboro Street
Boston, Massachusetts

George S. Amsden, M.D. (L)
Acworth, New Hampshire

Leslie R. Angus, M.D.
1120 East Market Street
Danville, Pennsylvania

Silvano Arieti, M.D.
103 East 75th Street
New York, New York

---

*(L) = Life Member. (H) = Honorary Member.
†Deceased.

330

Irma Bache, M.D. (L)
1 East 356
Pentagon Building
Washington, D.C.

Walter W. Baker, Ph.D.
Eastern Pennsylvania Psychiatric
    Institute
Henry Avenue & Abbottsford Road
Philadelphia, Pennsylvania

Lauretta Bender, M.D.
44 Malone Avenue
Long Beach, New York

Herbert Birch, Ph.D.
Department of Pediatrics
Albert Einstein College of Medicine
New York, New York

H. Waldo Bird, M.D.
School of Medicine
St. Louis University
1402 South Grand Boulevard
St. Louis, Missouri

James Birren, Ph.D.
Section on Aging
National Institute of Mental Health
Bethesda, Maryland

Eugene L. Bliss, M.D.
Salt Lake City General Hospital
156-168 Westminster Avenue
Salt Lake City, Utah

Joseph M. Bobbitt, Ph.D.
Manpower Development
National Institute of Child Health and
    Human Development
Bethesda, Maryland

Benjamin Boshes, M.D.
Department of Neurology and
    Psychiatry
Northwestern University
303 East Chicago Avenue
Chicago, Illinois

Wagner H. Bridger, M.D.
Department of Psychiatry
Albert Einstein School of Medicine
Bronx, N.Y.

Henry Brill, M.D.
Box 202
Pilgrim State Hospital
West Brentwood, L.I., New York

Eugene Brody, M.D.
University of Maryland
School of Medicine
Baltimore, Maryland

Albert Browne-Mayers, M.D.
147 East 50th Street
New York, New York

Hilda Bruch, M.D.
Department of Psychiatry
Baylor University
1200 Moursund Avenue
Houston, Texas

A. Louise Brush, M.D. (L)
55 East 86th Street
New York, New York

Dexter M. Bullard, Sr., M.D. (L)
M.H.A.
500 W. Montgomery Avenue
Rockville, Maryland

Eugene I. Burdock, Ph.D.
Psychiatric Institute
722 West 168th Street
New York, New York

Ernest W. Burgess, Ph.D.
University of Chicago
1225 East 60th Street
Chicago, Illinois

Enoch Callaway, M.D.
Chief of Research
The Langley Porter Neuropsychiatric
  Institute
401 Parnassus Avenue
San Francisco, California

D. Ewen Cameron, M.D.
Psychiatry and Aging Research
Veterans Administration Hospital
Albany, New York

Dale C. Cameron, M.D.
Saint Elizabeths Hospital
Washington, D.C.

Douglas G. Campbell, M.D.
490 Post Street
San Francisco, California

Eric T. Carlson, M.D.
60 Sutton Place South
New York, New York

Edward J. Carroll, M.D. (L)
121 University Place
Pittsburgh, Pennsylvania

James P. Cattell, M.D.
880 Fifth Avenue
New York, New York

Richard Allen Chase, M.D.
Department of Psychiatry
Neurocommunications Laboratory
The Johns Hopkins Hospital
Baltimore, Maryland

G. Brock Chisholm, M.D. (H)
Seawood, West Coast Road
R. R. 2, Victoria
British Columbia, Canada

John A. Clausen, Ph.D.
1963 Yosemite Road
Berkeley, California

Hollis E. Clow, M.D. (L)
121 Westchester Avenue
White Plains, New York

Robert A. Cohen, M.D.
4514 Dorset Avenue
Chevy Chase, Maryland

Jonathan O. Cole, M.D.
7111 Edgevale Street
Chevy Chase, Maryland

Oskar Diethelm, M.D. (L)
New York Hospital
525 East 68th Street
New York, New York

Simon Dinitz, Ph.D.
Department of Sociology
Ohio State University
Columbus, Ohio

Roy M. Dorcus, Ph.D.
University of California
Los Angeles, California

John M. Dorsey, M.D. (L)
Wayne State University
Detroit, Michigan

Leon Eisenberg, M.D.
2610 Whitney Avenue
Baltimore, Maryland

William W. Elgin, M.D. (L)
Sheppard & Enoch Pratt Hospital
Towson, Maryland

Joel Elks, M.D.
Johns Hopkins Medical School
Baltimore, Maryland

David M. Engelhardt, M.D.
208 Marlborough Road
Brooklyn, New York

Milton H. Erickson, M.D. (L)
32 West Cypress Street
Phoenix, Arizona

Jack R. Ewalt, M.D.
72-76 Fenwood Road
Boston, Massachusetts

Raymond Feldman, M.D.
708 Azalea Drive
Rockville, Maryland

Max Fink, M.D.
Missouri Institute of Psychiatry
5400 Arsenal Street
St. Louis, Missouri

Barbara Fish, M.D.
550 First Avenue
New York University
New York, New York

Arthur N. Foxe, M.D. (L)
9 East 67th Street
New York, New York

Jerome D. Frank, M.D.
Department of Psychiatry
Johns Hopkins University
Baltimore, Maryland

Richard L. Frank, M.D. (L)
15 East 91st Street
New York, New York

Shervert H. Frazier, M.D.
College of Medicine
Baylor University
Texas Medical Center
Houston, Texas

Alfred M. Freedman, M.D.
161 West 86th Stree
New York, New York

Daniel X. Freedman, M.D.
Department of Psychiatry
Yale University School of Medicine
333 Cedar Street
New Haven, Connecticut

Fritz A. Freyhan, M.D.
St. Vincent's Hospital
153 West 11th Street
New York, New York

Arnold J. Friedhoff, M.D.
32-25 168th Street
Flushing, New York

John Frosch, M.D.
1 Gracie Terrace
New York, New York

Daniel H. Funkenstein, M.D.
74 Fenwood Road
Boston, Massachusetts

W. Horsley Gantt, M.D.
Johns Hopkins Hospital
Baltimore, Maryland

Norman Garmezy, Ph.D.
Department of Psychology
University of Minnesota
Minneapolis, Minnesota

Bernard Glueck, Sr., M.D. (L)
University of North Carolina
Box 1020
Chapel Hill, North Carolina

Bernard Glueck, Jr., M.D.
Box 2070
Hartford, Connecticut

Murray Glusman, M.D.
722 West 168th St.
New York, New York

William Goldfarb, M.D.
530 West End Avenue
New York, New York

Sanford Goldstone, Ph.D.
5002 Glenmeadow
Houston 36, Texas

Jacques Gottlieb, M.D.
Lafayette Clinic
951 East Lafayette
Detroit 7, Michigan

Milton Greenblatt, M.D.
11 Burnside Road
Newton Highlands, Massachusetts

Samuel W. Greenhouse, M.A.
National Institute of Child Health and
    Human Development
Bethesda, Maryland

Roy R. Grinker, Sr., M.D.
Michael Reese Hospital
29th Street & Ellis Avenue
Chicago, Illinois

Ernest M. Gruenberg, M.D.
722 West 168th Street
New York, New York

A. Irving Hallowell, Ph.D.
Box 14, Bennet Hall
University of Pennsylvania
Philadelphia, Pennsylvania

Ward C. Halstead, Ph.D.
5537 University Avenue
Chicago, Illinois

David Hamburg, M.D.
Department of Psychiatry
Stanford University Medical School
Palo Alto, California

Donald M. Hamilton, M.D. (L)
21 Bloomingdale Road
White Plains, New York

Irving B. Harrison, M.D.
159 Soundview Avenue
White Plains, New York

Lynwood Heaver, M.D.
2651 E. 21st Street
Tulsa, Oklahoma

Morris Herman, M.D.
30 East 40th Street
New York, New York

Harold E. Himwich, M.D.
State Research Hospital
Galesburg, Illinois

Hudson Hoagland, Ph.D.
Deerfoot Road
Southboro, Massachusetts

Leslie B. Hohman, M.D. (L)
Duke Medical School
Durham, North Carolina

Bernard Holland, M.D.
Emory University
Woodruff Building
Atlanta, Georgia

William A. Horwitz, M.D. (L)
722 West 168th Street
New York, New York

Joseph Hughes, M.D.
111 North 49th Street
Philadelphia, Pennsylvania

Howard F. Hunt, Ph.D.
722 West 168th Street
New York, New York

William A. Hunt, Ph.D. (L)
Northwestern University
Evanston, Illinois

Paul E. Huston, M.D.
500 Newton Road
Iowa City, Iowa

Lissy Jarvik, Ph.D., M.D.
722 West 168th Street
New York, New York

George A. Jervis, Ph.D., M.D.
Letchworth Village
Research Department
Thiells, Rockland County, New York

Lothar B. Kalinowsky, M.D. (L)
115 East 82nd Street
New York, New York

Abram Kardiner, M.D. (L)
1100 Park Avenue
New York, New York

Martin M. Katz, Ph.D.
Psychopharmacology Service Center
National Institute of Mental Health
National Bank Building
Bethesda, Maryland

Solomon Katzenelbogen, M.D. (L)
9305 Parkhill Terrace
Bethesda, Maryland

William Raymond Keeler, M.D.
484 Avenue Road
Toronto, Ontario, Canada

Edward J. Kempf, M.D. (L)
Wading River
Long Island, New York

Isabelle V. Kendig, Ph.D. (L)
Sandy Springs, Maryland

Richard D. Kepner, M.D. (L)
P. O. Box 3119
Honolulu, Hawaii

Seymour S. Kety, M.D.
National Institute of Mental Health
Laboratory of Clinical Sciences
Bethesda, Maryland

H. E. King, Ph.D.
University of Pittsburgh Medical
   School
3811 O'Hara Street
Pittsburgh, Pennsylvania

Gerald L. Klerman, M.D.
Boston Psychopathic Hospital
72-76 Fenwood Road
Boston, Massachusetts

Lawrence Kolb, Sr., M.D. (L)
6645 32nd N.W.
Washington, D.C.

Vojtech Adalbert Kral, M.D.
4145 Blueridge Crescent
Montreal, Canada

Morton Kramer, Sc.D.
9612 Sutherland Road
Silver Spring, Maryland

Rema Lapouse, M.D.
111 Irving Terrace
Buffalo, New York

Emma Layman, Ph.D.
104 West 2nd Street
Mt. Pleasant, Iowa

Zigmond M. Lebensohn, M.D.
2431 K St., N.W.
Suite 215
Washington, D.C.

Heinz E. Lehman, M.D.
6603 LaSalle Boulevard
Montreal, Quebec, Canada

Alexander H. Leighton, M.D.
319 Rand
Cornell University
Ithaca, New York

Paul V. Lemkau, M.D.
615 N. Wolfe Street
Baltimore, Maryland

David M. Levy, M.D.
47 East 77th Street
New York, New York

Sir Aubrey J. Lewis (H)
The Maudsley Hospital
Denmark Hill, S.E. 5
London, England

William T. Lhamon, M.D.
Cornell University Medical School
525 East 68th Street
New York, New York

W. T. Liberson, Ph.D., M.D.
Chief, Physical Education
  and Rehabilitation Service
Veterans Administration Hospital
P.O. Box 28
Hines, Illinois

Ogden R. Lindsley, Ph.D.
Children's Rehabilitation Center
University of Kansas Medical Center
Kansas City, Kansas

Maurice Lorr, Ph.D.
1521 Erskine Street
Washington, D. C.

Reginald S. Lourie, M.D. (L)
Children's Hospital
Washington, D.C.

John W. Lovett-Doust, M.D.
University of Toronto
2 Surrey Place
Toronto, Ontario, Canada

Hans Lowenbach, M.D.
Duke University Medical Center
Durham, North Carolina

Donald J. MacPherson, M.D. (L)
1101 Beacon Street
Brookline, Massachusetts

Sidney Malitz, M.D.
722 West 168th Street
New York, New York

Robert Malmo, Ph.D.
1025 Pina Avenue, West
Montreal, Canada

Benjamin Malzberg, Ph.D. (L)
Research Foundation for
  Mental Hygiene, Inc.
217 Lark Street
Albany, New York

Amadeo S. Marrazzi, M.D.
Department of Pharmacology
University of Minnesota School of
  Medicine
Minneapolis, Minnesota

Edwin E. McNiel, M.D. (L)
3875 Wilshire Boulevard
Los Angeles, California

Sarnoff Mednick, M.D.
Department of Psychology
University of Michigan
Ann Arbor, Michigan

James G. Miller, M.D.
Mental Health Research Institute
University of Michigan
Ann Arbor, Michigan

Neal E. Miller, Ph.D.
Department of Psychology
Yale University 333 Cedar Street
New Haven, Connecticut

John Money, Ph.D.
Phipps 400, The Johns Hopkins
  Hospital
Baltimore, Maryland

Thomas Verner Moore, Ph.D., M.D.(H)
Ven. P.D. Pablo Maria Moore
O. Cart.
Cartuja de Miraflores
Apartado 43
Burgos, Spain

Robert S. Morrow, Ph.D.
16 Piatro Place
Dobbs Ferry, New York

Leon Moses, M.D.
19 East 74th Street
New York, New York

Hobart Mowrer, Ph.D.
445 Gregory Hall
University of Illinois
Urbana, Illinois

Harry M. Murdock, M.D.
Shappard and Enoch Pratt Hospital
Towson, Maryland

Henry A. Murray, M.D. (L)
48 Mount Auburn Street
Cambridge, Massachusetts

J. Martin Myers, Jr., M.D.
Institute of Pennsylvania Hospital
111 North 49th Street
Philadelphia, Pennsylvania

Leo P. O'Donnell, M.D. (L)
36 Elm Street
Pawling, New York

Raymond L. Osborne, M.D. (L)
140 East 54th Street
New York, New York

Joseph B. Parker, Jr., M.D.
University of Kentucky
Medical Center
Lexington, Kentucky

Benjamin Pasamanick, M.D.
Illinois State Psychiatric Institute
1601 W. Taylor Street
Chicago, Illinois

Grosvenor B. Pearson, M.D. (L)
3101 W. DeBazan Avenue
St. Petersburg, Beach 6, Florida

Harris P. Peck, M.D.
120 Woodridge Place
Leonia, New Jersey

Zygmunt A. Piotrowski, Ph.D. (L)
1025 Walnut Street
Philadelphia, Pennsylvania

Philip Polatin, M.D. (L)
5281 Independence Avenue
New York, New York

Max Pollack, Ph.D.
Hillside Hospital
Glen Oaks
Long Island, New York

Hyman L. Rachlin, M.D. (L)
35 Park Avenue
New York, New York

Sandor Rado, M.D. (L)
New York School of Psychiatry
Manhattan State Hospital
Ward's Island
600 East 125th Street
New York, New York

John Rainer, M.D.,
9 Innisfree Place
Eastchester, New York

F. C. Redlich, M.D.
333 Cedar Street
New Haven, Connecticut

Julius B. Richmond, M.D.
Department of Pediatrics
State University of New York
Upstate Medical Center
766 Irving Avenue
Syracuse, New York

David McK. Rioch, M.D. (L)
4607 Dorset Avenue
Chevy Chase, Maryland

Janet MacKenzie Rioch, M.D.
(Mrs. Philip Bard)
6 Meadow Road
Baltimore, Maryland

Margaret Rioch, Ph.D.
4607 Dorset Avenue
Chevy Chase, Maryland

Eli Robins, M.D.
Department of Psychiatry
Washington University School of
   Medicine
St. Louis, Missouri

Fred V. Rockwell, M.D. (L)
Grasslands Hospital
Valhalla, New York

Howard P. Rome, M.D.
Mayo Clinic
Rochester, Minnesota

David Rosenthal, Ph.D.
National Institute of Mental Health
Bethesda, Maryland

Saul Rosenzweig, Ph.D.
Department of Psychology
Washington University, Box 150
St. Louis, Missouri

Mathew Ross, M.D.
333 Commonwealth Avenue
Chestnut Hill, Massachusetts

Theodore Rothman, M.D.
415 North Camden Drive
Beverly Hills, California

Eli A. Rubinstein, Ph.D.
Training and Manpower Resources
   Branch
National Institute of Mental Health
Bethesda, Maryland

William S. Sadler. M.D. (L)
533 Diversey Parkway
Chicago. Illinois

George S. Saslow, M.D.
University of Oregon
Medical School
Portland, Oregon

Isidor W. Scherer, Ph.D.
8934 Bradmoor Drive
Bethesda, Maryland

G. Wilson Shaffer, Ph.D. (L)
Johns Hopkins University
Baltimore, Maryland

Charles Shagass, M.D.
1301 Spruce Lane
Wyncote, Pennsylvania

David Shakow, Ph.D. (L)
National Institute of Mental Health
Clinical Center
Bethesda, Maryland

Alexander Simon, M.D. (L)
Langley Porter Clinic
San Francisco, California

John L. Smalldon, M.D. (L)
Denver Hospital & State School
Taunton, Massachusetts

George W. Smeltz, M.D. (L)
Marlborough-Blenheim Hotel
Atlantic City, New Jersey

Lauren H. Smith, M.D. (L)
111 North 49th Street
Philadelphia, Pennsylvania

Harry C. Solomon, M.D. (L)
74 Fenwood Road
Boston, Massachusetts

Rene A. Spitz, M.D.
12 Rue Robert de Traz
Geneva, Switzerland

Edward J. Stainbrook, M.D.
1200 N. State Street
Los Angeles, California

Gregory Stragnell, M.D.
388 Homewood Road
Los Angeles, California

Joseph G. Sutton, M.D.
5 Roosevelt Place
Montclair, New Jersey

Hans C. Syz, M.D. (L)
The Lifwynn Foundation
52 South Morningside Drive
Westport, Connecticut

George Tarjan, M.D.
The Neuropsychiatric Institute
760 Westwood Plaza
Los Angeles, California

William S. Taylor, Ph.D. (L)
27 Langworthy Road
Northampton, Massachusetts

Harry A. Teitelbaum, M.D.
5605 Greenspring Avenue
Baltimore, Maryland

William B. Terhune, M.D. (L)
Silver Hill Foundation
Box 1114
New Canaan, Connecticut

Charles B. Thompson, M.D.
The Lifwynn Foundation
52 South Morningside Drive
Westport, Connecticut

Kenneth J. Tillotson, M.D. (L)
1265 Beacon Street
Brookline, Massachusetts

Harvey J. Tompkins, M.D.
Department of Psychiatry
St. Vincent's Hospital
New York, New York

James S. Tyhurst, M.D.
University of British Columbia
Vancouver 9, British Columbia
Canada

Vladimir G. Urse, M.D. (L)
Cook County Hospital
Polk and Wood Streets
Chicago, Illinois

Roy McL. Van Wart, M.D. (L)
10431 Bellogio Road
Los Angeles, California

Harold M. Visotsky, M.D.
646 N. Michigan Avenue
Chicago, Illinois

Raymond W. Waggoner, M.D.
121 Westchester Avenue
White Plains, New York

James Hardin Wall, M.D. (L)
University Hospital
1313 East Ann Street
Ann Arbor, Michigan

David Wechsler, Ph.D.
Bellevue Hospital
New York, New York

Edith Weigert, M.D.
12 Oxford Street
Chevy Chase, Maryland

Edwin A. Weinstein, M.D.
7101 Pyle Road
Bethesda, Maryland

Livingston Welch, Ph.D.
Hunter College
695 Park Avenue
New York, New York

Frederick L. Weniger, M.D.
108 Franklin Road
Pittsburgh 9, Pennsylvania

Louis J. West, M.D.
University of Oklahoma
Medical Center
800 N.E. 13th Street
Oklahoma City, Oklahoma

Robert W. White, Ph.D.
Department of Social Relations
Harvard University
Cambridge, Massachusetts

John C. Whitehorn, M.D.
210 Northfield Place
Baltimore, Maryland

Abraham Wikler, M.D.
Department of Psychiatry
University of Kentucky College of
  Medicine
Lexington, Kentucky

George B. Wilbur, M.D. (L)
Cove Road
South Dennis, Massachusetts

William Preston Wilson, M.D.
Duke University
Medical Center
Durham, North Carolina

George Winekur
Rennard Hospital
4940 Audubon Avenue
St. Louis, Missouri

Cecil L. Wittson, M.D.
9651 North 29th Street
Omaha, Nebraska

Joseph Wolpe, M.D.
Department of Behavioral Science
Eastern Pennsylvania Psychiatric
  Center
Henry Avenue and Abbottsford Road
Philadelphia, Pennsylvania

S. Bernard Wortis, M.D. (L)
410 East 57th Street
New York, New York

Eugene Ziskind, M.D.
2007 Wilshire Boulevard
Los Angeles, California

Joseph Zubin, Ph.D.
722 West 168th Street
New York, New York

PAST AND PRESENT OFFICERS OF THE
AMERICAN PSYCHOPATHOLOGICAL ASSOCIATION

Presidents

1912	Adolf Meyer	1940	Douglas A. Thom
1913	James T. Putnam	1941	Roscoe W. Hall
1914	Alfred R. Allen	1942	Roscoe W. Hall
1915	Alfred R. Allen	1943	Frederick L. Wells
1916	Adolf Meyer	1944	Frederick L. Wells
1917	Adolf Meyer	1945	Bernard Glueck
1918	Smith Ely Jelliffe	1946	Robert P. Knight
1921	William A. White	1947	Frederick L. Wells
1922	John T. MacCurdy	1948	Donald J. MacPherson
1923	L. Pierce Clark	1949	Paul Hoch
1924	L. Pierce Clark	1950	William B. Terhune
1925	Albert M. Barrett	1951	Lauren H. Smith
1927	Sanger Brown II	1952	Joseph Zubin
1928	Ross McC. Chapman	1953	Clarence P. Oberndorf
1929	Ross McC. Chapman	1954	David McK. Rioch
1930	William Healy	1955	Merrill Moore
1931	William Healy	1956	Oskar Diethelm
1932	J. Ramsey Hunt	1957	Howard S. Liddell
1933	Edward J. Kempf	1958	Leslie B. Hohman
1934	Edward J. Kempf	1959	Harry C. Solomon
1935	Nolan D. C. Lewis	1960	David Wechsler
1936	Nolan D. C. Lewis	1961	William Horsley Gantt
1937	Nolan D. C. Lewis	1962	Lauretta Bender
1938	Samuel W. Hamilton	1963	D. Ewen Cameron
1939	Abraham Myerson	1964	Jerome D. Frank
		1965	Franz J. Kallmann

Vice-Presidents

1924	William Healy	1931	J. Ramsay Hunt
	George H. Kirby		Herman N. Adler
1925	J. Ramsay Hunt	1933	Albert M. Barrett
	Sidney L. Schwab		Trigant Burrow
1927	Ross McC. Chapman	1934	Albert M. Barrett
	Edward J. Kempf		Trigant Burrow
1928	Edward J. Kempf	1935	J. Ramsay Hunt
	E. Stanley Abbott		Smith Ely Jelliffe
1929	Edward J. Kempf	1936	J. Ramsay Hunt
	E. Stanley Abbott		Smith Ely Jelliffe
1930	J. Ramsay Hunt	1937	Samuel W. Hamilton
	Herman N. Adler		Ray G. Hoskins

Vice-Presidents

1938	Lydiard H. Horton	1950	Harry M. Murdock
	Hans Syz		William S. Taylor
1939	Roscoe W. Hall	1951	Harry M. Murdock
	Douglas A. Thom		Lauretta Bender
1940	George S. Sprague	1952	William Horowitz
	Bernard Glueck		S. Bernard Wortis
1941	Frederick L. Wells	1953	David McK. Rioch
	Lowell S. Selling		Merrill Moore
1943	Frederick L. Wells		Howard S. Liddell
	Lowell S. Selling	1955	Oskar Diethelm
1944	Lowell S. Selling		Howard S. Liddell
	Flanders Dunbar	1956	Leslie B. Hohman
1945	Thomas V. Moore	1957	David Wechsler
	Robert P. Knight	1958	David Wechsler
1946	Paul H. Hoch	1959	Clara Thompson
	Thos. A. C. Rennie	1960	Theodora M. Abel
1947	William C. Menninger	1961	Donald M. Hamilton
	Ruth Benedict	1962	D. Ewen Cameron
1948	Ruth Benedict	1963	Jerome D. Frank
	Lauren H. Smith	1964	Franz J. Kallmann
1949	Arthur N. Foxe	1965	Bernard C. Glueck, Jr.
	Norman Cameron		

Secretaries

1921	H. W. Frink	1940-1948	Merrill Moore
1922-1926	Sanger Brown, II	1944-1951	Samuel W. Hamilton
1927-1929	Martin W. Peck	1952-1960	Donald M. Hamilton
1930-1939	L. Eugene Emerson	1961-1965	Fritz A. Freyhan

Treasurers

1924-1942	William C. Garvin	1952-1964	Bernard C. Glueck, Jr.
1943-1951	Joseph Zubin	1965	Howard F. Hunt

INDEX